The Nature of Parasitism

THEORETICAL AND EXPERIMENTAL BIOLOGY

An International Series of Monographs

CONSULTING EDITOR

J. F. Danielli

King's College, University of London, England

Volume 1 J. L. Cloudsley-Thompson, Rhythmic Activity in Animal Physiology and Behaviour. 1961

Volume 2 W. P. Rogers, The Nature of Parasitism: The Relationship of Some Metazoan Parasites to Their Hosts. 1962

ACADEMIC PRESS • New York and London

The Nature of Parasitism

The Relationship of Some Metazoan Parasites to Their Hosts

W. P. ROGERS

Department of Zoology, University of Adelaide

1962

ACADEMIC PRESS
NEW YORK and LONDON

ACADEMIC PRESS INC.
111 Fifth Avenue
New York, 3, N.Y., U.S.A.

United Kingdom Edition
Published by
ACADEMIC PRESS INC. (London) Ltd.
Berkeley Square House, Berkeley Square, London W.1.

LIBRARY OF CONGRESS CATALOG CARD NUMBER 61-12281

PRINTED IN GREAT BRITAIN BY WILLMER BROTHERS AND HARAM LTD.

Preface

A CONSIDERATION of host–parasite relationships raises a number of basic problems. What are the features of the parasite and the host that allow infection to occur? What are the physiological characters that distinguish a parasite from its free-living relatives? What are the features of the environments of parasites which affect specificity? To these sorts of questions our present knowledge provides only general answers. Until we have more precise answers we cannot begin to understand the basic features of the host–parasite relationship and the nature of parasitism.

My chief aim in writing this book has been to provoke interest in these sorts of problems; I have been concerned not so much to summarize our knowledge as to stimulate research on parasitism. Most of the book concerns metazoan parasites, chiefly nematodes and platyhelminths. I have grouped chapters in four parts which correspond roughly to different stages in the association between the metazoan parasite and its host. Part I, speculations on the host–parasite relationship, gives a general introduction and a brief statement of a hypothesis about some aspects of parasitism, especially in relation to parasitic nematodes. Part II deals largely with the stage in the association between the parasite and the host when infection occurs. The chapters here deal with factors that lead to infection, the life cycle of the parasite and the special character of the infective stage, the physiology of the free-living and infective stages, and finally, the physiology of infective processes. In Part III is discussed what I regard as the second stage in the association between the parasite and the host. Infection has occurred and the parasite now needs nutrients, oxygen and other factors from the host if it is to survive. In this part of the book these needs and the general physiology of parasitic stages are discussed. The last part of the book is concerned with factors which affect the propagation and maintenance of parasites as species; so the chapters deal with reproduction, specificity and the evolution of parasitism.

In an attempt to interest readers who may not have a detailed knowledge of parasitology I have used the more common parasites and hosts as examples whenever possible. The special language of parasitology has been avoided as much as possible, but some terms which parasitologists use in a different way from other biologists are included in the text. Thus the word "egg" is used for what might be more properly described as a "capsule", and includes the embryo, its membranes, and the shells of the egg. And the term "larvae" or "larval stages" used to denote the immature stages in the life cycle of nematodes may also be misleading to some biologists. These stages are juveniles, not larvae.

I am deeply indebted to Dr R. Dubos of the Rockefeller Institute for Medical Research who reviewed the chapters on more general aspects of parasitism, and to Dr E. Bueding of Johns Hopkins University who reviewed chapters on the physiology of parasites. Many of my colleagues at the University of Adelaide, especially Dr G. Mayo of the Department of Genetics, also gave me helpful advice for which I am most grateful. I wish also to thank the many authors whose illustrations I have used and whose work I have quoted; individual acknowledgements are given in legends.

I am most grateful to Mrs M. Ross, who is a member of the staff of the University of Adelaide, for the many drawings she prepared for me. My warmest thanks are due to my wife, Lillian Rogers, who did most of the typing and some of the drawings, who checked references and polished at least some of the rough spots in the manuscript.

W. P. ROGERS

University of Adelaide
December 1961

Contents

Preface v

PART I

SPECULATIONS ON THE HOST–PARASITE RELATIONSHIP

General Introduction 3

1 The Study of Parasitism 5
Infectiousness and parasitism 5
The relationship between nematode parasites and their hosts 9
Summary 11
References 11

2 The Nature of Parasitism 12
The environment of parasites 13
The dependence of the parasite on the host 18
Stages in the host–parasite association 19
Summary 23
References 23

PART II

THE PROBLEM OF INFECTIOUSNESS

General Introduction 27

3 Life Cycles and Infection 29
The life cycle of nematodes 31
A physiological basis for the life cycle of nematodes 38
Life cycles in other metazoan parasites 44
Summary 46
References 46

4 The Physiology of Free-living Stages 48
Free-living stages of nematodes 49
Free-living stages of other metazoan parasites 64
Summary 65
References 66

5 The Physiology of Infection 68
Infection via the gut of the host 70
Infection via the surface of the host 87
Discussion 91
Summary 92
References 93

PART III

THE LIFE OF PARASITES

General Introduction 97

6 Physiology of Parasitic Stages 99
Intermediary metabolism of parasitic nematodes. 100
Nerve-muscle physiology 111
Osmoregulation 115
Intermediary metabolism in the Acanthocephala and parasitic Platyhelminthes 119
Nerve-muscle physiology in parasitic Platyhelminthes. . . 124
Osmoregulation in parasitic Platyhelminthes and Acanthocephala 126
Summary 128
References 130

7 The Oxygen Requirements of Parasites 134
Oxygen in the environments of parasites 136
The oxygen requirements of nematode parasites 137
The transport of oxygen in nematode parasites 149
The significance of aerobic metabolism in nematode parasites 159
The oxygen requirements of parasitic Platyhelminthes and Acanthocephala 161
Summary 164
References 164

8 The Nutrition of Parasites. 167
Nutrition of parasitic nematodes 168
The nutrition of other metazoan parasites. 180
Effects of the host's hormones on parasites. 189
References 189

PART IV

THE DEVELOPMENT AND MAINTENANCE OF PARASITISM

General Introduction 197

9 The Propagation of Parasites 199
The eggs and sperm of nematode parasites 200
The formation of the egg-shell 201
The production of eggs and sperm in parasitic Platyhelminthes and Acanthocephala 212
The sex ratios 214
Parthenogenetic and asexual reproduction 214
Nutrition and reproduction 215
Summary 216
References 217

10 The Specificity of Parasites 219
Specificity in the first stage of the association of the parasite with the host 221
Specificity in the second stage of the association of the parasite with the host 230
Specificity in the third stage of the association of the parasite with the host 237
Summary 239
References 239

11 The Evolution of Parasitism 242
Ecological factors in the origin of parasitism 244
Infection of the prospective animal host 244
Infection of the plant host 248
Adaptations in parasites and their hosts 249
Pathogenicity and parasitism 256
Summary 257
References 258

Author Index 261
Subject Index 269

PART I

Speculations on the Host–Parasite Relationship

General Introduction

MANY parasitologists accept the view that adaptation to a life of commensalism or mutualism precedes adaptation to a parasitic mode of life, though there seems no good reason why parasitism should not develop without these intermediary conditions. The morphological changes, such as the increased development of organs for attachment to the host or the loss of digestive organs, are frequently found as adaptations to a parasitic mode of life and they tell us something about the relationship of the parasite to the host. But adaptations of this sort must have occurred after the assumption of a parasitic mode of life. The morphological characters which might be necessary for the establishment of parasitism, such as thickness of the cuticle or the nature of the feeding mechanism, are more difficult to visualize. So it must be with the physiological adaptations to parasitism. We need to know not only those characters of a parasite which determine its dependence on the host, but also those which made it possible for the ancestors of parasites to move from the environment of the free-living forms and enter the environment on or in the host and survive there.

The infective stage of modern parasites is specialized to move from one sort of environment to another. Does it represent physiologically the stage in the life cycle of the free-living ancestor which was best adapted to invade the host and so "pre-adapted" for starting a parasitic mode of life? Are the sorts of adaptations to parasitism likely to be different in different stages of the life cycle so that the relationship of the parasite to the host changes?

After entering the host the infective agent is exposed to an environment from which it must obtain the factors necessary for its growth and development. It must also overcome the toxic and damaging features of the environment. These opposing conditions, the one favourable, the other unfavourable, are the major components which must be considered in the study of host–parasite relations. But there is another factor of importance in the relationship between many metazoan parasites and their hosts. Infection often requires the hatching of the egg of the parasite, or excystment or moulting. Until this occurs the infective agent may be isolated from the host by a barrier formed of the egg-shell, the cyst-wall, or sheath. Thus the host must provide the right conditions for certain changes in the infective agent before either the favourable or unfavourable components in the environment can affect many parasites.

A parasite may influence the favourable or unfavourable features of its environment. As an isolated system the host–parasite complex may be represented as host $\rightleftharpoons$ parasite's environment $\rightleftharpoons$ parasite. Though not all changes in the environment caused by the host would affect the parasite and *vice versa* there would be considerable feedback in the system which would be more closely coupled than in most free-living systems. In the relationship between the parasite and the host, negative feedback would lead to a steady-state condition with the survival of the host and the parasite; positive feedback would lead to the death of the host or the parasite. A negative feedback system in the host–parasite relationship thus might have selective value for the parasite.

CHAPTER I

The Study of Parasitism

THE relationship of macroscopic parasites to disease has been recognized, in general terms, from early times. As a consequence, the motivation for research in parasitology has arisen largely from the desire to cure or to prevent disease. Thus studies on host–parasite relationships have been concerned largely with pathology and immunology, and the bulk of research in parasitology, dealing with the natural history of parasites, has sought in studies on life cycles and in ecology to provide means whereby infection could be prevented. From the time of Koch's demonstration that disease in human beings could be caused by bacteria, studies on parasitic micro-organisms have followed similar lines. But because parasitic micro-organisms are of special importance in human disease, their study has been regarded as a special field outside what is conventionally called parasitology, and the organisms themselves are called pathogens, rather than parasites.

INFECTIOUSNESS AND PARASITISM

It is often implied that an understanding of virulence or pathogenicity is basic to an understanding of parasitism. This is not necessarily true. What is more important is an understanding of infectiousness—the capacity of the organism to infect the host and live as a parasite. In order to infect and live in the host the parasite must be able to counter the toxic actions of the host and it must obtain, under the right conditions, certain substances from the host. So to understand parasitism we want information about the needs of the parasite and its defence mechanisms rather than about the damage it does to the host. One way of obtaining this information is to study the metabolism of the parasite. This approach is thought to have a practical value also because it may show biochemical differences between the host and the parasite which might be exploited by selectively toxic compounds.

Studies on the Metabolism of Parasites

In discussing the contribution that studies on bacterial metabolism have made to the understanding of parasitism by micro-organisms, Dubos (1954, p. 12) said

> . . . all textbooks of infectious diseases dutifully begin with chapters devoted to metabolic chemistry. But like the religious convocation which opens political or other lay gatherings, this chapter has little to do with, and is never mentioned in, subsequent proceedings. In practice metabolic knowledge is not used in the analysis of reactions between host and bacteria. The reason is simply that despite the spectacular advances during the past three decades, the science of bacterial metabolism has contributed but little to the understanding of infectious processes.

Has this statement any special significance to those who study metazoan parasites? I think it has. By and large our research on the biochemistry of animal parasites has shown that the basic ground plan of their metabolic processes is similar to that in other sorts of animal cells. Surely this is not surprising. Long before the free-living ancestors of metazoan parasites appeared the most efficient and adaptable basic metabolic pattern for cellular function must have evolved. We might expect that this ground plan would be modified only in minor respects in different sorts of animals or even in different sorts of tissue. It may be, however, that some parasites have lost the power to synthesize coenzymes or other substances which are important in metabolism and so they become dependent upon the host for the supply of these substances. As yet no evidence to this effect has come from studies on metazoan parasites.

If it is difficult in studies on the basic metabolism of parasitic bacteria to discover the mechanisms of infectiousness as Dubos suggests, it is likely to be even more difficult with metazoan parasites. From an evolutionary point of view these animals are much more closely related to their hosts than are parasitic bacteria. Moreover, they seldom multiply within the host. On the other hand, the greater complexity of metazoan parasites should provide wider avenues for biochemical research which might lead to an understanding of infectiousness, but these I believe must be based on a deeper knowledge of the biology of parasitism than we have at present.

An example from outside parasitology may best explain what I mean here. The problem, let us say, is to discover the essential biochemical differences between muscle and liver. We might start, without any knowledge of the biology of these tissues, by studying their basic metabolism—aerobic and anaerobic respiration, the general processes of nitrogen catabolism and the mechanisms of synthesizing new tissue. The results would show that different parts of the basic ground plan of metabolism would have different emphasis in the different tissues as well as other minor variations. Even the synthetic mechanisms would probably be basically the same though the substances synthesized would differ. Gradually, however, information would accumulate which the inspired biochemist could interpret to show that the essential biochemical differences were those which concerned the contractile function of muscle and the storage function of the liver. Would this information have come more quickly if we had started with our biological knowledge about the functions of liver and muscle? I think so. This may seem a gross exaggeration of the situation of research on parasitism. But one must agree, for instance, that more information on the biology of infectiousness and the host as an environment for the parasite is needed as a basis for biochemical studies on parasitism.

One of the ways in which information about infectiousness and the requirements of metazoan parasites from their hosts might be found is the study of the biochemistry of the life cycle of parasites and the processes which lead to infection of the host. There is a wide background knowledge of the natural history of life cycles and the experimental biologist has also entered this field so that some of the problems are open to biochemical investigation. Problems of this sort are comparable with those in which the parasite has lost some power of synthesis and so becomes dependent on the host for a coenzyme or essential metabolite. Consider, for instance, the parasite in which the infective stage is an egg. Part of the mechanism which causes hatching of the egg has been lost and the parasite becomes dependent on the host to make good this loss.

This approach to the study of parasitism has been used to suggest a hypothesis about the relationship of nematode parasites to their hosts which will be discussed later.

Studies on the Culture of Parasites in vitro

It is the hope of most parasitologists that the culture of metazoan parasites *in vitro* will provide opportunities for great advances in our knowledge of parasite physiology from which will come an understanding of infectiousness and parasitism. Though this has not proved true in work on parasitic bacteria (Dubos, 1948) the differences between parasitic bacteria and metazoan parasites are so great that parasitologists generally have remained hopeful. Now that two specialized nematode parasites, *Nippostrongylus muris* and *Haemonchus contortus*, have been cultured through their whole life cycles from egg to adult (Weinstein and Jones, 1956; Silverman, 1959), the value of this approach should soon appear. These two parasites are closely related taxonomically so it is not surprising that the same basic medium serves for their cultivation. But the host preferences and life cycles are quite different. *Haemonchus contortus*, a parasite of ruminants, has a histotrophic larval stage in the walls of the abomasum and the adult lives on the host blood and tissues of the mucosa of the same organ. *Nippostrongylus muris* has a life cycle which takes it via the blood stream to the lungs and thence up the trachea and down the œsophagus to the small intestine. The adult, a parasite primarily of rodents, lives on blood and tissue of the mucosa of the small intestine. In view of the differences between these two parasites it seems that it may be possible to alter the basic medium so that it would support one but not the other. This may give information on specificity. But the difficulty here is that many aspects of specificity may not depend on nutrition. Thus the nutritional needs of *Nippostrongylus muris* and *Haemonchus contortus*, blood and mucosal tissue, may well be the same. But the environments are quite different: the one highly acid, containing pepsin and the fermentation products from the rumen which are undergoing peptic digestion; the other weakly acid or alkaline, containing the juices from intestinal cells, the bile, pancreatic secretions and the partly digested products from the stomach of an omnivore. The physical organization of the habitat *in vivo* is such that the parasites can live in one medium and feed on something quite different. Specificity and infectiousness may depend more on the total environment, physical as well as chemical, than on the nature of the nutrients, especially for endoparasites.

This problem may be posed in another way. To explain infectiousness and parasitism it is not only necessary to demonstrate what factors in the environment the host must provide for the parasite; it is necessary also to show what prevents the saprophytic form from living in such an environment (Rogers, 1954). It may be asked then if the medium in which parasites like *Nippostrongylus muris* and *Haemonchus contortus* will grow *in vitro* will support the growth of saprophytic nematodes. As for bacteria it may prove that most saprophytes will grow as well as the parasite *in vitro* and that factors other than those directly concerned with nutrition are important in determining infectiousness. Thus the parasitic habits of nematodes which live in the alimentary canal may be determined by their resistance to the action of the gut contents as much as by nutritional demands.

The properties of the gut contents that limit infectiousness may not be the same as those that function in other parts of an animal's body or in plants. A general statement on this subject has been made by Lewis (1953) who suggested that parasitism is the result of a balance in the host's capacity to provide substances which favour the growth of parasites and those which inhibit. Such substances commonly occur among the metabolites of many different species. Though the examples which Lewis gives are drawn from bacterial and fungal parasites there seems no reason why his hypothesis should not apply to animal parasites as well (see Chapter 8).

Studies on the cultivation of metazoan parasites *in vitro* may be used to examine the "balance hypothesis". Presumably the role of more complex inhibitors, antagonists and antibodies, which form part of the more established theories of resistance and susceptibility, and which are important in acquired as well as natural immunity, can also be studied in this way.

The Relationship between Nematode Parasites and Their Hosts

Most of the detailed discussion in this book concerns nematode parasites and chiefly nematode parasites of the gut. Other metazoan parasites are referred to, but generally in less detail. I have selected nematode parasites because they, especially those which live in the alimentary canal, are the animals which I have studied in my own research work. But there are other reasons:

(a) Nematodes are very successful animals; free-living forms, plant and animal parasites are common and widely distributed and show little morphological specialization. The basic physical organization of nematodes (Harris and Crofton, 1957) seems to be suitable for a variety of environments, and parasitism has not given rise to specialization to the degree found in other groups. Physiological specialization may not be as great either. This certainly applies to the physiology of digestion and absorption. In any case, information about physiological specialization may be sought by comparing free-living and parasitic forms. This may be especially useful in comparing, for instance, the capacity of saprophytic and parasitic forms to live in special media *in vitro*. This would not be possible with many other groups of metazoan parasites in which free-living species suitable for comparison often cannot be obtained.

(b) Because there are a large number of species which are parasites of the gut it seems reasonable to suppose that this organ presents less formidable barriers to the establishment of parasitism than many other organs. In some groups the adults are found only as parasites of the alimentary canal. The alimentary canal has features which are not commonly found in other environments and which give a starting point for the study of parasitism.

(c) The processes of reproduction and the life cycles of nematode parasites are generally relatively simple and similar to those of free-living forms. This again suggests that the parasitic forms are relatively unspecialized as compared with the Trematoda and Cestoda, for instance.

Though the fundamental character of parasitism is the same whatever the parasite or the host, the actual relationship between the parasite and the host may vary from species to species. Thus the degree and nature of the dependence of the parasite on the host may vary greatly. In discussing this, factors in the host–parasite relationship that relate to (a) the process of infection, (b) the maintenance of the parasite within the host and (c) the production of infective agents are my primary concern. These factors will be discussed in detail later. A hypothesis on the nature of parasitism based on these factors in the host–parasite relationship is briefly summarized below.

(i) The basic feature of parasitism lies in the unusual sort of environment needed by the parasites and in the capacity of the parasite to penetrate and resist the protective mechanisms of the host that provides the environment. The important components of the environment are the substances and conditions which the parasite requires of the host. None of these substances need be unique in itself. The specific features of the environment of a parasite may lie in the pattern of the components rather than in the individual components.

(ii) The life cycle of many parasites may involve systems of secretions within the parasite which govern certain processes of development such as the hatching of eggs and the moulting of larvae of nematodes. The infective stage, egg or larva, may be regarded as a "resting" stage in which activity of the normal system of internal secretions is suspended.

(iii) Part of the pattern which the parasite requires from the host might be formed of factors which act primarily by stimulating the infective stage to recommence production of internal secretions, so leading to a resumption of development. Other factors may be required, also as stimuli, for starting changes, such as moults and metamorphoses, which occur later during the parasitic phase of the life cycle.

(iv) After the initial process of infection the pattern of substances and conditions required from the host would be those concerned in the growth and maintenance of the parasites. The components of the pattern might here include such things as nutrients, osmotic pressure, oxygen tension and redox potential. As well as factors favouring the growth of parasites there would be in the environment metabolites, antagonists and antibodies which inhibit growth. The balance of favourable and unfavourable factors would determine the success or failure of the parasite in maintaining its place in the host.

The pattern needed for mature parasites might change again, qualitatively and quantitatively, to meet the needs of reproduction, and especially for the production of the large numbers of sperm and eggs usually needed for the successful maintenance of the species.

(v) The various patterns of the environment necessary for a parasite to complete its life cycle both within and without the host determine the specificity of the parasite and may throw light on the evolution of parasitism.

Summary

For the study of parasitism, factors in the host–parasite relationship that are concerned with the process of infection and the survival of the parasite within the host are of chief importance. Studies on the basic metabolism of parasites have not as yet thrown light on this problem. It is suggested that research on problems where there are clear-cut biological distinctions between the parasite and the host, and between the parasite and its free-living relatives, might be profitable.

A hypothesis concerning the relationship between parasites, especially nematode parasites, and their hosts is briefly stated.

References

Dubos, R. J. (1948) *Bact. Rev.* **12**, 173.

—— (1954) "Biochemical Determinants of Microbial Diseases". Harvard University Press, Cambridge, Mass.

Harris, J. E. and Crofton, H. D. (1957) *J. exp. Biol.* **34**, 116.

Lewis, R. W. (1953) *Amer. Nat.* **37**, 273.

Rogers, W. P. (1954) *Rep. Aust. Ass. Adv. Sci.* **30**, 105.

Silverman, P. H. (1959) *Nature, Lond.* **183**, 197.

Weinstein, P. P. and Jones, M. F. (1956) *J. Parasit.* **42**, 215.

CHAPTER 2

The Nature of Parasitism

ALL except the most simple animals are heterotrophic and depend upon the activities of other organisms for their survival. Indeed many animals can live only in close association with other living organisms; the environment in which they live is the immediate product of other living organisms. Associations of this sort may be between individuals of the same or different species and may involve animals and plants. The closeness of the association may vary considerably. Thus in commensalism the association is a loose one with varying degrees of permanence and profit for one or both partners. In symbiosis the association is more intimate and both partners profit. As might be expected there are no clear-cut distinctions between the different degrees of association found in commensalism (Caullery, 1952, pp. 1–30).

Like commensalism, parasitism is a type of association between two organisms, but one, the parasite, is dependent on and lives at the expense of the other, the host. The host provides the environment in which the parasite lives. In using the environment the parasite injures the host, directly by depriving it of some of its food, or by destroying tissue, and indirectly by chemical or physical toxic actions. As in commensalism, the closeness of the association between the parasite and the host varies greatly (Caullery, 1952, pp. 30–39). There are even special circumstances when a host may profit temporarily from an association with a parasite (Chitwood, 1951; Chitwood *et al.*, 1952). On the whole, however, the host always does better without the parasite but, on the other hand, the host is essential for the parasite because it is only on or in the host that the parasite can obtain the environment it needs for its survival.

A major feature of parasitism is the provision by the host of the environment for the parasite. What it is that is unique in the physics and chemistry of the environment of parasites is not known.

This description of parasitism could be enlarged greatly with details of different sorts of parasites and different sorts of hosts; but this type of information rarely helps to explain parasitism in physiological terms. Indeed, there is little in the literature about the physiology of animal parasites to which one could point and say "that makes this organism a parasite". Even the extensive studies which have been carried out with *Ascaris lumbricoides* (Fairbairn, 1957) do not give an answer to this question. In fact there is no satisfactory explanation, in physiological terms, for the parasitic habits of any animal parasite.

One way in which the problem of parasitism might be approached is to ask the question "What does the parasite require from its host?" Of course not all the things that the parasite gets from its host are necessarily directly concerned in parasitism. For example, as it grows the parasite must obtain water from the host; but it is not the need for water which primarily makes the parasite dependent on the host. If it could be shown that the dependence of the parasite on the host was due to the need for certain factors in its environment which could be obtained only in or on a living organism, then the knowledge of these factors and the use the parasite made of them would be of fundamental importance in understanding parasitism. It is the unusual nature of the environment required by the parasite which gives parasitism, like symbiosis, its novel character. The basic problem of parasitism is thus an ecological problem—the analysis of the relationship of an organism to its environment. This problem is difficult because the environment is complex and because the relationship between host and parasite is in a steady-state condition which is easily disturbed by experimental intervention.

It is often implied and sometimes specifically stated "that the host provides the parasite with substances it has elaborated, and that are essential for the parasite's nutritional requirements" (Baer, 1952, p. 6). It is the need for these nutrients, it is thought, which makes the parasite dependent on the host, and which determines host specificity. These views may be correct but there is as yet little evidence to support them as far as metazoan parasites are concerned. It seems reasonable, therefore, to examine the possibility that the unique features of the environments of at least some species of parasites might be due to components other than essential nutrients.

The Environment of Parasites

The environment required by a parasite for its survival, though it must normally be provided by a living organism, will not differ in principle from other sorts of environments. The difference in the components in the environments in which free-living and parasitic animals live must lie in the nature of some of the substances and the unusual combinations of physical and chemical properties on or in living organisms. In addition, the environments provided by healthy living organisms will usually be maintained within a narrow range of steady-state conditions not commonly found in non-living systems. The chief ways in which the environments of parasites might differ from the environments of free-living organisms would thus be (a) the presence of special substances; (b) special combinations of substances which are not unique in themselves; (c) physical properties, and (d) stability.

The hazards of the environment to which parasites might be subjected also differ from those which free-living organisms would meet. Metabolites produced by the host, complex substances which affect resistance and susceptibility, and changes in the physical and physico-chemical features of the environment may have unfavourable effects on parasites. Some of these unfavourable components of the environment have no exact counterpart in the environments of free-living organisms.

Animal ecologists have several ways of describing an environment in terms of its components. Allee *et al.* (1949, p. 1) regarded the environment as including "biotic factors"—the living organisms and non-living organic matter—and "physical factors". Others discuss environment in terms of "density-responsive" or "non-reactive" factors. Here the components of the environment are characterized according to whether the influence they exert on the rate of increase or decrease of a population of organisms is dependent on or independent of the number of organisms per unit space (Varley, 1947; Nicholson, 1954). Andrewartha and Birch (1954, p. 26) chose to divide the environment of animals into four components: weather; food; other animals, and organisms causing disease; and a place in which to live.

The factors that are required in the environments of metazoan parasites have not been rigidly determined except for one or two species which have relatively simple needs (see Chapter 8). For the purpose of the present discussion the scheme which is briefly outlined below, though deficient in many respects, seems to be suitable.

A. Basic Nutrients that are needed by the Parasite for obtaining Energy and for the Synthesis of Tissue: Salts, Water

Viruses and those protozoan parasites which are intracellular may be so highly adapted to a parasitic mode of life that the usual sources of energy, such as glucose, are replaced by compounds of "high phosphate-bond energy", such as the phosphagens and adenosine-triphosphate which have been synthesized by the host. Metazoan parasites are extracellular and even when they ingest blood or tissue there is no evidence to suggest that the basic sources of energy are not carbohydrates, fats and amino acids, as in the host. On the contrary, it is clear that metabolism for the production of energy is similar in principle to that in the host animals (see Chapter 6). Little is known about the basic materials needed for the synthesis of tissues in parasites; presumably most of their requirements would be the same as for free-living animals.

None of these substances is likely to be unique; but the proportions in which some of them are needed or the amounts required of one or other of them, as in the cestodes (Read and Rothman, 1957), may not be found commonly outside living animals.

B. Nutrients required for Specific Metabolic Functions in the Parasite

Many highly adapted unicellular parasites have lost the ability to synthesize coenzymes and other substances which play a special part in metabolic processes (Lwoff, 1933). There is as yet little direct evidence to suggest that this is also a feature of parasitism involving metazoan animals. Nevertheless it is often implied that it is the need for essential nutrients which determines the dependence of the parasite on the host. Moreover it has been suggested that this dependence may determine specificity. The chief compounds which give the specific characters of the host are macromolecules, proteins and nucleic acids; molecules of low molecular weights are less likely to vary greatly except among more widely separated taxonomic groups. High specificity in parasites, if it is dependent primarily on the provision of unique substances occurring only in the susceptible species of host, might thus be expected to involve macromolecules synthesized by the host. Hawking (1955), writing about protozoan parasites, suggested that the "narrow specificity of certain parasites for certain hosts e.g. *Plasmodium vivax* for *Homo sapiens*, is due to the close adaptation of the parasites to proteins of the host". It is not known whether metazoan parasites can use unaltered proteins and nucleic acids of the host as nutrients.

C. Substances that have a Specific Stimulating Action on Parasites

Many components of the environments of free-living animals, in addition to any direct actions they may have on metabolism, may have indirect effects which regulate the activities of animals. These components of the environment may be relatively complex organic substances, such as glutathione which "triggers" the feeding activity of *Hydra* (Loomis, 1955), or simple substances, like dissolved gaseous carbon dioxide which stimulates sexual reproduction in the same animal (Loomis, 1957).

Is it possible that substances provided by the host might serve some such functions for parasites? Could stimuli like these govern such activities as feeding, development and migration of parasites within the host? Certainly the exsheathing and hatching of infective agents of several species of nematodes are stimulated by factors in the environment provided by the hosts (Rogers and Sommerville, 1957; Rogers, 1958). None of these factors, undissociated carbonic acid and dissolved gaseous carbon dioxide, Eh and pH, is unique in itself, but different combinations of them do give some degree of specificity (Rogers, 1960).

The "hatching factor" for the eggs of *Heterodera rostochiensis* produced by the plant hosts also acts as a stimulus (Ellenby and Gilbert, 1957). It is a relatively complex substance excreted by a small range of host plants and it is evidently at least partly responsible for the specificity of the parasite.

D. *Dissolved Gases in the Medium*

It is known that the tensions of both oxygen and carbon dioxide in the medium may be important in the economy of parasites and it is not unreasonable to class them as nutrients. Thus carbon dioxide has a marked sparing effect on the use of carbohydrate reserves of the nematode parasite *Heterakis gallinae* (Fairbairn, 1954) and it is fixed by this parasite and probably by several other species.

All the parasites which have been examined so far (von Brand, 1952) have the capacity to use oxygen when it is present in the medium, and the survival of many *in vitro* is shortened by the withdrawal of oxygen (Davey, 1938*a*). In most tissues of host animals, oxygen is freely available to parasites. In the contents of the alimentary canal, however, except close to the mucosa, oxygen is likely to be absent or present only in small amounts (von Brand and Weise, 1932; Rogers, 1949) and so may limit the distribution of some species of parasites.

E. *Antibodies and Toxic Substances produced by the Host*

Even when the environment contains all the components needed for the parasite, infection may not occur if substances such as antibodies or toxins which attack the parasite are produced by the host. Just how far the innate or acquired capacity of host animals to produce such substances limits the host range of metazoan parasites is unknown. Mechanisms of this sort certainly limit the range of hosts which can be infected with some parasitic protozoa. Thus infections with some trypanosomes are maintained only because the parasite has the capacity to change its antigenic structure at intervals during the course of infection (Browning, Adamson and Keppie, 1953).

F. *Other Organisms*

Though predators are not commonly found in the environments of internal parasites, the presence of individuals of other species, or even the same species, can affect the environment. This may occur indirectly via the host, i.e. the organisms may affect the health of the host to such a degree that the environment becomes unsuitable. Or it may occur directly due to the production of excretory products or through the physical effects of crowding (see, for example, Read, 1951). Also the parasites themselves may have a favourable effect on the environment. They might, for instance, produce basic or acidic substances, or enzymes, or inhibitors of enzymes (Collier, 1941) which counteract unsuitable conditions.

G. *A Supporting Medium of Suitable Physico-chemical Properties*

Properties of this sort may depend largely on the proportions of salts and other simple substances in the environment which go to make up the "balanced medium" of appropriate hydrogen ion concentration, oxidation-reduction potential or osmotic pressure. These features may be basic for the pattern of requirement for parasites and some may have specific stimulating effects on parasites as well. They may be important in determining the sort of organ, or site in the alimentary canal, in which a parasite may live (Davey, 1938*b*; Rogers and Sommerville, 1957).

Many physico-chemical properties arise partly from unspecific processes. Thus a variety of oxidizing or reducing substances might contribute to the oxidation-reduction potential but, so long as the potential falls within certain limits, the actual nature of the compounds might not always be of importance. Similarly, suitable hydrogen ion concentrations and osmotic pressures could be obtained with a number of different substances.

H. *The Physical Properties of the Medium*

Physical properties like temperature and mechanical pressure have little specificity but they are important features of the environment required by some parasites. They are important because, if the environment is complete except in these respects, some vital feature of development fails. The rise in temperature that many parasites experience when they are transferred from an intermediate host to a warm-blooded definitive host is a signal for developmental changes certainly in one tapeworm (Smyth, 1952) and may be of some general significance. And a simple lack of mechanical pressure may lead to failure in fertilization and to the production of infertile eggs (Smyth, 1954).

It seems reasonable to suppose that other physical properties such as viscosity, the rate of movement of the supporting medium, and purely structural features of the environment such as the size of pores in a membrane, the diameter of blood vessels, or folds on the surfaces of membranes may be important features of the environment of different parasites.

The Dependence of the Parasite on the Host

Most components of the environment of parasites could be placed in one of the categories A to H. Some might go into more than one category because they may have more than one effect on the parasite. Thus glucose could serve as a nutrient (A) and affect the osmotic pressure as well (G); glutathione might be an essential nutrient (B) as well as an influence on the redox potential. Moreover, the components in different categories could be interdependent; e.g. the requirement of a native protein as a nutrient for a parasite (B) might set a limit to the pH range of the environment.

In this classification of the components of the environment of a parasite, B, E, F and part of A and C could be regarded as "biotic" factors, and the remainder as "physical" factors. Or a part of A, B and C might be classed as "food"; D, G and part of A as "weather"; E and F as "other living organisms", and H as "a place in which to live". Just how far components of the environment would be "density-responsive" would depend upon the capacity of the host to keep within the limits tolerated by the parasites independently of size of the infection. Even the temperature of the environment, which in warm-blooded animals is dependent upon the health of the host, could be a "density-responsive" factor.

The relative importance of these different categories in the environment in determining the dependence of the parasite on the host is unknown. For some parasites the provision of a special nutrient or the nature of the defence mechanism of the host might be critical. But it is possible that the unusual characters of the environment of a parasite might not be due to the presence of any component which does not occur in the environments of free-living animals. Indeed all the components might be commonplace so that the unusual character of a parasite's environment might be due to the unusual proportions of the components. For some parasites even the structure, stability or regular change in the environment might be more critical than the need for special nutrients.

The components of the environment of a parasite may be regarded as forming a pattern. The limits of variation of the pattern would depend on the parasite and the inter-relations of different parts of the pattern. For some parasites at least, parts of the pattern can vary widely. Thus some nematode parasites can withstand salt concentrations equivalent to 50 to 230 mM sodium chloride *in vitro* (Panikkar and Sproston, 1941; von Brand and Simpson, 1942). Other helminths are similar in their resistance to changes in osmotic pressure (Stephenson, 1947; Van Cleave and Ross, 1944). Apart from a little information of this sort, however, there is no direct evidence about the variation in the environment that parasites can withstand. The indirect evidence comes (i) from our knowledge of the specificity of parasites and (ii) from experiments on the cultivation of parasites *in vitro*.

Specificity of Parasites

A parasite that can live only in one, or in a few species of hosts is likely to be highly exacting in its pattern of requirements; and an unspecific parasite can live in a wide variety of environments. Thus the adult *Taenia saginata*, for which man is the only definitive host, seems to require an environment which can be provided only in one organ of one species of animal. *Trichinella spiralis*, on the other hand, which can live in most warm-blooded animals, makes a much less critical demand on its environment. Evidence of this sort, however, must be assessed with care; the difference in specificity of *Taenia saginata* and *Trichinella spiralis* could be due to the different abilities of the two parasites to resist the attack of the hosts rather than to the capacities of the hosts to supply the components of the environments needed by the parasites. Also, matters other than the final environment in which the parasite lives must be considered. For instance, the behaviour of the infective stage of the parasite and of the host may affect specificity. In Chapter 10 factors in the relationship between the parasite and the host which affect specificity are discussed in more detail.

The Cultivation of Parasites in vitro

The sort of medium in which parasites can be cultured might be expected to show how exacting the requirements of parasites might be. Unfortunately, only a few parasites have been cultured successfully and then only in complex media of which the precise chemical composition is unknown.

Stages in the Host–Parasite Association

The essential components of the environment may vary *in vivo*, not only from one species of parasite to another, but also during the life cycle of a particular parasite, i.e. the needs of the parasite will vary with its stage of development within or on the host. This means that the requirements of a parasite would not only form a pattern at any one time, but there might also be a definite sequence of changes in the pattern which would be necessary for the parasite to complete its life cycle. This view is supported by the results of Rogers and Sommerville (1957) who showed that the optimum conditions for bringing about the first changes towards the parasitic stages in the life cycles of some parasites of sheep occurred in those regions of the gut of the host which preceded the final sites of the adult parasites.

In some parasites at least, the process of infection is started by a

TABLE I

Relationships between the Parasite and the Host

Stage in the association between the parasite and host	Some of the biological processes involved in the different stages of the association	Some features of the environment which might have special significance in the different stages
Stage I Infection via the gut or skin of the host	Hatching of eggs; exsheathment of larvae; evagination of cysticercus; loss of cilia as the miracidium penetrates the host	Physico-chemical conditions such as oxidation-reduction potential, gas pressures; special substances such as bile salts and the eelworm hatching factor; temperature; digestive enzymes
Stage II Maintenance of the individual parasite in the host	Feeding, growth, respiration, migration in the host, moulting of nematodes	Nutrients, oxygen, and salts in the medium; osmotic pressure, pH; toxins and antibodies produced by the host
Stage III Reproduction and the production of infective agents; maintenance of the species	Asexual reproduction; production of eggs and sperm, fertilization; dispersal of infective agents; specificity and the evolution of parasitism	Increased quantities of basic nutrients; changes in temperature; mechanical factors; toxins and antibodies produced by the host

stimulus from the host which leads to such changes as the hatching of infective eggs (Rogers, 1958). Without this stimulus infection cannot occur. But even if infection takes place, the absence of nutrients and a suitable supporting medium would make it impossible for the parasites to maintain themselves in the host. Further, all factors may be present for infection and for the maintenance of parasites, but other factors needed for reproductive activity and for the production of fertile eggs may be absent, or present in inadequate amounts. Thus the pattern of requirements for *Schistocephalus solidus* includes simple physical factors which are required specifically for the production of fertile eggs (Smyth, 1954). Another possible example here is *Ascaridia galli* which feeds on the gut contents of the host (Rogers and Lazarus, 1949). Egg production of nematodes necessitates a considerable intake of phosphorus in one form or another (Martin and Ross, 1934). If the intake of phosphorus in the diet of chickens harbouring *Ascaridia galli* was inadequate, the pattern of requirements for the production of eggs might not be complete.

It seems reasonable to suppose, then, that the needs of many parasites will vary with the stage of development in the life cycle, and at least three stages might be recognized: when the pattern has features predominantly concerned with the process of infection of the host; when the needs are largely for the growth and maintenance of the parasite as an individual; and when additional requirements, for the maintenance of the parasite as a species by sexual or asexual reproduction, have to be met. Some of the chief features which might be concerned with the pattern of requirements of parasites in the three main stages of association with the host are summarized below and in Table I. Some host–parasite relationships are also shown diagrammatically in Fig. 1.

The First Stage in the Association between the Host and the Parasite

This is concerned with the processes which lead to the infection of the host. Free-living stages, if they precede the infective stage, are involved, but the direct association between the parasite and the host starts when the infective agent becomes a parasite in the new host. If the infective agent is a free-living stage the process of infection frequently involves the removal of outer layers of the organism. These outer layers may be protective like the shells of eggs, cyst-walls and the sheaths of larvae of nematodes; or they may be concerned with dispersal like the ciliated epithelium of miracidia.

The important components in the environment in which the first stage of association takes place are those which start development of the infective stage as true parasites. In general, these components need not be highly specific. It is sufficient to ensure that the infective stage does not lose the material and physiological properties which protect it as an infective agent until it enters an environment with the components needed for the second stage of the association.

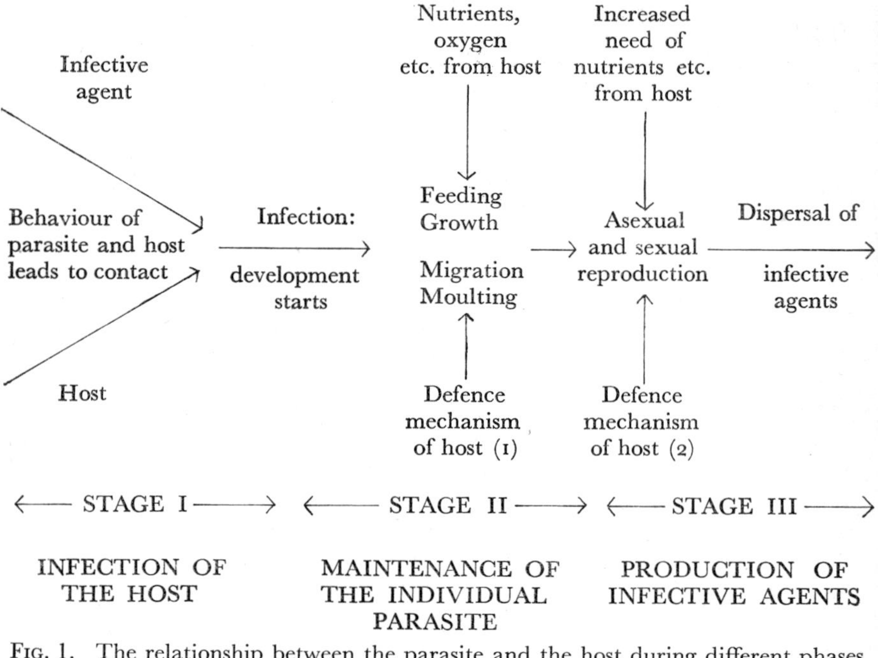

FIG. 1. The relationship between the parasite and the host during different phases of the life cycle.

The Second Stage of the Association

Here the relationship between the parasite and the host must be closer than in the first stage because the environment must contain all the components which lead to growth and, in some parasites, migration, moulting, and even metamorphosis. Moreover, during this stage the parasite is more open to the attack of the host by normal physiological processes or by the action of antibodies and non-specific tissue reactions.

The Third Stage of the Association

The maintenance of a parasite as a species is dependent on its capacity to infect the new host. This in turn depends upon the number of infective agents the parasite produces and their chances of meeting the new host. The probability that the infective agent will meet the host may be increased by the intervention of an intermediate host with the appropriate pattern of behaviour. Alternatively, the parasite might simply produce large numbers of infective agents which are well protected against harmful components of the environment until they are taken up, largely by chance, by the host. In both these sorts of life cycles the needs of the parasite might differ in many respects from its needs in the first and second stages of the association of the parasite with the host. Thus for many parasites such as *Ascaris lumbricoides* and *Haemonchus contortus* the production of eggs is so great that added demands must be made on the environment for substrates for energy and for the building blocks for the synthesis of the materials in the eggs. Similarly the production of vast numbers of cercariae must require an increased supply of nutrients for rediae or sporocysts.

In the following chapters some components in the environments and related factors which influence the three stages in the association between parasites and their hosts will be discussed in more detail.

Summary

In order to infect the host and to survive, the parasite must obtain substances from the host, under the proper conditions. Some of these substances and conditions, or combinations of substances and conditions, would occur rarely except on or in the host. The need for these special features of the environment determines the parasitic habit of an organism. But in addition to having needs which can be fulfilled only by the proper host, the parasite must be able to resist the unfavourable factors—toxins, antibodies, physical conditions—in the environment provided by the host.

The needs of the parasite, and its capacity to resist unfavourable conditions, may vary throughout the life cycle. Thus special conditions may be necessary in order that infection may occur; and the needs for the growth of the parasite may change, at least in degree, during the reproductive period of the cycle.

References

Allee, W. C., Emerson, A. E., Park, O., Park, T. and Schmidt, K. P. (1949) "Principles of Animal Ecology". W. B. Saunders, Philadelphia.
Andrewartha, H. G. and Birch, L. C. (1954) "The Distribution and Abundance of Animals". University of Chicago Press, Chicago.
Baer, J. G. (1952) "Ecology of Animal Parasites". University of Illinois Press, Urbana.
Browning, C. H., Adamson, H. and Keppie, A. A. N. (1953) *J. Path. Bact.* **65**, 137.
Caullery, M. (1952) "Parasitism and Symbiosis". Sidgwick and Jackson, London.
Chitwood, B. G. (1951) *Plant & Soil*, **3**, 47.
——, Specht, A. and Havis, L. (1952) *Plant & Soil*, **4**, 77.
Collier, H. B. (1941) *Canad. J. Res.* **B19**, 91.

Davey, D. G. (1938*a*) *J. exp. Biol.* **15**, 217.
—— (1938*b*) *Parasitology*, **30**, 278.
Ellenby, C. and Gilbert, A. B. (1957) *Nature, Lond.* **180**, 1105.
Fairbairn, D. (1954) *Exp. Parasit.* **3**, 52.
—— (1957) *Exp. Parasit.* **6**, 491.
Hawking, F. (1955) *In* "Mechanisms of Microbial Pathogenicity", 5th Symp. of Soc. gen. Microbiol. (J. W. Howie and A. J. O'Hea, eds.), Cambridge University Press, Cambridge.
Loomis, W. F. (1955) *Fed. Proc.* **14**, 247.
—— (1957) *Science*, **126**, 735.
Lwoff, A. (1933) *Ann. Inst. Pasteur*, **51**, 55.
Martin, C. J. and Ross, I. C. (1934) *J. Helminth.* **12**, 137.
Nicholson, A. J. (1954) *Aust. J. Zool.* **2**, 9.
Panikkar, N. K. and Sproston, N. G. (1941) *Parasitology*, **33**, 214.
Read, C. P. (1951) *J. Parasit.* **37**, 174.
—— and Rothman, A. H. (1957) *Exp. Parasit.* **6**, 294.
Rogers, W. P. (1949) *Aust. J. sci. Res.* **B2**, 157.
—— (1958) *Nature, Lond.* **181**, 1410.
—— (1960) *Proc. roy. Soc.* **B152**, 367.
—— and Lazarus, M. (1949) *Parasitology*, **39**, 245.
—— and Sommerville, R. I. (1957) *Nature, Lond.* **179**, 619.
Smyth, J. D. (1952) *J. exp. Biol.* **29**, 304.
—— (1954) *Exp. Parasit.* **3**, 64.
Stephenson, W. (1947) *Parasitology*, **38**, 116.
Van Cleave, H. J. and Ross, E. (1944) *J. Parasit.* **30**, Suppl. 7.
Varley, G. C. (1947) *J. animal Ecol.* **16**, 139.
von Brand, T. (1952) "Chemical Physiology of Endoparasitic Animals". Academic Press, New York.
—— and Weise, W. (1932) *Z. vergl. Physiol.* **18**, 339.
—— and Simpson, W. F. (1942) *Proc. Soc. exp. Biol. Med.* **49**, 245.

PART II

The Problem of Infectiousness

General Introduction

By infectiousness I mean the capacity of an organism to live as a parasite. If the infective stage is free-living, infectiousness is the capacity to change from this stage into a true parasite living within or on the host. If there is an intermediate host in the life cycle infectiousness may be the ability to change from a parasite in one host to a parasite in another sort of host. Infectiousness also includes the capacity of an organism to maintain a parasitic mode of life on or in the new host. This part of the book is concerned only with the initial changes which occur when the infective stage becomes parasitic. If, for example, the infective stage is an egg, the importance here is the hatching of the egg so that the embryo can emerge and start living as a parasite; or, if the infective stage is the sheathed larva of a parasitic nematode, the importance is with the processes that complete the moult and free the parasitic larva. This is what I refer to as "the process of infection" with eggs or sheathed larvae. The advantage of starting with processes like this in the study of infectiousness is that morphological changes which are easily observed occur during infection. Frequently, of course, changes like this do not occur. Nevertheless, the change from an infective stage to a parasitic stage must always involve physiological changes because growth is suspended in the infective stage and is restarted only when infection occurs.

In the next three chapters some of the factors which influence the infection of the host are discussed from three points of view:

(i) the special role of the infective agent in the life cycles of parasites and the sort of adaptations which might best allow it to act as a "bridge" from one sort of environment to another;

(ii) the physiological characteristics of free-living stages and how they are concerned in the process of infection;

(iii) the physiological relationship between the infective stage and the host, and the components of the environment provided by the host which initiate the development of the first parasitic stage.

Though the life cycles of parasites and the physiology of the free-living stages have been studied extensively, little of this work has been directly concerned with the mechanisms by which the hosts become infected. It is difficult, therefore, to make generalizations about the processes which lead to the first stage in the association between the parasite and the host. Nevertheless there is some justification for advancing a hypothesis which deals with a restricted group of nematode parasites—those which infect the host *via* the alimentary canal.

CHAPTER 3

Life Cycles and Infection

PARASITIC species are found in almost all the phyla of animals and in many it is possible to compare the life cycles of the parasitic species with those of the related free-living forms. From such comparisons it is often found that parasites may have more simple life cycles as in the parasitic Cirripeda in which larval stages may be shortened and merged into one another. Among the groups of parasites which no longer have closely related free-living species, stages in the simplification of the life cycles can be seen by comparing different species of parasites. In the Cestoda, for instance, complexity in the life cycle ranges from *Diphyllobothrium latum* with two intermediate hosts and one optional "transport" or "paratenic" host, to *Hymenolepis nana* in which the whole life cycle may be condensed to take place in the one host (Baer, 1952, pp. 147, 148).

But in many ways parasitism involves an increase in the complexity of life cycles. Thus the free-living nematode *Panagrellus redivivus* can repeat its whole life cycle in the one medium, whereas the filarial worm *Wuchereria bancrofti* has a complex cycle because it requires two very different hosts, an insect and a mammal.

Most of the adaptations to parasitism in the life cycles of modern parasites are those which increase the probability that the infective stage will reach the next host. These adaptations usually take one of two forms: (i) increases in the numbers of infective agents which are resistant to the environmental conditions, and (ii) the development of patterns of behaviour which lead to increased contacts between the host and the parasite. *Taenia saginata*, which may live in man for ten years, producing 50 to 150 million eggs per year, and *Ascaris lumbricoides*, which produces 200,000 eggs per day for about a year, are examples of parasites which produce large numbers of infective agents. Most parasites, however, have a lower egg output than this, especially when efficient means of spreading infection have been developed. In parasitic molluscs, for instance, egg production is often lower than in related free-living species. Resistance to the hazards of the environment such as high and low temperatures and shortage of water is frequently increased by the production of thick-shelled eggs, or by the process of incomplete moulting which leaves a larva protected by the uncast cuticle of an earlier stage. The behaviour of the infective stage also influences its chance of reaching the host. The migration of infective larvae onto the grass, which makes them more easily available to grazing animals, is a simple example of this sort of adaptation. Sometimes it is the introduction of an additional host in the life cycle that increases greatly the chance of infection. The behaviour of the intermediate host is such that it can form a link between the habitat where its own infection is most likely to take place, and the habitat where the infection of the final host is most likely to occur.

The adaptations which increase the chance of contact between the infective stage and the host are, however, the sort which might arise very largely *after* an organism had established a parasitic mode of life. The sort of character which would be needed so that an organism would *become* a parasite might be quite different. A requirement in the life cycle for the starting of parasitism would be that at least one stage of the organism should be able to come in contact with the host and be able to "infect" it; i.e. the presumptive parasite must have a stage which could attach itself to the host and survive long enough to produce material which could ultimately re-infect the host. To achieve this the "infective stage" must have unusual characters. It must be able to move from the one environment where it lives as a free-living organism to a very different type of environment where it lives on or in the host. And the sort of environment in which the infective stage must live as a free-living organism is often restricted because it must be one in which the parasite can make contact with the host. To do this the infective stage must often live in places where it is exposed to hazards such as shortage of water and extremes in temperature. Thus on the one hand it must be able to meet extremes in the weather of its environment; on the other it must be capable of resisting the "biological attacks" of the host—hazards which are not found in the environment of free-living animals.

In many species of parasites the change in environments which occurs during the life cycle is lessened by the acquisition of an additional host, especially when free-living stages are entirely eliminated from the life cycle. Nevertheless, infective stages in the life cycles of this kind still have definite characteristics which can be recognized in infective stages in general.

The problem of moving from one environment to another has been solved by many species of free-living animals. As a rule, problems of this sort are met by sudden changes in anatomy and physiology which take place during the life cycle of the animal. Thus in the Amphibia a metamorphosis takes place at the end of the aquatic phase to give an adult more fitted for life in a terrestrial environment. Among invertebrates the most dramatic changes of this kind are found in the Insecta. In this group also, metamorphosis may be accompanied by a period of rest or diapause, which allows for different time relationships between the two environments. Thus the metamorphosis of the pupa to adult in some species is delayed over winter by a period of diapause.

Is it possible that the mechanisms by which the infective stages of parasites pass from one type of environment to another are similar to the mechanisms found in free-living animals which allow them to live in two different environments during their life cycles? Certainly the infection of the host is often accompanied by marked changes in the anatomy and presumably in the physiology of the parasite which in many species amounts to a metamorphosis. In this chapter these questions are discussed; in particular, the general characters of the infective stage which might distinguish it from other stages of the life cycles of parasites are examined. Only nematode parasites are discussed in any detail. The uniformity of the life cycles of this group in comparison with most of the other groups of parasites makes it easier to summarize the information.

The Life Cycle of Nematodes

The basic life cycle of nematodes, whether they are free-living or parasitic, has six stages separated by four moults (Maupas, 1899; Seurat, 1920; Filipjev and Michajlova, 1924; Filipjev and Schuurmans Stekhoven, 1941). The egg hatches to give the first larval stage (more correctly, the first juvenile stage) which moults to give the second larval stage. This process is repeated until the fourth stage moults to give the adult. During this process gradual changes occur; size increases steadily except for a short period before and during each moult. Growth continues in the adult. The lengths of specimens of *Hyostrongylus rubidus* during development to the adult male are graphed in Fig. 2. Alicata (1935) found that the growth was slow but steady up to the time of the second moult; at the infective stage growth ceased and did not start again until some time after infection had occurred. Thereafter the rate of growth increased rapidly. The short periods when growth ceased at each moult were not recorded but the difference between the infective stage and other stages in the life cycle was clear.

In most species of nematodes growth is due to an increase in the size of cells rather than an increase in the number of cells. The reproductive and nervous systems increase steadily in complexity but at moulting sudden changes sometimes occur in parts of the alimentary

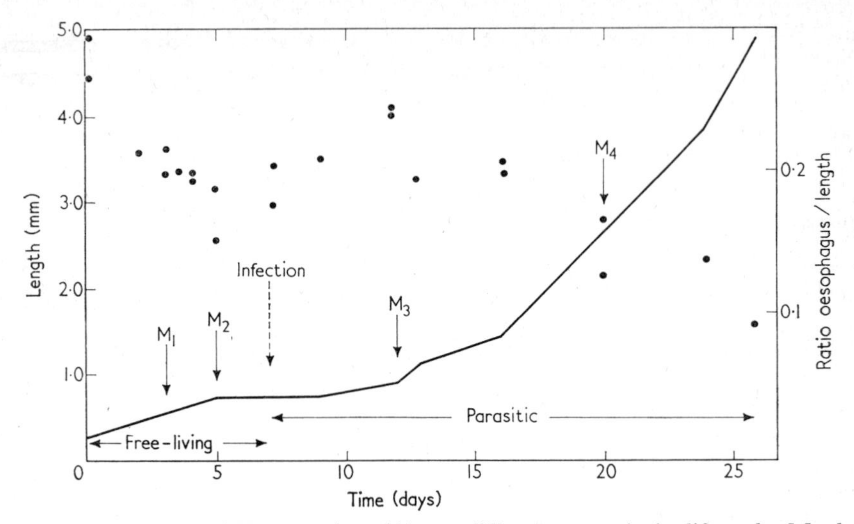

FIG. 2. The length of *Hyostrongylus rubidus* at different stages in its life cycle. Moults are shown as M_1, M_2, M_3 and M_4. Growth was measured from the time the eggs hatched, and the free-living stages were cultured at 22° to 24°C. The points show the values of the ratio, length of œsophagus/length of body, at different times during the life cycle. The measurements were taken from Alicata (1935).

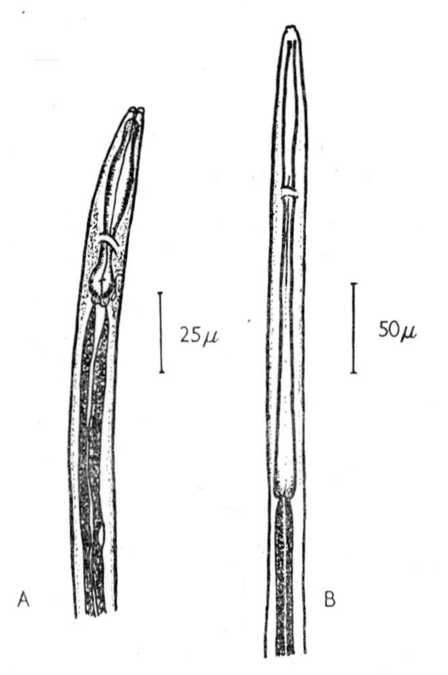

FIG. 3. Anterior parts of larvae of *Strongyloides ransomi* showing,
A, the rhabditiform œsophagus of a free-living stage, and
B, the filariform œsophagus of the infective stage (from Alicata, 1935).

canal. In free-living stages of *Strongyloides,* for instance, the rhabditiform œsophagus has an anterior swelling followed by a posterior bulb (Fig. 3A). The infective and parasitic stages have a filariform œsophagus which has no anterior swelling (Fig. 3B). Moreover, the ratio of the length of the œsophagus to the length of the whole worm changes rapidly from about $\frac{1}{4}$ to $\frac{1}{2}$ in some species of *Strongyloides*. In many other nematodes, however, the changes in the proportions of the body take place gradually throughout the life cycle (Fig. 2). Thus a metamorphosis like that in the Arthropoda does not occur in nematodes. Even the pronounced changes in shape which occur in *Tetrameres* and *Spaerularia* (Fig. 4) are due largely to the increase in the size of the female reproductive system and cannot be regarded as a metamorphosis.

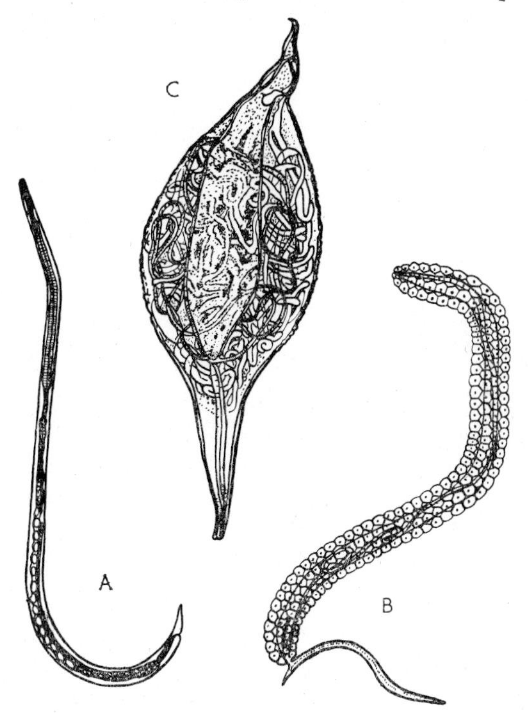

FIG. 4. The morphology of adult nematode parasites: A, parasitic female of *Strongyloides stercoralis* (after Faust, 1949); in B, *Spaerularia bombi*, and C, *Tetrameres fissispina*, the bodies are distorted by the enlarged uterus (after Leuckart, 1887; Travassos, 1919).

The Egg as the Agent of Infection

The basic life cycle has been modified in many parasitic nematodes. It is probable, however, that most forms undergo all the moults characteristic of the basic life cycle (see, for instance, Chandler *et al.*, 1940,

p. 267), though the early moults may take place within the egg-shell. For instance in *Metastrongylus* spp. the first moult occurs before the egg hatches, and in *Ascaris lumbricoides* and *Syngamus trachea* two or three moults take place within the egg-shell. In *Heterodera rostochiensis* development continues to the second larval stage within the egg-shell, which in turn is further enclosed in a cyst formed from the body wall of the parent. These changes in the life cycle are adaptations for the protection of pre-parasitic stages. In some species they also aid in spreading infection because the eggs are often better placed than larvae to be dispersed by wind and water. The delay in the hatching of eggs which is basic to these adaptations is not uncommon among parasitic nematodes; it is, however, rare in free-living species.

In a number of parasites development proceeds to the infective stage, which, according to the species, may be the first, second or third larval stage, within the egg-shell. As the egg must hatch within an appropriate host and not before, a feature of parasitism in these species is that the process of hatching of the egg becomes more complex because it requires the intervention of the host. In this respect the modifications of the life cycle are related to the components of the environment provided by the host which lead to the hatching of the egg and so to infection.

The Ensheathed Larva as an Agent of Infection

Moulting in nematodes is a relatively simple process similar to that in the Kinorhyncha (Hyman, 1951, pp. 181, 454). The entire cuticle of the body surface, including the lining of the buccal capsule, the excretory canal, rectum and vagina, is shed as a thin transparent membrane. In the few species which have been examined in detail during the process of moulting the cuticle becomes loosened from the underlying hypodermis at the anterior and posterior ends of the worm. The areas of loosened cuticle then increase towards the middle of the worm where they meet. The larva emerges from the old cuticle either through a slit in the anterior part or by shedding the anterior end of the cuticle as a small cap. The active movements of the worm are important in both these processes.

In many nematodes one of the moults takes place in two distinct phases. During the first phase the cuticle is loosened but it is not thrown off. In this condition the organism is enclosed in two cuticles, the outer one, thin and transparent, forming an envelope outside the cuticle proper. This is seen in free-living and parasitic species. In *Rhabditis coarctata* the larval stage (Fig. 5A) by which dispersion is effected is ensheathed in this way (Triffitt and Oldham, 1927). The second-stage larva (Fig. 5B) which emerges from the egg-shell of *Ascaris lumbricoides* is loosely enclosed in the thin cuticle of the first stage (Alicata,

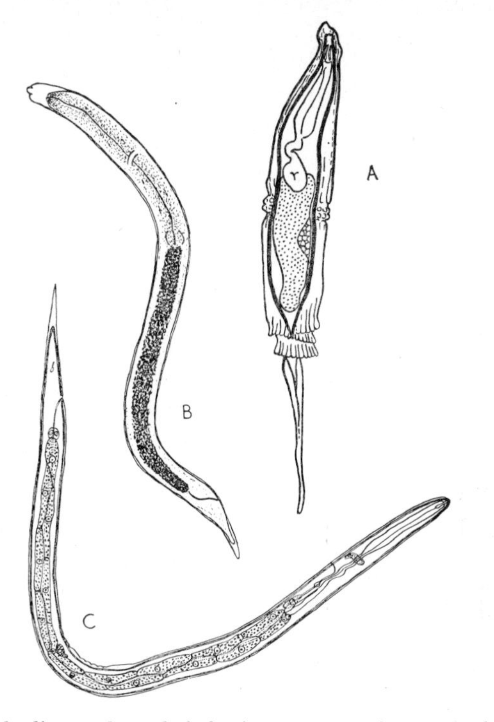

Fig. 5. Ensheathed dispersal and infective stages of nematodes: A, *Rhabditis coarctata;* B, *Ascaris lumbricoides;* C, *Trichostrongylus axei* (after Triffitt and Oldham, 1927; Alicata, 1935; Chitwood and Chitwood, 1940).

1935). The infective (third) stage of many trichostrongyle parasites is enclosed in a closely-fitting "sheath" formed from the uncast cuticle of the second stage (Fig. 5C). In many species the third stage emerges soon after ingestion by the host, after the anterior end of the sheath has been thrown off as a small cap. This, it seems, is achieved by the active movements of the juvenile nematode after the cuticle has become weakened at the base of the cap (Veglia, 1915; Lapage, 1935; Rogers and Sommerville, 1960). Ensheathed forms which enter the host through the skin, e.g. *Ancylostoma duodenale*, shed the sheath as they penetrate the outer layers of the skin (Looss, 1911).

The division of the process of moulting into two phases may thus have some significance in parasitism because it can give rise to an ensheathed infective stage. In many species in which the exsheathment occurs in or on the host as a prelude to infection the intervention of the host is required for the completion of moulting. Here again, then, the modifications of the life cycle of the parasites are related to the components of the environment provided by the host.

Like the process of moulting, the process of development of larval stages between moults may be divided into two phases.

In his description of the life cycle of the nematode parasite of sheep *Haemonchus contortus*, Veglia (1915) gave a detailed account of the two phases in each of the four larval stages. He found that just after the hatching of the egg or after the completion of a moult the newly-emerged larvae moved and fed actively; granules accumulated in the cells of the intestine and the length of the worm increased. After twelve hours the activity gradually decreased until the animals stopped feeding and became motionless. This second phase, which Veglia called "lethargus", also lasted about twelve hours. In this period the larvae remained rigid while changes in their internal structure took place. Size decreased rather than increased (see also Stoll, 1940). Activity, which restarted when the new cuticle was fully formed, led to the casting of the old cuticle except in the third stage when it remained as a sheath. The process was then repeated with the newly-emerged larva feeding and growing until the lethargic phase was again reached.

This division of each stage into periods of activity and inactivity has not been reported for many species. Looss (1911) in a detailed discussion of the development and life cycle of *Ancylostoma duodenale* did not remark particularly upon this matter. It is probable, however, that it is a common feature of development, though often without the clear distinction between the two phases which Veglia (1915) reported. Because the quiescent period is one in which reorganization of some of the internal structure and the musculature takes place, the animal might be expected to be sluggish or motionless. And the loosening of the old cuticle in the buccal capsule could prevent feeding.

Though there are some features which are common to the quiescent phase and the period when the larvae are ensheathed (for instance neither growth nor feeding occurs) there must be marked physiological differences. In fact, the ensheathed period corresponds more closely to the active period before lethargus.

The Physiological Function of Moulting

The significance of moulting in the life cycle of nematodes is not clear. In unspecialized species it may be primarily a mechanism of growth related to the properties of the cuticle. Thus this noncellular outer covering may limit the size of each larval stage, and its periodic removal at each moult may be necessary for increases in size of the worm (Looss, 1911).

The importance of the elastic properties of the cuticle in determining the movements and structure of *Ascaris lumbricoides* (Harris and Crofton, 1957) probably applies to many nematodes. This suggests that moulting is related to growth and is necessary so that, among other things, the elastic properties of the cuticle are retained as the organism increases in size. It is clear that the cuticle is extensible to some degree because the new cuticle formed under the old one is always smaller and the newly-moulted larva is smaller than its predecessor though it soon increases in size. Also the cuticle of adult worms must often be highly extensible; sometimes the increase in the size of adults is more than in all the preceding stages together. In some species moulting takes place without any increase in size. *Meloidogyne*, for instance, moults several times without casting any of the cuticles so that the larva is sometimes enclosed in several layers at once. Thus moulting may take place without growth; and growth may take place without moulting. Whatever the relationship was between moulting and growth in unspecialized nematodes no satisfactory generalizations can be applied to many modern species.

Moulting might be a mechanism for getting rid of nitrogenous waste materials. This is a questionable hypothesis, however, because it seems that nitrogenous wastes are excreted by larvae without difficulty (Weinstein and Haskins, 1955). And ammonia and urea can be excreted even through the adult cuticle of *Ascaris lumbricoides* and *Ascaridia galli* (Rogers, 1952).

The Significance of Moulting in Parasitism

Whatever the physiological functions of moulting, it appears that it in some way facilitates entry into a new environment.

Like the wholly free-living organism, the pre-parasitic stage of a nematode parasite needs certain components in its environment. The step from the free-living stage to the parasitic stage involves a sudden change in the nature of these requirements. This change usually occurs at times in the life cycle when the normal processes of development have been interrupted just after a moult. Whatever the infective stage, egg or larva, development does not continue, even slowly, until infection occurs (e.g. see Fig. 2). At infection development is restarted rather than accelerated. The infective stage is thus a "resting" stage in the life cycle. Though it may move about actively it does not feed, nor does it grow, and it is dependent upon reserve materials, usually fat (Payne, 1923; Rogers, 1939), for its continued existence.

This is generally true even when an intermediate host is involved in the life cycle. Once the infective stage is reached inside the intermediate host development seldom goes any further.† But here again a sudden

†*Dracunculus medinensis* is a rare exception in this respect (Moorthy, 1938*a*) in that the third-stage larva in *Cyclops*, which is infective to the final host, increases slightly in size after moulting.

change in environment occurs before development is started in the final host. The infective stage forms a "bridge" which enables the parasite to go from one sort of environment to another. In wholly free-living nematodes the dispersal form sometimes is similar to the infective stage of a parasitic species because it has to be transported to a fresh site before development can be restarted.

Except in rare instances, such as *Camallanus sweeti* in which the first larval stage may be infective (Moorthy, 1938*b*), the formation of an infective stage is immediately preceded by a moult or partial moult. The moult which gives rise to the infective stage is usually the first, as in many Ascaroidea (Alicata, 1934), or the second, as in many Strongyloidea (Looss, 1911; Veglia, 1915; Alicata, 1935). In a number of parasites the life cycle is not known in detail and it is uncertain how many moults precede the development of the infective stage but there is sufficient evidence to suggest that in different species almost any stage in the life cycle except the adult may become the infective stage for the vertebrate, invertebrate or plant host.

The change in the physiology of the larva which gives rise to a dispersal stage or infective stage probably takes place when moulting occurs. Thus the structural changes which occur at moulting are here accompanied by profound physiological changes which will allow the animal to enter a new, and often very different, environment. And until the new environment is reached development ceases completely; the infective stage "rests" until some factor in the new environment promotes further development. This suggests that the changes preceding dispersal or infection which take place in the larva are not complete and that the new environment must itself, directly or indirectly, complete the process.

A Physiological Basis for the Life Cycle of Nematodes

It was pointed out in the beginning of this chapter that many animals undergo a metamorphosis when, in the course of their normal life cycles, they leave one environment and enter another. In this process the action of the environment is always indirect, i.e. the components of the environment do not themselves act on the tissues of the animals. Instead metamorphosis is brought about by internal secretions which are secreted as a result of a stimulus from the environment acting on receptors. In many species the course of events is: component of environment→ receptor→ nervous system→ gland A →gland B →tissue reactions. The importance of the different steps in this system varies. Some may be absent, others may be added. Thus it is frequently found that vertebrates and invertebrates can pass through a complex life cycle involving a metamorphosis in a constant environment. In these animals the changes are brought about by internal secretions, independently, very often, of the environment. Even when the events in the life cycle are simple, as in the moulting of early juveniles of many arthropods, development is controlled in ways similar to this.

Could processes like this control the moulting and development of nematodes? Though these animals lack the anatomical complexity of the Arthropoda a number of "gland cells" have been described in their tissues. However, the main features in the life cycle of parasitic nematodes, which point to a general hypothesis about the underlying physiological processes controlling moulting and development, might be listed as follows:

(1) The life cycle of nematodes, though it does not involve a metamorphosis, does include well-defined moults. The period between moults may be divided, more or less distinctly, into a phase of active feeding and a quiescent phase.

(2) In parasitic species the formation of the infective stage is usually preceded by a moult or partial moult. Whether the life cycle is direct or indirect, the infective stage is a "resting" stage in which the normal processes of development are suspended.

(3) The infective, "resting" stage does not resume development until it reaches the appropriate host. In different species the infective stage may be any of the four larval stages; the adult does not normally occur as an infective stage.

(4) In many species the infective stage is enclosed within an egg-shell, or a partly-cast cuticle or sheath. In these species the first changes which take place during infection are the hatching of the egg or the exsheathment of the larva.

(5) In species which migrate inside the host, moulting is often correlated with movement from one site to another during the parasitic phase of development; i.e. moulting is often associated with a change in environment within the host.

The time taken for free-living nematodes to pass through the life cycle is influenced by factors in the environment such as temperature and food supply, but there must also be some internal mechanism within the worms which is largely responsible for the duration of the different phases of development. It seems that some timing mechanism must at intervals set in motion the processes which lead to such events as the hatching of eggs, the moulting of larvae, and the development of adult features. These events, which often require the co-ordination of changes throughout the whole organism, might be brought about either by a system of internal secretions or by the nervous system. From the nature of the changes that take place in nematodes it seems that co-ordination by internal secretions is the more likely. The secretions could be distributed throughout the body of the nematode via the body fluid, or simply by diffusion from cell to cell.

The basic life cycle of a free-living nematode might be idealized in the form shown in Fig. 6. Here "development" includes an increase both in the number of cells and in the size of the cells. Before hatching, for instance, "development" would be largely an increase in the number of cells; after hatching, the principal indication of development would be an increase in cell size in most species.

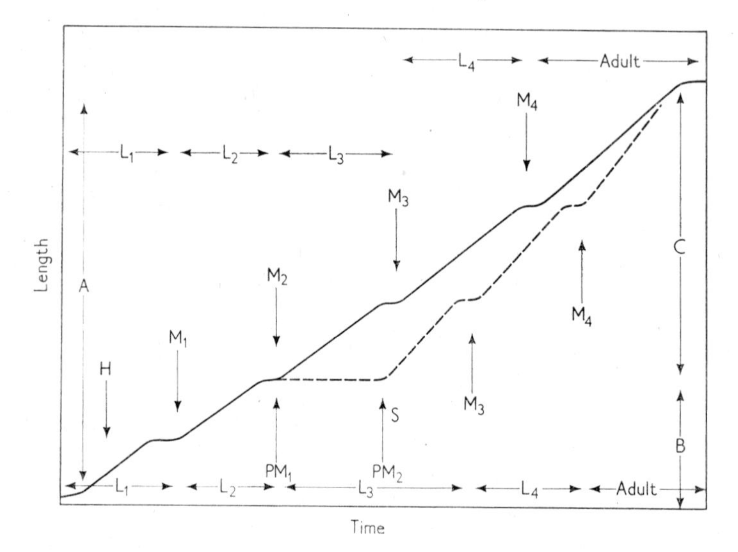

FIG. 6. An idealized form of the basic life cycle of nematodes (hypothetical). The solid line represents the life cycle in which "internal secretions" are produced regularly to promote hatching (H) and moulting (M_1– M_4). The broken line represents a life cycle in which a change of environment is necessary to stimulate (S) the completion of the second moult. A, B and C are different environments.

Development, it is suggested, would take place in a series of steps. At each step it would at first be rapid, gradually slowing to a period of quiescence during which the substances which governed and co-ordinated the developmental changes would be released in the tissues of the larva and these would give rise to minor rearrangements in structure culminating in a moult (M_1, M_2, M_3, M_4). The first three moults might be influenced by a "juvenile hormone" which would delay the development of the primary sex organs until after the fourth moult.

In an unspecialized nematode with this basic life cycle there would be five periods of development, one ending with the hatching of the egg and four ending with a moult, all of which, it is suggested, would be governed by some sort of internal regulating mechanism. In the life cycle of free-living nematodes the periods between moults would be largely controlled by the internal mechanism. This mechanism would not be dependent upon specific changes in the environment except where one of the larval stages was specialized for dispersal.

The underlying physiological mechanism which controls development in free-living nematodes may be similar in some respects to that of the Insecta (Wigglesworth, 1954). Adaptations to parasitism would require that the host in some way should influence the mechanism controlling development.

Adaptations for Infection with Larvae

A species of nematode with the basic life cycle would have the capacity to pass through all its stages in the one environment (A, Fig. 6). Adaptations which allowed a species to spend part of its life in one environment (B) and part in another (C) would be correlated with changes in the cycle of "internal secretions". If, for instance, the production of substances which led to moulting became dependent, at a particular larval stage, upon the presence of a certain component (S) in the environment, moulting would be delayed until that environment was reached. And if feeding, growth and internal changes could not occur until moulting had taken place, the larva would form a "resting stage" and act as a bridge between two sorts of environments, the one lacking the component which stimulated the internal secretion, the other providing the stimulus. The resting larva would thus constitute a dispersal stage or an infective stage.

A life cycle which is similar to this is shown by *Rhabditis coarctata* (Triffitt and Oldham, 1927; Oldham, 1937*a*). The eggs of this species are laid in dung where they hatch and the larvae feed and grow to the pre-encystment stage. At this stage they collect on arthropods where they undergo a partial moult and adhere to the transport hosts as cysts which are protected by the sheaths. Here the larvae remain quiet until favourable conditions for exsheathment are met. When the arthropod bearing the cysts reaches a fresh patch of dung the conditions for further development are attained and the larva exsheaths and grows to an adult in the dung. Specificity for the transport host is low. Living mites, beetles and caterpillars will serve, and encystment occurs under the stimulus of the movement of the host (Oldham, 1937*b*, p. 429). The change in environment required for the completion of the life cycle is merely from one lot of dung to another.

The life cycle of a parasitic nematode like *Haemonchus contortus*, of which the third-stage larva is ensheathed and infective, might be described as follows (Fig. 6). Development up to the second quiescent period would proceed normally in a free-living environment and under the control of internal secretions which govern the hatching of the egg (H), the first moult (M_1) and the second "partial moult" (PM_1). At this time the internal secretion, it is suggested, is incomplete, and only the first part of the moult takes place, leaving the second-stage larva ensheathed in the uncast cuticle of the first stage so that the physiological changes concerned with feeding and growth are suspended. This suspension of development will continue until some component or pattern of components in the new environment provided by the host (S) stimulates the completion of the internal secretion leading to the completion of the physiological changes in the second larval stage, i.e. exsheathment occurs and feeding and growth are resumed (PM_2).

The environment of the parasitic phase (C) may also change. Thus *Haemonchus contortus* and other trichostrongyle parasites have a histotrophic stage during which they spend part of the life cycle in the mucosa of the alimentary canal before they become adult and live close to the mucosa in the lumen of the gut (Stoll, 1943; Sommerville, 1954). One or two moults, according to the species of parasite, take place during the histotrophic stage, and this again may be associated with a change in the environment. This is more clearly seen in species which undergo more complex migrations. Thus *Nippostrongylus muris*, of which the third-stage larva infects the host through the skin, shows a lag in growth which persists for most of the time it is in this part of the host. This lag may correspond to the quiescent period at the end of the third stage. After the larvae have been in the lungs for about 15 hours, growth slows down again and the third moult occurs (Twohy, 1956). The fourth moult occurs when the parasite is in the final environment, the small intestine (Yokogawa, 1922).

The specialization of the third larval stage for dispersal may be likened to the specialization in which the ensheathed third stage becomes an agent of infection in the life cycle of the parasitic species. The infective stage is a "bridge" which carries the animal from the environment of the free-living stages to that of the parasite within the host. However, the pattern which provides the stimulus for restarting development in the infective stage is more exacting and is provided only at certain sites in certain hosts (Rogers and Sommerville, 1957; Rogers, 1960). As yet, it is not known whether specific components of the environment are needed to stimulate moulting at other times during the parasitic phase of the life cycle.

In species where an intermediate host is involved, two stages in the life cycle of the parasite are specialized as infective stages. Here the mechanisms controlling development would be suspended in both stages and activity would be restored by the appropriate host.

Adaptations for Infection with Eggs

In unspecialized nematodes with the basic life cycle the egg hatches and the first-stage larva emerges. Under normal circumstances this occurs without a halt in the development of the embryo. It seems that at a certain stage in development the process which leads to the hatching of the egg and the escape of the larva is started, and the timing of this process, though influenced by some factors in the environment, is due largely to the internal regulating mechanism within the embryo.

When the egg is the infective agent of a nematode parasite, the development of the embryo stops at the infective stage while it is still enclosed in the egg-shell. This may be at the end of the first larval stage (as in the Trichuroidea), the second stage (some Ascaroidea), or the third stage (some Strongyloidea); (for references see Chandler *et al.*, 1940). Thus the development of the embryo continues beyond the point at which hatching occurs in unspecialized species. The internal mechanism which normally starts the process of hatching is stopped until the egg reaches the right site in the right host. It appears that this is an adaptation to parasitism which helps to ensure that hatching occurs in an environment suitable for the future development of the larva as a parasite.

One hypothesis may thus be applied whether the infective agent is an egg or a larva. In both instances, as an adaptation to parasitism, the mechanism within the worms which times developmental changes is suspended in the infective stage. Components in the environment provided by the host are necessary for restarting the mechanism.

Other changes in the mechanism of hatching of eggs might also be involved because the body fluids of the host in which the infective eggs of internal parasites must hatch differ in their physico-chemical properties from the environments in which the eggs of free-living nematodes hatch. For example, the osmotic pressure of the body fluids is high compared to most other environments. And as osmotic pressures often affect the hatching of eggs of invertebrates (Davis, 1959) adaptations to allow the hatching of infective eggs in solutions of relatively high osmotic pressure might be needed (see Chapter 5).

Alternative Hypotheses for Adaptations for Infection

There are at least two ways in which the suspension of the timing mechanism might arise.

(1) It might be lost entirely and replaced by a stimulus provided by the host. But this seems unlikely because the timing mechanism would probably be concerned in initiating later moults. It seems more probable that the stimulus from the host would be needed merely to restore the action of the timing mechanism. The results obtained by

Rogers and Sommerville (1957) and Rogers (1958, 1960) give some support to this argument.

(2) The timing mechanism would stop if the larva failed to synthesize some essential component of the system. The host could then restart development by supplying the missing component. In other words, the host provides the factor controlling development which is absent from the nematode rather than the stimulus needed for the production of the factor. There seems no reason why a host should not produce substances which have a highly specific role in the physiology of nematodes. But there are a number of objections to such a hypothesis; it would be necessary, for instance, that the controlling factor produced by the host should penetrate into the tissues of the larva through the cuticle and, in many species, through the highly impermeable egg-shell as well. Nevertheless, as discussed later, it seems possible that the "hatching factor" for the eggs of *Heterodera rostochiensis*, which is produced by the host plant, might act in some such way.

These hypotheses suggest that the role of the host is to provide substances which restore the development of the parasite by *indirect* means; i.e. the host's action on the parasite is mediated through the system which would normally control development in free-living unspecialized nematodes. An alternative to this is the hypothesis that the host produces substances which start the development of the parasites by *direct* action on the infective stage. Such a process may be visualized most clearly when the infective stage is enclosed in a sheath or egg-shell. These structures form a barrier between the infective larva and the environment and so prevent many substances reaching the larva. If the host provided substances which removed the sheath or the shell of the egg, the larvae might obtain the nutrients and other factors needed for the resumption of development.

The view that the host might provide substances which remove the egg-shells or sheaths from infective larvae seems to have been the unstated hypothesis of many workers who have tried to cause hatching of eggs or the exsheathment of larvae with digestive enzymes or similar preparations from the gut of the host. These experiments with the infective stages of nematode parasites have not been successful.

Life Cycles in other Metazoan Parasites

Moulting is not a common feature of the life cycle of parasites. It occurs in the Nematomorpha, a group closely related to the Nematoda, the Pentastomida, and in the parasitic arthropods. Though our understanding of the physiological basis of moulting and metamorphosis of invertebrate animals comes largely from studies on the Arthropoda and especially the Insecta (Wigglesworth, 1954) little is known of the changes in the mechanism controlling development which are associated with parasites of this group.

Though moulting does not occur in other groups of parasites, changes in anatomy during the life cycle are common. These changes usually take place immediately after the parasite has entered the intermediate or final host but they are much more pronounced than those which occur when infection with nematodes takes place. Thus in the digenetic Trematoda there is a metamorphosis which takes place when the miracidium enters the molluscan host (Dawes, 1959). The miracidium is a ciliated, actively moving organism which does not feed. When infection occurs the ciliated epidermis and several structures within the body are lost and the rounded or vermiform hollow sporocyst begins to take in nutrients from the tissues of the host (Fig. 7).

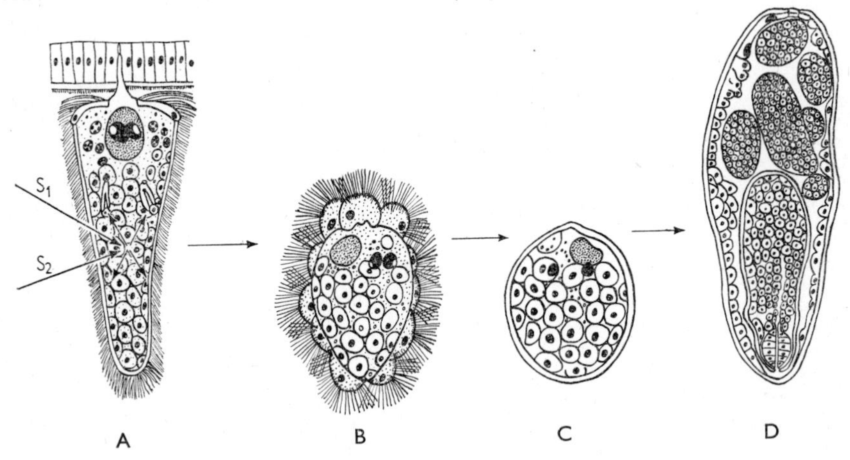

FIG. 7. The metamorphosis of the miracidium of *Fasciola hepatica*. A shows a miracidium entering the tissues of the snail; B and C show stages in the metamorphosis to the mature sporocyst, D (after Thomas, 1883). The host provides a stimulus (S_1) which replaces the "internal secretions" that would be produced during metamorphosis in a free-living organism, or the host provides a stimulus (S_2) for the release of the internal secretions. The internal secretions organize and co-ordinate the changes during metamorphosis (A, B and C).

Metamorphoses which are more or less far-reaching occur when infection takes place with metacercariae, and in the life cycles of cestodes. A distinct metamorphosis occurs in the life cycle of the Acanthocephala (Baer, 1952, p. 111). In some species of groups such as the parasitic molluscs and Crustacea, pronounced structural changes which are a consequence of parasitism are seen (Lapage, 1958, pp. 139–49). But these changes occur slowly as a steady "degeneration" of the organism. The processes which underlie this de-differentiation of cells and tissues are unknown but they must differ in several respects from those which take place during a metamorphosis and they are not included in this discussion.

The changes in anatomy and physiology which constitute a metamorphosis must be co-ordinated within the parasite. And they must be set in train by the act of infection. Co-ordination could be achieved by the diffusion of substances through the tissues, or, more rapidly, through the nervous system or some fluid-transporting mechanism. Metamorphosis could be the result of direct action of substances provided by the host or the infective agent. Or the host might act indirectly by stimulating the parasite itself to secrete internally the necessary substances. In either case it would seem that a system of this sort could be a basic adaptation in an organism which assumes a parasitic mode of life because it would ensure that the infective stage would remain in a "resting" condition, so conserving food reserves until the appropriate host was reached.

Summary

Free-living nematodes undergo a series of moults during their life cycles and in parasitic species the infective stage is preceded by a moult. Thereafter development is suspended until the infective agent reaches the appropriate host. The infective stage is thus a resting stage which acts as a bridge by which the parasite passes from an environment in one part of its life cycle to a different environment in another part of its life cycle.

In arthropods moulting is controlled by internal secretions and a similar mechanism controls the metamorphoses which many animals, vertebrate and invertebrate, undergo when they pass from one environment to another in the course of their normal life cycles. Is it possible that the life cycles of nematodes are also controlled by internal secretions? If so, it seems reasonable to suggest that in the infective stage the normal system which controls development is suspended and that a stimulus from the host is required to start it going again.

References

Alicata, J. E. (1934) *Proc. helm. Soc. Wash.* **1**, 12.

—— (1935) *Bull. U. S. Dep. Agric.* No. 489.

Baer, J. G. (1952) "Ecology of Animal Parasites". University of Illinois Press, Urbana.

Chandler, A. C., Alicata, J. E. and Chitwood, M. B. (1940) *In* "Introduction to Nematology". (J. R. Christie, ed.), M. B. Chitwood, Babylon, New York.

Chitwood, B. G. and Chitwood, M. B. (1940) *In* "Introduction to Nematology". (B. G. and M. B. Chitwood, eds.), M. B. Chitwood, Babylon, New York.
Davis, C. C. (1959) *Biol. Bull., Woods Hole*, **116**, 15.
Dawes, B. (1959) *Nature, Lond.* **184**, 1334.
Faust, E. C. (1949) "Human Helminthology". Henry Kimpton, London.
Filipjev, I. N. and Michajlova, E. (1924) *Zool. Anz.* **59**, 212.
—— and Schuurmans Stekhoven, J. H. (1941) "A Manual of Agricultural Helminthology". E. J. Brill, Leiden.
Harris, J. E. and Crofton, H. D. (1957) *J. exp. Biol.* **34**, 116.
Hyman, L. H. (1951) "The Invertebrates" Vol. III. McGraw-Hill Book Co., New York.
Lapage, G. (1935) *Parasitology*, **27**, 186.
—— (1958) "Parasitic Animals". Heffer and Sons, Cambridge.
Leuckart, R. (1887) *Abh. sächs. Ges. (Akad.) Wiss.* **13**, 565.
Looss, A. (1911) *Rec. Sch. Med. Cairo*, **4**, 452.
Maupas, E. (1899) *Arch. Zool. exp. gén. (3)*. **7**, 563.
Moorthy, V. N. (1938*a*) *Amer. J. Hyg.* **27**, 437.
—— (1938*b*) *J. Parasit.* **24**, 323.
Oldham, J. N. (1937*a*) *J. Helminth.* **13**, 13.
—— (1937*b*) *In* "Papers on Helminthology Published in Commemoration of the 30-year Jubileum of K. J. Skrjabin". Moscow.
Payne, F. K. (1923) *Amer. J. Hyg.* **3**, 584.
Rogers, W. P. (1939) *J. Helminth*, **17**, 195.
—— (1952) *Aust. J. sci. Res.* **B5**, 210.
—— (1958) *Nature, Lond.* **181**, 1410.
—— (1960) *Proc. roy. Soc.* **B152**, 367.
—— and Sommerville, R. I. (1957) *Nature, Lond.* **179**, 619.
—— (1960) *Parasitology*, **50**, 1.
Seurat, L. G. (1920) "Histoire naturelle des Nématodes de la Berbérie". *Trav. Lab. Zool. gén. de l'Université d'Alger*, vi.
Sommerville, R. I. (1954) *Aust. J. agric. Res.* **5**, 130.
Stoll, N. R. (1940) *Growth*, **4**, 383.
—— (1943) *J. Parasit.* **29**, 407.
Thomas, A. P. W. (1883) *Quart. J. micr. Sci.* **23**, 99.
Travassos, L. (1919) *Mem. Inst. Osw. Cruz*, **11**, 71.
Triffitt, M. J. and Oldham, J. N. (1927) *J. Helminth.* **5**, 33.
Twohy, D. W. (1956) *Amer. J. Hyg.* **63**, 165.
Veglia, F. (1915) *Rep. vet. Res. S. Afr.* **3 and 4**, 349.
Weinstein, P. P. and Haskins, W. T. (1955) *Exp. Parasit.* **4**, 226.
Wigglesworth, V. B. (1954) "The Physiology of Insect Metamorphosis". Cambridge University Press, Cambridge.
Yokogawa, S. (1922) *Parasitology*, **14**, 127.

CHAPTER 4

The Physiology of Free-living Stages

MANY parasites spend part of their life cycles as free-living stages, one or two of which are specialized for infecting the host or hosts. During this part of the life cycle the features which help the infective stage to make contact with the host and infect it are developed. These features include such things as changes in behaviour so that the infective stage reaches material which might be eaten by the host, or, if infection is through the integument, so that it will come into contact with the surface of the host. In addition, changes in structure and metabolism may take place so that the infective stage will be better adapted to survive in these new situations. Of course, if the egg is the infective stage, the behaviour of the embryo does not affect the chances of infecting the host, though the structure of the egg-shell and the metabolism of the embryo are important because they affect the period the egg may survive.

In some groups e.g. the Mermithoidea in the Nematoda, the Gordiacea, and the parasitic gastropods, it is the larval stages which are parasitic and the adults are free-living. Generally, however, the adult is parasitic, and free-living stages, if they occur at all, are found among the juveniles or larvae. The significance of this is not clear, but as the need for food and energy for the production of large numbers of eggs is probably greater than the needs for growth (see Chapter 9) there seem to be more advantages in the parasitic life for the adult. This view is supported by the fact that in the Mermithoidea and Gordiacea the food reserves which are accumulated during the parasitic stages serve for the adults which do not feed.

In the Cestoda and Acanthocephala the egg is an infective stage and it is free-living except in *Hymenolepis nana* which can pass the whole of the life cycle in the one host. In these two groups parasitism is highly developed. Many of their infective stages are parasitic and so they are less exposed to varying environments. Development outside the host is usually restricted to the "embryonation" of the egg.

The other major group of highly specialized internal parasites is the digenetic trematodes. These parasites have several free-living stages, the egg, the miracidium, the cercaria and often the metacercaria, all of which may be infective in one species or another. In this group also, development outside the host is more extensive. Not only does embryonation occur in a free-living stage but, in the metacercaria of some species, reproductive organs are almost fully developed.

In the Nematoda all degrees of specialization in the life cycle for a parasitic mode of life can be seen, from species with a completely free-living cycle to those which are entirely parasitic. Some, like the oxyurids *Probstmyaria* and *Atractis*, can pass through a number of generations in the one host, i.e. there is no halt in the life cycle for an infective stage; but there is some doubt whether these organisms are true parasites (Baer, 1952, p. 98). The infective stage of *Trichinella spiralis* is parasitic as, for example, are both infective stages in the Filaroidea. In these the life cycle stops at the infective stage and development is not resumed until after a new host is infected. For many nematode parasites of animals the egg is infective and requires a period outside the host for development; for others which are parasitic in plants and animals free-living larval stages serve as infective stages.

The physiology of the free-living infective stages has not been examined extensively and there is as yet no information which suggests that there are any characteristic features in their metabolism. As they do not feed until they become parasitic the infective stages are dependent on food reserves built up during earlier stages in the life cycle. When the egg or miracidium is the infective stage the reserves are formed by the adult which is usually a parasite, but in some species of nematodes the food reserves are built up by free-living larval stages. This, though common in the Nematoda, is rare in most other groups of parasites.

Free-living Stages of Nematodes

The Food Reserves

As yet no pronounced differences have been reported between the metabolism of infective eggs and that of eggs that hatch outside the host to give a free-living larva. The food reserves must be greater in the infective egg because the embryo can remain alive for long periods—many months in some species—without external supplies. On the other hand, eggs that hatch to give a free-living larva normally do so within a few days, or at most in a few weeks after they have been laid. Reserve deposits of fats and carbohydrates are found in eggs (Fauré-Fremiet, 1913; Giovannola, 1936; Rogers, 1948; Elliott, 1954; Passey and Fairbairn, 1957; Fairbairn and Passey, 1957) and histological studies have shown that both these substances are used during the development of the embryo. Only with eggs of *Ascaris lumbricoides* and *Parascaris equorum* have detailed chemical investigations of the changes in food reserves during development been carried out (Fairbairn, 1957). In *Ascaris lumbricoides* the total lipids form about 35% of the total solids of eggs which have been washed in alkali to remove the outer coat of protein on the shell. The lipids are largely triglycerides and "ascarosides" (glycosides of hydroxyhentriacontane or 2, 6-dihydroxyhentriacontane, and a 3, 6-deoxyaldohexose; Polonsky *et al.*, 1955; Fouquey *et al.*, 1957). The total alkali-stable carbohydrate, made up of about equal amounts of glycogen and trehalose, forms about 16% of the total egg solids (Passey and Fairbairn, 1957).

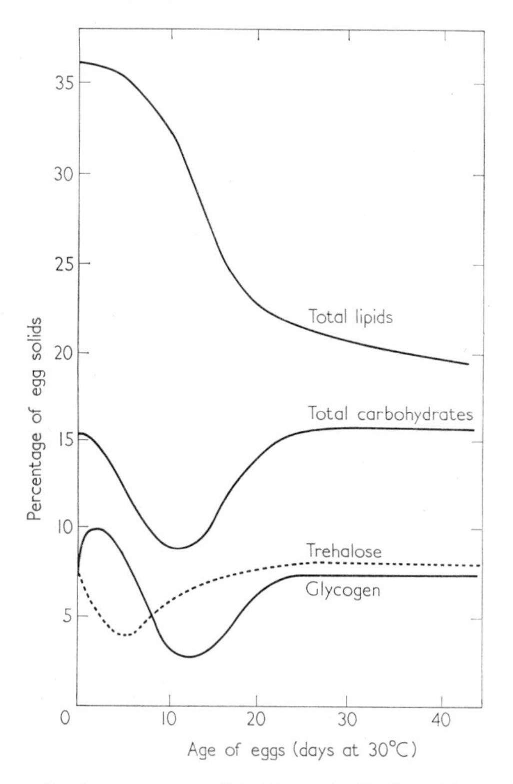

FIG. 8. The changes in the amounts of lipid, total alkali-stable carbohydrate, glycogen, and trehalose during the development of eggs of *Ascaris lumbricoides*. The results are given as the percentage of the different substances in the solids of eggs from which the outer coat has been removed by treatment with alkali (after Passey and Fairbairn, 1957).

In the early stages of development the embryo of *Ascaris lumbricoides* uses both lipid and carbohydrate, but after about twelve days at 30°C carbohydrate is synthesized from lipid. Thus in the infective embryo, after about eighteen days at 30°C, the total carbohydrate is about the same as in the early stages of development but the lipid is considerably reduced. Thereafter in the "resting" infective stage there is a slow reduction in lipid and carbohydrate reserves (Passey and Fairbairn, 1957 and Fig. 8).

Elliott (1954), who used histological methods, studied the relationship between the fat content, age and infectivity of the eggs of *Ascaridia galli*. She found that the fat content at first decreased rapidly and then more slowly until little remained when the eggs had been kept for 300 days at 28°C. Infectivity did not fall until the 200th day; thereafter it fell rapidly until the 300th day when very few eggs were infective.

Most of the information we have about infective larvae comes from studies with species of strongylid nematodes in which the free-living stages—egg, first and second larvae—precede the development of the infective stage. The first two larval stages behave quite differently from the infective stage. They live in moist contaminated soil where they feed and rapidly increase in size. Bacterial cells probably form a large part of their diet. Indeed, McCoy (1929*a*, 1929*b*) and Lapage (1933) were able to grow infective larvae of hookworms and trichostrongylids from eggs in culture with single strains of bacteria as food. Growth to the infective stage did not take place with heat-killed bacteria. Histological methods have shown that both fat and glycogen are built up as reserve materials in these rhabditiform larvae (Giovannola, 1936). In filariform larvae of *Strongyloides ratti*, Jones (1955) found that glycogen, estimated by chemical methods, formed 0.5% of the wet tissue (about 2.5%, dry weight).

The axenic culture of the free-living stages of *Haemonchus contortus*, two species of hookworms, and *Nippostrongylus muris* has been carried out with media of which the most successful have contained chick embryo extract, liver extract and serum as basic components (Glaser and Stoll, 1938; Lawrence, 1948; Weinstein, 1953; Weinstein and Jones, 1956; Silverman, 1959). The filariform larvae obtained in these cultures were sometimes slightly smaller than those produced in bacterial cultures but they were normal in other respects, and they were infective.

Filariform infective larvae do not feed and they migrate out of the soil to sites where they are likely to make contact with the host, either in its food or on its surface (Rogers, 1940*a*; Crofton, 1948*a*, 1948*b*). Associated with this change in behaviour there is an increased resistance to some features of the environment (Lucker, 1941*a*, 1941*b*; Kates, 1950) and fat becomes the major food reserve. During the infective stage the amount of histologically demonstrable fat, stored largely in the cells of the gut, is decreased (Fig. 9). The rate at which it disappears is related to the activity of the larvae, and infectivity is roughly proportional to the amount of fat present (Payne, 1922, 1923*a*, 1923*b*; Rogers, 1939, 1940*b*).

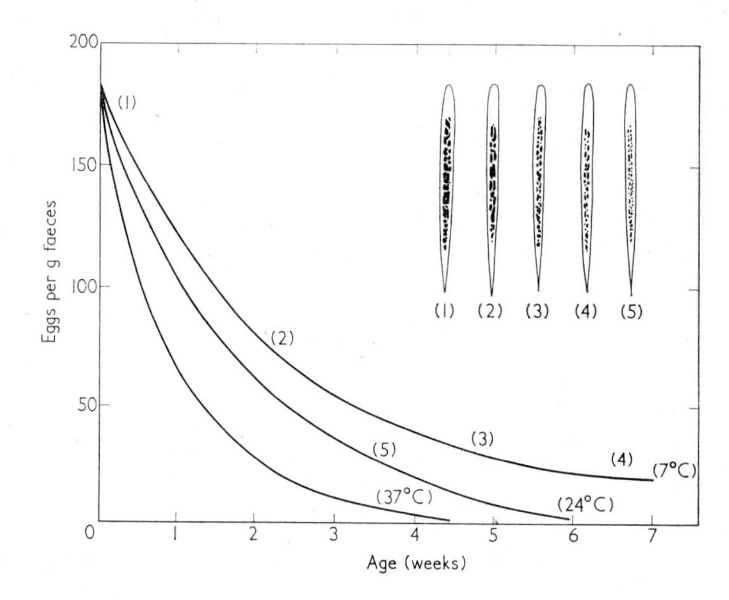

FIG. 9. The changes in infectivity of larvae of *Haemonchus contortus* measured as the egg output in goats each given one dose of 1000 larvae which had been aged for different periods at 7°C, 24°C and 37°C. The fat content of larvae of different ages, demonstrated by histological methods, is indicated by the figures in parenthesis in the graphs which correspond to the sketches of the larvae containing fat stained with Sudan IV (after Rogers, 1940*b*).

Oxygen Requirements

The eggs of a number of species of nematodes, e.g. *Ascaris lumbricoides, Parascaris equorum, Ancylostoma caninum, Trichuris trichiura, Haemonchus contortus,* and *Nippostrongylus muris* have been examined and all were found to consume oxygen. When the pO_2 in the environment is lowered development is slowed. Thus at a pO_2 of 3 mm of mercury the rate of development of *Ascaris lumbricoides* is halved; and at 10 mm the embryonation of *Ancylostoma caninum* proceeds very slowly. Under anaerobic conditions development is stopped (Brown, 1928; McCoy, 1930; Dinnick and Dinnick, 1937) though it is resumed when oxygen again becomes available. According to Brown (1928) the eggs of *Ascaris lumbricoides* can survive without oxygen for more than six weeks. Eggs of

Ancylostoma caninum and *Trichuris trichiura* resumed development after 9 or 10 days under anaerobic conditions (McCoy, 1930; Dinnick and Dinnick, 1937). Results of a similar sort have been obtained with eggs of other species (Nolf, 1932; Lapage, 1937, p. 64) and it seems probable that the eggs of nematodes that hatch outside the host as well as those which form the infective stage require oxygen for development though they can survive for long periods without it. On the other hand, anaerobic conditions, or very low oxygen tensions, are suitable for the hatching of the infective eggs of a number of species of nematodes (Rogers, 1960). As hatching of infective eggs occurs in the lumen of the gut of the host where oxygen tensions must be very low, this may be a general adaptation to parasitism in all nematodes with life cycles which have infective eggs.

Brown (1928) found that the eggs of *Ascaris lumbricoides* consumed 2.5×10^{-6} ml of oxygen per egg during the period of development from the one cell stage to the motile embryo. This figure was not greatly affected by changes in the rate of development brought about by raising the temperature. Other workers (Huff, 1936; Jaskoski, 1952; Passey and Fairbairn, 1955) found the oxygen consumption in similar experiments to be about 4×10^{-6} ml per egg. Huff (1936) found that the oxygen consumed was increased by removing the outer protein coat from the eggs; Jaskoski (1952), however, did not confirm this. The consumption of oxygen for the embryonation of eggs of *Parascaris equorum* was found to be 9×10^{-6} ml per egg (Fauré-Fremiet, 1913). The eggs of *Trichuris trichiura*, which take 21 days at 30°C to develop to the embryonated stage, consume 2.9×10^{-6} ml of oxygen per egg (Nolf, 1932). Though the corresponding period for the development of the eggs of *Ancylostoma caninum* which hatch outside the host to give a free-living larva is only 24 hours, about the same amount of oxygen is used (McCoy, 1930). The Q_{O_2} of eggs of different species therefore varies greatly; measured at 30°C the slowly-developing eggs of *Ascaris lumbricoides* gave values less than 1 (Passey and Fairbairn, 1955) whereas for the rapidly-developing eggs of *Haemonchus contortus* it was about 10 (Rogers, 1948).

The detailed changes in oxygen uptake which take place during the course of development of the embryo are known only for *Ascaris lumbricoides* (Passey and Fairbairn, 1955). Sufficient results are available, however, from the eggs of *Haemonchus contortus* and *Nippostrongylus muris* to allow comparison up to the stage when these eggs hatch (Rogers, 1948). In the eggs of *Ascaris*, after a sharp fall, the Q_{O_2} rises steadily from about 0.3 for the early morula to about 0.8 for the motile vermiform embryo. This rise was also found during the development of the eggs of *Haemonchus* which gave values of 9.7 (early morula), 10.7 (late blastula) and 12.6 (motile, vermiform embryo). At this stage the eggs of *Haemonchus contortus* hatch but, in *Ascaris*, development continues within the egg-shell where the Q_{O_2} of the embryo falls rapidly from 0.8 to about 0.15 on about the 25th day. Thereafter it falls slowly to reach 0.01 on the 140th day (Passey and Fairbairn, 1955). Presumably the rapid fall is associated with the "lethargus" preceding the first moult, and the "resting" period of the infective stage.

Studies on the oxygen uptake of eggs of *Parascaris equorum* during development have been briefly reported by Hopkins (1955). A notable point in these results was the sudden rise and fall in oxygen consumption that occurred during the embryonic moult after 8 or 9 days' incubation at 25°C.

Little is known about the oxygen requirements of the free-living first and second larval stages though some experiments have been carried out with filariform infective larvae. These larvae consume oxygen when it is available and do not survive for long periods under anaerobic conditions. Thus, Costello and Grollman (1958) regard the filariform larvae of *Strongyloides papillosus* as "strict aerobes"; other species of this genus are also sensitive to lack of oxygen (Fülleborn, 1924; Lucker, 1934). The larvae of *Ancylostoma caninum* are less sensitive; they will live for days without oxygen (McCoy, 1930).

The Q_{O_2} of free-living and parasitic infective larvae varies greatly in different species and Costello and Grollman (1958) have suggested that there might be an inverse relationship between the survival of different species and their oxygen uptake (Table 2). The Q_{O_2} of infective larvae of *Haemonchus contortus* and *Nippostrongylus muris* decreases as the larvae become older (Rogers, 1948; Schwabe, 1957).

The relationship between pO_2 and oxygen uptake of third-stage larvae of parasites of the horse (primarily *Cylicocylus*, *Cylicocercus*, *Cylicostephanus*, and *Cyathostomum*) has been examined by Bair (1955). These larvae showed a low oxygen uptake which was almost constant at pressures of oxygen from 38 to 339 mm of mercury. In comparison, a free-living nematode, *Rhabditis elegans*, showed an increasing oxygen consumption up to a pO_2 of 120 mm. And for a facultative parasite, *Rhabditis strongyloides*, from a skin lesion in a cow, the critical pO_2 was 58.5 mm (Fig. 10). Bair pointed out that the oxygen relations of the larvae fitted them particularly for a parasitic life in tissue of low oxygen tension. *Rhabditis strongyloides*, though better fitted for a parasitic life than *Rhabditis elegans*, would be unlikely to extend its parasitic habitat beyond the skin lesions or similar localities with a pO_2 between that of venous and arterial blood. Bair concluded that one of the adaptations necessary for a parasitic mode of life is an adjustment of oxygen requirements.

TABLE II

The Relationship between Longevity and Q_{O_2} in Nematode Larvae (Costello and Grollman, 1958)

Species	Type of larva	Longevity	Q_{O_2}	Authors
Strongyloides papillosus	infective, filariform (free-living)	7 days	28.5	Costello and Grollman (1958)
Nippostrongylus muris	infective, filariform (free-living)	30 days	18.4	Rogers (1948)
Haemonchus contortus	infective, filariform (free-living)	90 days	12.6	Rogers (1948)
Trichinella spiralis	infective, encysted (parasitic)	5 years	2.35	Stannard *et al.* (1938)
Eustrongylides ignotis	infective, encysted (parasitic)	4 years	0.56	von Brand (1952)

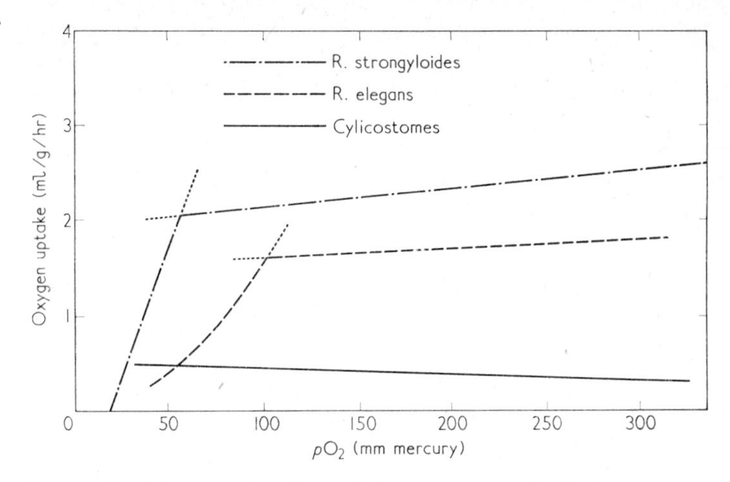

FIG. 10. The relation between the pO_2 and the oxygen uptake (ml per g wet wt. per hr) of *Rhabditis elegans* which is entirely free-living; *Rhabditis strongyloides*, a free-living form which can live as a parasite in skin lesions of a cow; and the free-living infective larvae of cylicostome parasites of the horse (after Bair, 1955).

Metabolism

Carbon dioxide is produced by free-living larvae and eggs. The respiratory quotient for the eggs of *Ascaris lumbricoides* and *Parascaris equorum* in the early stages of development is about 0.8, rising to 1.0 in the later stages (Fauré-Fremiet, 1913; Huff, 1936; Jaskoski, 1952). Passey and Fairbairn (1955) reported that carbon dioxide production in eggs of *Ascaris lumbricoides* paralleled the disappearance of oxygen but at a somewhat lower level. They found, however, that the direct method of Warburg was unsuitable for measuring carbon dioxide production in their experiments and so gave their results only in general terms.

For the eggs of *Haemonchus contortus* and *Nippostrongylus muris*, which hatch to give free-living larvae, the respiratory quotient is lower, usually about 0.6. For the infective larvae of these species it usually ranges between 0.6 and 0.7 (Rogers, 1948; Schwabe, 1957). Though chemical and histological tests suggest that both fats and carbohydrates are metabolized by infective eggs, whereas fat is the major substrate used by the larvae, these values should be interpreted with caution. It is quite possible that the low quotients could be due to other features of metabolism (Richardson, 1929).

Carbon dioxide is used by the eggs of *Ascaris lumbricoides* during development. Passey and Fairbairn (1957) found that the carbon of carbon-14 dioxide entered the glucose of glycogen and trehalose in the embryos largely at the 3 and 4 positions. This indicates that fixation, probably limited to a net exchange of carbon brought about by the Wood-Werkman or similar reaction (Ochoa, 1951), had occurred.

The respiration of eggs that hatch outside the host and of infective eggs is strongly inhibited by cyanide. Thus potassium cyanide, 10^{-3}M in neutral solution, caused 60 to 70% inhibition of the oxygen uptake of the eggs of *Haemonchus contortus* and *Nippostrongylus muris* (Rogers, 1948). With the eggs of *Ascaris lumbricoides* Passey and Fairbairn (1955) found that, though undissociated hydrogen cyanide strongly inhibited development and respiration (87% at 4.6×10^{-4}M), cyanide ions had little effect. Similar results were obtained with hydrazoic acid and azide ions. Carbon monoxide in the dark was also an effective inhibitor. The inhibition caused by all these substances was largely reversible.

The action of these inhibitors suggests that respiration of the embryos of *Ascaris lumbricoides* takes place through a cytochrome–cytochrome oxidase chain of carriers and enzymes, or something rather similar. It seems unlikely that flavoproteins or phenol oxidases would be important. Passey and Fairbairn (1955), who put forward these views, gave supporting evidence from their studies on the relation between respiratory rate of the embryos and oxygen pressure. They found that the affinity of the embryo for oxygen was high; the Q_{O_2} in air was only about twice the Q_{O_2} at a pO_2 of 20 mm of mercury (Fig. 11). However,

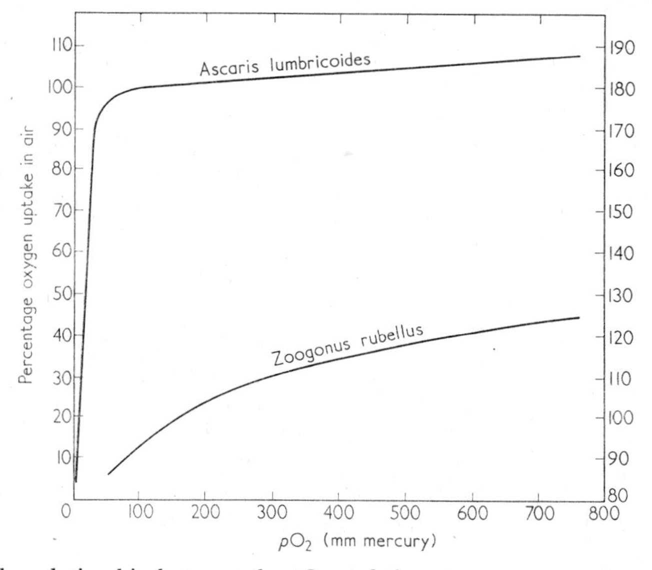

FIG. 11. The relationship between the pO_2 and the oxygen consumption of infective eggs of *Ascaris lumbricoides* (after Passey and Fairbairn, 1955), and infective cercariae of *Zoogonus rubellus* (after Hunter and Vernberg, 1955). The left hand scale refers to the eggs; the right hand one to the cercariae. The figures for the cercariae are means of results which showed a wide variation.

Passey and Fairbairn were unable to show the presence of cytochrome *c* or cytochrome oxidase in developing eggs.

Little is known about the intermediary metabolism of infective larvae. Schwabe (1957) found that in the presence of appropriate co-factors, glucose, glycerophosphate, pyruvate, succinate, α-ketoglutarate, all increased the respiratory rate of minced third-stage larvae of *Nippostrongylus muris*. He concluded that the glycolytic reaction sequence and the tricarboxylic acid cycle were present, at least in part, in these organisms. More definite evidence for the functioning of the Krebs tricarboxylic acid cycle and the cytochrome system in the filariform larvae of *Strongyloides papillosus* has been obtained by Costello and Grollman (1958, 1959). In a related species, *Strongyloides ratti*, glycolysis which is similar to that in vertebrate tissues also occurs. Lactic acid is an end-product of anaerobic metabolism; the phosphate esters, glucose-6-phosphate, glucose-1-phosphate, fructose-6-phosphate, fructose-1, 6-diphosphate, and triose phosphate are present. Adenosine monophosphate, diphosphate, and triphosphate as well as a phosphagen, probably arginine phosphate, have been identified in the tissues of these larvae (Jones, 1955).

In view of the failure of species of *Strongyloides* to survive for even short periods in the absence of oxygen it seems probable that the glycolytic mechanism is poorly developed and serves largely to provide pyruvate for a vigorous tricarboxylic acid cycle.

End-products of Metabolism

Little work on the nature of the excretory products of infective stages of nematodes has been carried out, and, apart from carbon dioxide, the end-products of carbohydrate or fat metabolism have not been generally identified. Presumably the 1, 2-dicarboxylic acids produced by the filariform larvae of *Nippostrongylus muris* (Weinstein and Haskins, 1955) are products of carbohydrate metabolism but it is not known if these substances are excreted by other species of larvae.

The end-products of nitrogen metabolism of larvae of *Nippostrongylus muris* have also been examined by Weinstein and Haskins (1955) who showed by means of qualitative tests that ammonium salts and primary aliphatic amines were excreted. The amines were ethylene diamine, cadaverine, ethanolamine, methyl amine, propyl amine and butyl amine. The fluid in the eggs of *Ascaris lumbricoides* contains a variety of amines which are produced by the embryos (Haskins and Weinstein, 1957).

As it seems probable that at least some of these amines are expelled from the larvae via the excretory pore, the so-called excretory system of nematodes may in fact have an excretory function (Weinstein and

Haskins, 1955). It has also been shown that this system is concerned with water balance. Pulsations of the excretory ampulla, sometimes leading to the release of droplets from the excretory pore, have been noted in several species of larval and adult worms (Eisma, 1932; Raven and Schuurmans Stekhoven, 1934); and Weinstein (1952) showed that the rate of pulsation was generally inversely proportional to the sucrose or sodium chloride content of the medium in which filariform larvae of *Nippostrongylus muris* or *Ancylostoma caninum* were kept. In distilled water these larvae must carry out a considerable amount of work to maintain a water balance; larvae of *Nippostrongylus muris* excrete an amount of water equal to their own volume in 10.8 hours. For larvae of *Ancylostoma caninum* the same task took 74.9 hours (Weinstein, 1952).

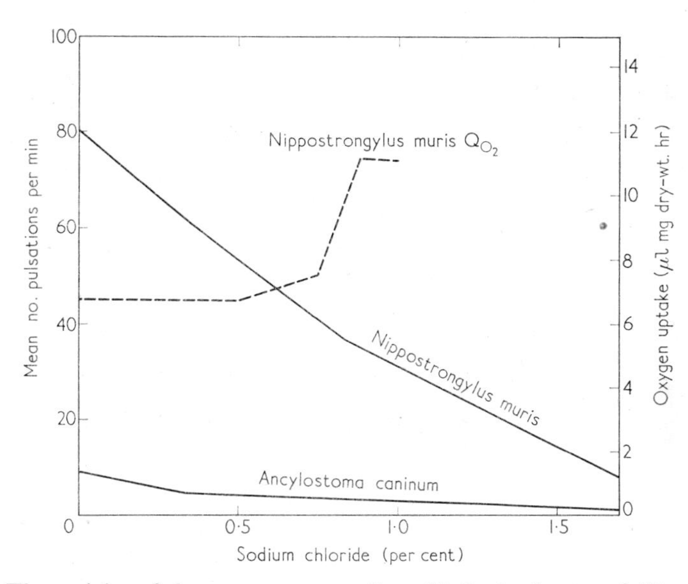

FIG. 12. The activity of the excretory ampullae of infective larvae of *Nippostrongylus muris* and *Ancylostoma caninum* in solutions of sodium chloride of different concentrations (after Weinstein, 1952) and upper curve, the oxygen uptake of larvae of *Nippostrongylus muris* in similar solutions (after Schwabe, 1957).

Schwabe (1957) measured the oxygen uptake of the larvae of *Nippostrongylus muris* in solutions of different concentrations of sodium chloride at 37°C. Though there was a considerable variation between different lots of larvae the level of oxygen uptake was always greatest at concentrations between 0.13 and 0.17M (0.75 to 1.0%). There seems, therefore, to be little correlation between work carried out to maintain water balance and the respiratory rate (Fig. 12).

Developmental Physiology

The term "developmental physiology" may be used to cover the physiology of unfertilized eggs and sperm, the zygote, and other stages up to the adult. Here the developmental physiology of the parasite in its free-living stages until contact is made with the host is discussed. The developmental changes which are part of the process of infection, such as the hatching of eggs and the exsheathment of larvae, are discussed in Chapter 5. The physiology of fertilization, maturation, and the synthesis and structure of egg-shells, are discussed in detail in Chapter 9.

The metabolic processes which take place during the development of the free-living stages of parasitic nematodes must be co-ordinated with the more clear-cut morphological and physiological changes such as the hatching of eggs and the moulting of larvae. As yet the physiology of these changes which take place outside the host, i.e. before infection occurs, has not been examined extensively. Except in a few instances it is not possible therefore to compare these changes which seem to be largely independent of the environment with those that require the intervention of the host when infection occurs, or when parasitic stages undergo migration in the tissues of the host during development. However, the value of the information on the developmental physiology of free-living stages in indicating possible adaptations which might be necessary for a parasitic mode of life can be illustrated by the work of Wilson (1958) on the hatching of the eggs of *Trichostrongylus retortaeformis*.

An understanding of the mechanism of hatching of eggs requires some knowledge of the structure of the egg-shell. Basically, the egg-shell of nematodes is a primary egg envelope composed of an inner "vitelline membrane" largely of lipid, a thicker middle layer of chitin and some protein, and an outer layer of protein. A tertiary envelope of protein may surround the primary egg envelope. The lipid layer is probably most important in governing the permeability of the whole egg-shell, while the chitin and protein layers give mechanical strength. The shells of eggs of parasitic nematodes which hatch outside the host are generally thinner and more fragile (Monné and Hönig, 1955) than those of eggs which hatch within the host (Monné and Hönig, 1954, 1955). Thus the envelopes of eggs of the Strongyloidea, with the exception of *Nematodirus*, *Nematodirella* and *Syngamus*, are thin, and the isotropic lipid layer does not adhere tightly to the outer shell, which is formed largely of quinone-tanned protein and contains little if any chitin (see Chapter 9).

The hatching of eggs of nematodes outside a host has generally been attributed to the activity of the enclosed larvae which were thought to force their way through the egg-shell by their movements (Veglia, 1915). Looss (1911) thought that hatching of eggs of *Ancylostoma duodenale* was brought about by an increase in hydrostatic pressure in the egg fluid resulting from a change in the properties of the lipid membrane of the egg-shell which made it semipermeable at the time of hatching. This conclusion was based on the finding that eggs could be collapsed more easily in strong salt solutions when hatching was due to commence. Wilson (1958) pointed out, however, that the collapse of the contents of eggs of *Trichostrongylus retortaeformis* in saturated solutions of sodium chloride shows that the egg membranes are not semipermeable in the way Looss suggested (i.e. preferentially permeable to water) as only the larva is distorted under such conditions.

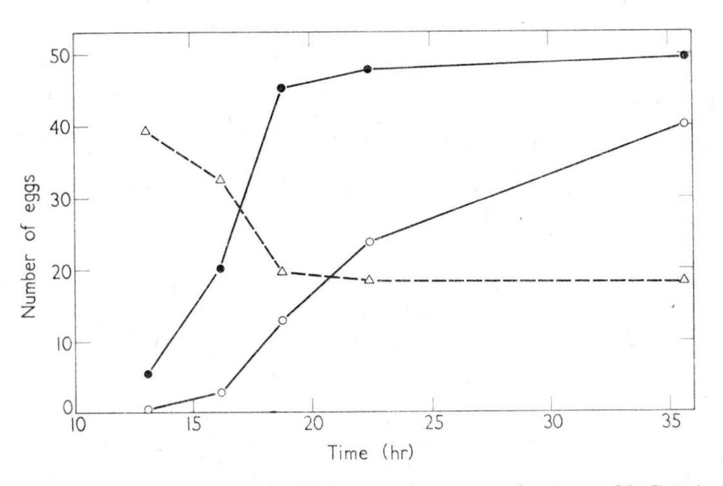

FIG. 13. The hatching of eggs of *Trichostrongylus retortaeformis* at 30°C (○); water permeability of the egg estimated by plasmolysis in saturated sodium chloride (●), and mobility of unhatched larvae (△) (after Wilson, 1958).

Wilson suggested that the hatching of eggs of *Trichostrongylus retortaeformis* involves two processes, one depending on the breakdown of the inner lipid membrane of the egg (Fig. 13) and an increase in the hydrostatic pressure inside the larva, and a subsequent process which normally controls the rate of hatching when there are no ions in the solution. The breakdown of the lipid membrane he attributed to movements of the larva in the fluid of the egg in the presence of an emulsifying agent; the increase in hydrostatic pressure within the larva enables it to exert more pressure on the rigid egg-shell. The second process Wilson regarded as a chemical weakening of the protein layer of the shell which lies outside the layer of lipid.

The hatching of the eggs of *Trichostrongylus retortaeformis* was retarded by dilute salt solutions (Fig. 14) which delayed the breakdown of the lipid membrane. Dropkin *et al.* (1958) showed that the hatching of eggs of *Heterodera rostochiensis, Meloidogyne arenaria* and *Ditylenchus dipsaci* was also reversibly inhibited by salt solutions. Even at a concentration as low as 0.1M, sodium chloride showed this effect on some species.

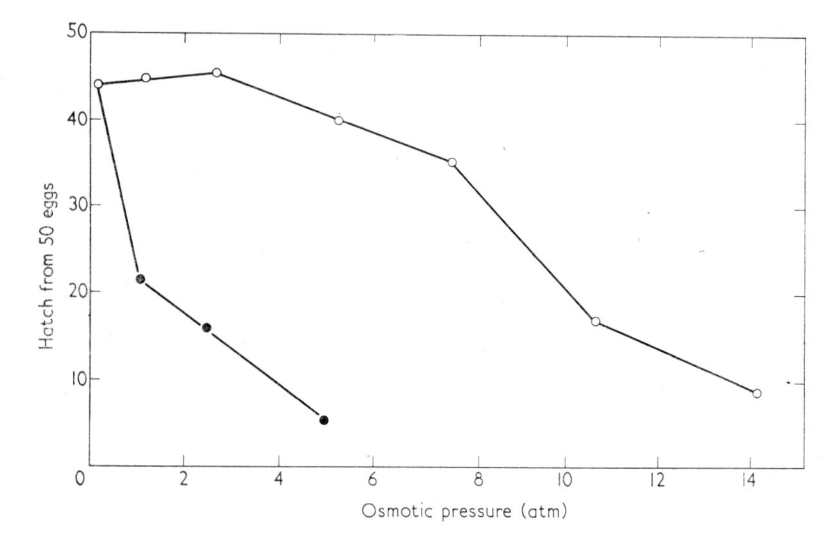

FIG. 14. Hatching of eggs of *Trichostrongylus retortaeformis* incubated in solutions of sucrose and sodium chloride for 136 hours at 30°C; O, mean hatch in ten sucrose cultures; ●, mean hatch in ten sodium chloride cultures (after Wilson, 1958).

The Special Physiology of Free-living Infective Stages

Free-living infective stages must have the capacity to survive in two very different sorts of environments. Also, they must be able to "recognize" a suitable host in the sense that they should not shed the protective mechanisms suited to the free-living environment until they have reached the right environment for development as a parasite (see Chapter 5). It might be expected, then, that the physiological characteristics of infective stages might fall somewhere between those of free-living stages and those of the parasitic stages. This can be seen in the oxygen relationships of some infective agents.

Free-living stages are sensitive to a lack of oxygen. Without it development does not proceed, and even in the free-living infective stages, in which no development occurs, the presence of oxygen prolongs survival. Nevertheless the sensitivity of the infective stages varies considerably from species to species and this may be related to the site in the host where infection occurs. Thus the eggs and third-stage larvae of the nematodes which infect the host via the alimentary canal are relatively resistant to a lack of oxygen. This may be an adaptation of some significance because it appears that the hatching of these eggs and the exsheathing of these larvae take place at sites in the host where oxygen is absent or at very low pressures (Rogers, 1960). On the other hand the infective larvae of species of *Strongyloides* are very sensitive to the lack of oxygen and this may be related to the route of infection which is through the skin of the host. Some infective larvae, like those of *Nippostrongylus muris* and *Ancylostoma caninum* which, though normally infecting the host through the skin, have some capacity for entering the host via the alimentary canal, are more resistant to the lack of oxygen than species of *Strongyloides*.

It seems characteristic of free-living infective stages that they do not feed. Evidently the requirements for feeding as a free-living organism and as a parasite are not commonly reconciled within one stage of the life cycle. The economic use of food reserves in the free-living infective stage is therefore of importance. For this reason presumably, these stages are predominantly aerobic in their metabolism and those which enter a habitat low in oxygen are also necessarily adapted for survival at low partial pressures of oxygen (Bair, 1955). It would be interesting to know if the efficiency of aerobic metabolism in infective stages, as judged by the Pasteur effect for instance, is greater than in adult parasites.

The importance of the "critical oxygen tension" (the point in the pO_2 $-Q_{O_2}$ curve where the oxygen uptake suddenly falls away) in relation to a parasitic way of life has been discussed by several workers (e.g. Bair, 1955). The critical tension may be a particularly important physiological parameter for infective stages which pass from an environment where air is available to one in which the pO_2 is low. In these organisms adaptations which allow respiration to continue at relatively low oxygen pressures could be a basic necessity (Bair, 1955). And in some respects it seems to be an added advantage if the respiratory rate in air is relatively low because this leads to the conservation of reserve materials and allows the infective stage to survive longer (see Table II) and so increases its chances of reaching a host. Unfortunately only a few results are available for the examination of these suggestions. The infective eggs of *Ascaris lumbricoides* have a critical tension of about 40 mm of mercury, and, as Passey and Fairbairn (1955) pointed out, at a pO_2 of 20 mm they can respire at about half the rate in air. The migrating larvae in the tissues of the host, free of the egg-shells which might limit the diffusion of oxygen, may therefore respire quite actively. The critical pressure for the respiration of larvae of cylicostomes is less than 38 mm of mercury though the exact value has not been determined. It would be interesting to know if the critical pressure for these small organisms is determined by the penetration of oxygen to central tissues by diffusion alone, or whether it is effectively aided by oxygen- or electron-transport.

Shortage of water must be a hazard for infective stages of many species. This must be of special importance in infective eggs where the shell forms a "closed box". The classical view that fat catabolism is more efficient than carbohydrate catabolism for the provision of metabolic water suggests that fat might be metabolized preferentially by infective eggs. There is no evidence that this is so; both glycogen and fats form food reserves in eggs and the R.Q. is usually about 1. In many infective larvae, however, fat is the major food reserve and the R.Q. is low. The nature of the major nitrogenous end-product is usually associated with the availability of water; species of animals that suffer a shortage of water usually excrete nitrogen in a form which is less soluble and less toxic than ammonia. Infective larvae do not appear to be adapted this way. Ammonia is the major nitrogenous end-product, and though a considerable part of the excreted nitrogen is in the form of amines these compounds cannot be regarded as detoxication products of ammonia. The excretion of nitrogen by infective eggs has not been examined in detail, but at least one species produces a variety of amines.

Physiological characters of infective stages which are directly concerned with the process of infection of the host will be discussed in Chapter 5.

Free-living Stages of other Metazoan Parasites

As in the Nematoda, there are no known physiological characteristics which distinguish the free-living stages of the platyhelminths or Acanthocephala from the parasitic stages. Glycogen and fat are both present as reserve food materials though glycogen usually predominates in the relatively short-lived infective stages, miracidia and cercariae (von Brand, 1952; Axmann, 1947). All free-living stages of the platyhelminths which have been examined so far use oxygen when it is available. Though there is indirect evidence that the eggs of cestodes are resistant to the lack of oxygen, the free-living stages of many trematodes cannot live for long under anaerobic conditions. Those species of the free-living metacercariae and cercariae which have been examined (Stunkard, 1930; Olivier *et al.*, 1953) show a definite need for oxygen. As might be expected with such small organisms, the need may be met even at low pressures of oxygen. Thus the cercariae of *Schistosoma mansoni* lost their tails and died rapidly if no oxygen was available but they remained active and apparently undamaged when the pressure was about 7 mm of mercury. The cercariae of *Zoogonus rubellus* which, unlike those of *Schistosoma mansoni*, are sluggish and lack a tail, also showed a sensitivity to lack of oxygen; under anaerobic conditions they died in about 12 hours. Their oxygen uptake was not greatly affected by changes in the pO_2 from 38 to 760 mm of mercury (Fig. 11) so it is probable that they can survive for normal periods at relatively low tensions. No appreciable oxygen debt was incurred by exposing cercariae to anaerobic conditions for 10 hours (Hunter and Vernberg, 1955, 1957; Vernberg and Hunter, 1956).

The hatching of the eggs of several species of trematodes, where the hatching takes place outside the host, has been examined. Some workers regarded hatching as the outcome of movements of the miracidium which were considered to open the operculum in the shell in one way or another. However, Rowan (1956, 1957) showed in his experiments with eggs of *Fasciola hepatica* that the basic mechanism was the production of a proteolytic enzyme by the miracidium in response to exposure to light. The enzyme digested the material which bound the operculum to the shell and so allowed the escape of the miracidium. The hypertonicity of the contents of the egg rather than the muscular movements of the miracidium brought about its escape.

Summary

At present no clear-cut distinctions between the physiological characters of free-living stages and parasitic stages of metazoan parasites are known. In general, however, free-living stages have a predominantly aerobic metabolism and are more sensitive to a lack of oxygen than many parasitic stages. Resistance to the lack of oxygen can be correlated with the route of infection of the host in the infective agents of many species of nematodes.

The carbohydrate metabolism of those species of free-living stages which have so far been examined follows the more conventional routes of glycolysis and the tricarboxylic acid cycle. Phosphagen, probably arginine phosphate, which has not been found in adult parasites, is present in the infective larvae of at least one species.

The infective stages of nematode parasites are not generally adapted to a shortage of water as might be expected. Ammonia is the major end-product of nitrogen metabolism and fat is not always the major food reserve.

REFERENCES

Axmann, M. C. (1947) *J. Morph.* **80**, 321.
Baer, J. G. (1952) "Ecology of Animal Parasites". University of Illinois Press, Urbana.
Bair, T. D. (1955) *J. Parasit.* **41**, 613.
Brown, H. W. (1928) *J. Parasit.* **14**, 141.
Costello, L. C. and Grollman, S. (1958) *Exp. Parasit.* **7**, 319.
—— (1959) *Exp. Parasit.* **8**, 83.
Crofton, H. D. (1948*a*) *Parasitology*, **39**, 17.
—— (1948*b*) *Parasitology*, **39**, 26.
Dinnick, J. A. and Dinnick, N. N. (1937) *Med. Parasit., Moscow*, **5**, 603.
Dropkin, V. H., Martin, G. C. and Johnson, R. W. (1958) *Nematologica*, **3**, 115.
Eisma, M. (1932) *Acta leidensia*, **7**, 1.
Elliott, A. (1954) *Exp. Parasit.* **3**, 307.
Fairbairn, D. (1957) *Exp. Parasit.* **6**, 491.
—— and Passey, R. F. (1957) *Exp. Parasit.* **6**, 566.
Fauré-Fremiet, E. (1913) *C. R. Soc. Biol., Paris*, **75**, 90.
Fouquey, C., Polonsky, J. and Lederer, E. (1957) *Bull. Soc. Chim. biol., Paris*, **39**, 101.
Fülleborn, F. (1924) *Arch. Schiffs-u. Tropenhyg.* **28**, 144.
Giovannola, A. (1936) *J. Parasit.* **22**, 207.
Glaser, R. W. and Stoll, N. R. (1938) *Parasitology*, **30**, 324.
Haskins, W. T. and Weinstein, P. P. (1957) *J. Parasit.* **43**, 28.
Hopkins, C. A. (1955) *Trans. R. Soc. trop. Med. Hyg.* **49**, 12.
Huff, G. C. (1936) *J. Parasit.* **22**, 455.
Hunter, W. S. and Vernberg, W. B. (1955) *Exp. Parasit.* **4**, 427.
—— (1957) *J. Parasit.* **43**, 493.
Jaskoski, B. J. (1952) *Exp. Parasit.* **1**, 291.
Jones, C. A. (1955) *J. Parasit.* **41**, Suppl. 48.
Kates, K. C. (1950) *Proc. helm. Soc. Wash.* **17**, 39.
Lapage, G. (1933) *Nature, Lond.* **131**, 583.
—— (1937) "Nematodes Parasitic in Animals". Methuen, London.
Lawrence, J. J. (1948) *Aust. J. exp. Biol. med. Sci*, **26**, 1.
Looss, A. (1911) *Rec. Sch. Med. Cairo*, **4**, 349.
Lucker, J. T. (1934) *Bull. U. S. Dep. Agric.* No. 437.
—— (1941*a*) *Proc. helm. Soc. Wash.* **8**, 11.
—— (1941*b*) *J. agric. Res.* **63**, 193.
McCoy, O. R. (1929*a*) *Science*, **69**, 74.
—— (1929*b*) *Amer. J. Hyg.* **10**, 140.
—— (1930) *Amer. J. Hyg.* **11**, 413.
Monné, L. and Hönig, G. (1954) *Ark. Zool.* **6**, 559.
—— (1955) *Ark. Zool.* **7**, 261.
Nolf, L. O. (1932) *Amer. J. Hyg.* **16**, 288.
Ochoa, A. (1951) *Physiol. Rev.* **31**, 56.
Olivier, L., von Brand, T. and Mehlman, B. (1953) *Exp. Parasit.* **2**, 258.
Passey, R. F. and Fairbairn, D. (1955) *Canad. J. Biochem. Physiol.* **33**, 1033.
—— (1957) *Canad. J. Biochem. Physiol.* **35**, 511.
Payne, F. K. (1922) *Amer. J. Hyg.* **2**, 254.
—— (1923*a*) *Amer. J. Hyg.* **3**, 547.
—— (1923*b*) *Amer. J. Hyg.* **3**, 584.
Polonsky, J., Fouquey, C., Ferreol, G. and Lederer, E. (1955) *C. R. Soc. Biol., Paris*, **240**, 2265.

Raven, B. and Schuurmans Stekhoven, J. H. (1934) *Zool. Anz.* **106**, 17.
Richardson, H. B. (1929) *Physiol. Rev.* **9**, 61.
Rogers, W. P. (1939) *J. Helminth.* **17**, 195.
—— (1940*a*) *Parasitology*, **32**, 208.
—— (1940*b*) *J. Helminth.* **18**, 183.
—— (1948) *Parasitology*, **39**, 105.
—— (1960) *Proc. roy. Soc.* **B152**, 367.
Rowan, W. B. (1956) *Exp. Parasit.* **5**, 118.
—— (1957) *Exp. Parasit.* **6**, 131.
Schwabe, C. W. (1957) *Amer. J. Hyg.* **65**, 325.
Silverman, P. H. (1959) *Nature, Lond.* **183**, 197.
Stannard, J. N., McCoy, O. R. and Latchford, W. B. (1938) *Amer. J. Hyg.* **27**, 666.
Stunkard, H. W. (1930) *J. Morph.* **50**, 143.
Veglia, F. (1915) *Rep. vet. Res. S. Afr.* **3 and 4**, 349.
Vernberg, W. B. and Hunter, W. S. (1956) *Exp. Parasit.* **5**, 441.
von Brand, T. (1952) "Chemical Physiology of Endoparasitic Animals". Academic Press, New York.
Weinstein, P. P. (1952) *Exp. Parasit.* **1**, 363.
—— (1953) *Amer. J. Hyg.* **58**, 352.
—— and Haskins, W. T. (1955) *Exp. Parasit.* **4**, 226.
—— and Jones, M. F. (1956) *J. Parasit.* **42**, 215.
Wilson, P. A. G. (1958) *J. exp. Biol.* **35**, 584.

CHAPTER 5

The Physiology of Infection

INFECTION is the outcome of a complex series of events and processes. The success or failure of the infective agent to become established as a parasite depends partly on its own condition and partly on the condition of the host. The vigour of the infective agent depends on its genetical constitution and on the environment to which it has been exposed, whether it was free-living (Payne, 1923; Rogers, 1940) or parasitic in an intermediate host (Evans and Stirewalt, 1951), and the susceptibility or resistance of the host also depends upon genetical and environmental factors.

In the interaction between the vigour of the infective agent and the susceptibility of the host there is an event in the process of infection in some species which seems critical; if the infective egg, cyst or larva fails to hatch, excyst or exsheath, infection cannot occur. Of course, this sort of event can be no more critical than other physiological and morphological changes which take place if the infective stage is to change to a true parasite. Perhaps it is because the morphological changes which occur in the hatching, excysting or exsheathing of infective stages are clear-cut and easily seen that they may be regarded as critical in the sort of experimental approach which can be made at present in the study of the infective process. Further, these changes in the infective stage are the first which can be easily observed during the process of infection; they are the first indications that the infective stage has reached, in a host, an environment which contains some of the factors which are necessary for its success as a parasite. For these reasons the discussion on the physiology of infective processes given here is primarily concerned with changes of this sort.

In Chapter 3 it was suggested that processes in the life cycle of free-living nematodes such as the hatching of eggs and the moulting of larvae must be controlled and co-ordinated largely by some sort of mechanism within the nematodes. This might be achieved by a system of "internal secretions" which regulates the time of production of substances which cause hatching or moulting. In parasitic species part of this mechanism might be lost so that the parasite would be dependent on the host to replace it (see Chapter 3 and Fig. 15). For instance, the infective stage, lacking part of this system for restarting development, would remain in a "resting" condition until, in the right host, the missing components were provided. The missing components might function by providing (I) a stimulus which causes the infective stage to produce the internal secretions; or (II) by providing the substances which replace the missing internal secretions; or (III) by providing substances which cause exsheathment or hatching by their direct action on the sheath or egg-shell.

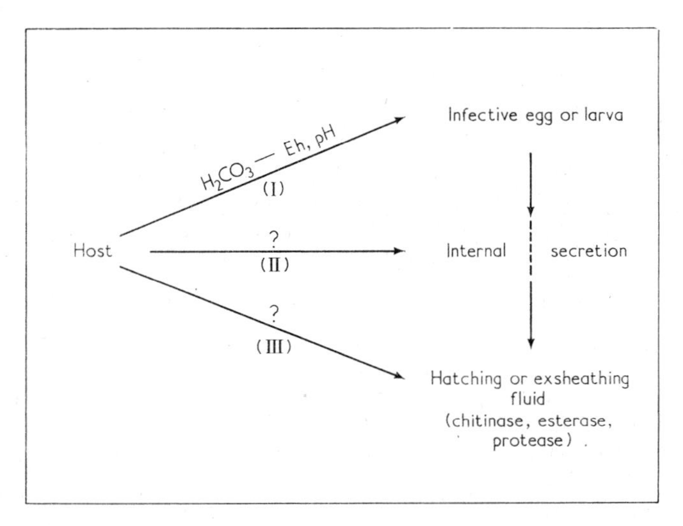

FIG. 15. Host–parasite relationships in the process of infection. The host may start infection by providing an environment (I) which stimulates the infective agent to produce, directly or indirectly, hatching or exsheathing fluids which contain certain enzymes. There is no evidence, as yet, to show that the host may function as in (II) or (III) (after Rogers, 1960).

There is evidence that at least part of this hypothesis is true. Thus it has been shown that a stimulus from the host is necessary to start infection via the gut with a variety of infective eggs and larvae of nematode parasites. The stimulus leads directly or indirectly to the secretion of hatching or exsheathing fluids by the infective agents themselves.

As the hosts do not normally produce the chitinases or the particular proteases needed to break down the outer coverings of nematode eggs or infective larvae, it is not usual for them to start the process of infection by direct action on the infective agents in this group. In the Acanthocephala also, which have a layer of chitin in the egg-shell (see Chapter 9), the action of the host in starting infection is probably indirect. There is evidence, however, that the direct action of the host on some infective cysts and larvae of parasitic platyhelminths is sufficient to start the processes of infection.

Though something is known about the actual mechanisms by which larval parasites penetrate the tissues of the host, the factors in the environment provided by the host which lead to infection via routes other than the alimentary canal have rarely been studied. No generalizations about the processes of infection which take place through the surface of the host can yet be made.

In this chapter the physiology of mechanisms which lead to infection via the gut and via the external surface of the host will be discussed separately. The significance of processes of infection in relation to the specificity of parasites and the evolution of parasitism will only be mentioned briefly. These subjects are discussed in more detail in Chapters 10 and 11.

Infection via the Gut of the Host

The first question here may be stated: Is it the properties of the contents in the lumen of the gut or the properties of the tissues of the walls of the gut which are concerned in the first processes of infection? In another way: Are the features of the environment which are important in starting the processes of infection found in the unorganized, somewhat unstable and relatively simple fluids of the gut contents, or in the organized, highly complex and stable tissues of the walls of the gut?

Clearly, for species in which the infective stage is enclosed within an egg-shell or cyst-wall, it must be factors in the contents of the alimentary canal which lead to the hatching of the egg or excystment. But when the infective agent is a larva which might be equipped to change its behaviour in response to a change in its environment, either the contents of the gut or its tissues might provide the stimulus. In some species, for instance, an infective larva might be swept along passively by movements of the fluids of the gut, until, at some point in the right host, a change in the properties of the fluid causes a change in the behaviour of the larva so that it retains its place in a selected region of the gut and infection takes place. On the other hand, an infective larva, as it is moved passively along the alimentary canal, might make random movements which could lead to a penetration of tissue only in certain regions. Even such simple features as the physical properties of the epithelium lining the gut could determine the region at which it was possible for this to occur.

General Features of Environments of Parasites of the Alimentary Canal

There are a number of summaries and reviews (Vonk, Mansour-Bek and Slijper, 1946; Hobson, 1948; Read, 1950; Spector, 1956) on the composition of the contents of the gut of vertebrates and invertebrates. Books dealing with groups of animals also refer to this subject (see, for instance, Day and Waterhouse, 1953, p. 311; Sturkie, 1954, p. 164; Barrington, 1957, p. 109). All this information cannot be summarized here. Instead, some of the principal features which tend to distinguish the contents of the gut from other sorts of environments will be briefly mentioned.

Physico-chemical features

The high hydrogen ion concentration of the gastric juice of many vertebrates makes the contents of the stomach an unusual sort of environment. Adaptations which allow parasites to live in this part of the gut seem to be rare, and nematodes are the only metazoan parasites which are commonly found in the stomach of warm-blooded animals. The contents of other parts of the alimentary canal are usually slightly acid; the range of hydrogen ion concentrations is similar to that found in the environments of free-living animals.

Other features of the contents of the gut which are relatively uncommon under natural conditions are the low oxidation-reduction potential (Bergeim, Kleinberg and Kirch, 1945; Dewey, Lee and Marston, 1958), low oxygen tension (von Brand and Weise, 1932) and, in some regions of the gut, a high concentration of dissolved carbon dioxide (Turner and Hodgetts, 1955). Apart from the alimentary canals of animals, conditions like these would occur rarely except as the result of the fermentative activity of micro-organisms as in sewage or mud (von Brand, 1946). The osmotic pressure of the gut contents of vertebrates, which is slightly hypotonic or similar to that of the blood (Follansbee, 1945; Hobson, 1948; Read, 1950), is higher than is commonly found in the environments of free-living animals with the exception, of course, of marine animals.

The physico-chemical properties of the contents of the alimentary canal not only vary along the length of the gut, but they also vary with the distance from the mucosa. Thus the oxygen pressure close to the mucosa is higher than in the bulk of the contents, especially where the diameter of the gut is small, as in the small intestine of the rat (Rogers, 1949). Other properties, such as the carbon dioxide tension and pH may also vary in this way (Read, 1950).

Chemical composition

The proportions and concentrations of salts in the contents of the gut do not seem to present any unusual features. Certainly body fluids and even some non-living systems show similarities. Most of the products of digestion, amino acids, monosaccharides, and lipids, occur in animals outside the alimentary canal; they also occur in the environment of free-living organisms as the result of autolysis or the action of micro-organisms on complex organic matter. Some regions of the gut must be unique, however, as sites where glucose, amino acids, fatty acids and neutral fats are provided at relatively high concentrations.

Though proteases, lipases and carbohydrases are found outside the gut, and though these enzymes catalyse reactions which are similar to those of digestive enzymes, they differ in many other respects so that the mixture of enzymes in the gut contents is rarely duplicated elsewhere. Other substances which are excreted or secreted in vertebrates, such as bile salts, bile pigments and mucin, do not commonly occur in the environments of free-living animals.

Physical characters

The physical factors which might be important for parasites which infect the host via the gut could be temperature (in warm-blooded animals), mechanical pressure, diameter and length of the intestine and rate and direction of movement of material in the lumen.

Factors such as these may be concerned in starting the process of infection (Smyth, 1947) as well as affecting the capacity of the infective agents to reach sites in the gut which favour their further development. One aspect of this has been examined by Larsh (1947, 1950) who showed that the infectivity of *Hymenolepis nana* and *Ascaris lumbricoides* for mice depended partly on the peristaltic activity of the small intestine.

Physical features may have a negative rather than a positive relation to the pattern of requirements of a parasite. Thus the absence of grinding surfaces in the gizzard makes the pigeon susceptible to infection with plerocercoids of *Schistocephalus solidus* (Clarke, 1953).

The Physiology of Infection with Eggs

The process of infection of nematode parasites of the alimentary canal has been examined with eggs of *Ascaris lumbricoides, Ascaridia galli* and *Toxocara mystax* (Rogers, 1958, 1960; Fairbairn, 1960). Infection with these parasites takes place in the small intestine of the host and requires that the embryo should pass through the egg-shell which has an inner layer of lipid, a "hard shell" composed largely of chitin and an outer layer of protein (see Chapter 9 for details). Eggs placed directly in the small intestine hatch normally; treatment of the eggs in organs anterior to the duodenum is unnecessary (Hansen, Terhaar and Turner, 1956).

Rogers (1958, 1960), who worked chiefly with the eggs of *Ascaris lumbricoides*, found that hatching took place *in vitro* when the contents of the egg were appropriately stimulated to produce "hatching fluid" which attacked the shell and so allowed the escape of the infective stage. The hatching fluid continued to act on the egg-shell, though slowly, after the stimulus was withdrawn (Fig. 16). Thus components

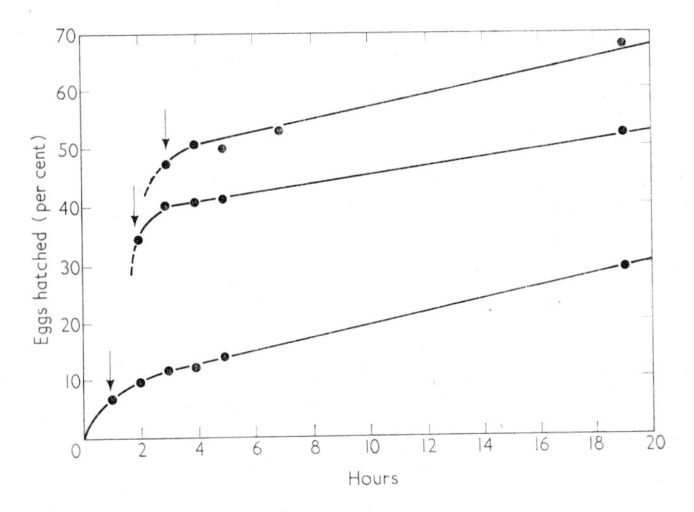

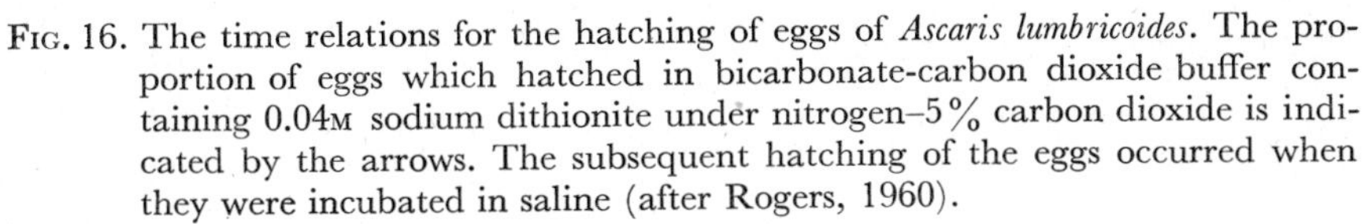
FIG. 16. The time relations for the hatching of eggs of *Ascaris lumbricoides*. The proportion of eggs which hatched in bicarbonate-carbon dioxide buffer containing 0.04M sodium dithionite under nitrogen–5% carbon dioxide is indicated by the arrows. The subsequent hatching of the eggs occurred when they were incubated in saline (after Rogers, 1960).

in the environment provided by the host, which constituted the stimulus for infection, acted indirectly; as expected, the host had no direct action on the egg-shells which could lead to the hatching of the eggs.

The stimulus for infection with nematode eggs

The hatching of eggs *in vitro* at 37°C took place when carbon dioxide was present in the gas phase and was favoured by the presence of a reducing agent. It seemed that it was the unionized components of bicarbonate–carbon dioxide buffer, undissociated carbon dioxide and dissolved gaseous carbon dioxide, which were primarily responsible for

TABLE III

The General Effect of Gases, pH, and Reducing Agents on Infective Larvae and Eggs

Composition of the medium				Exsheathment of larvae %		Hatching of eggs %	
"Buffer"	gas phase	pH	reducing agent	*Haemonchus contortus*	*Trichostrongylus axei*	*Toxocara mystax*	*Ascaris lumbricoides*
Phosphate	air	6.0	—	0	0	0	0
Phosphate	N_2	6.0	+	0	0	0	0
Phosphate	5% $CO_2 - N_2$	about 6.0	—	1	4	1	1
Phosphate	5% $CO_2 - N_2$	about 6.0	+	0	6	3	1
Bicarbonate	5% $CO_2 - N_2$	6.0	—	3	5	5	6
Bicarbonate	5% $CO_2 - N_2$	6.0	+	14	54	16	38
Bicarbonate	5% $CO_2 - N_2$	8.0	—	3	2	40	7
Bicarbonate	5% $CO_2 - N_2$	8.0	+	5	21	62	64
Bicarbonate	N_2	about 8.3	—	0	0	0	0
Bicarbonate	N_2	about 8.3	+	0	3	0	0

The reducing agent was 0.02M sodium dithionite except for *Toxocara mystax* for which 0.02M cysteine was used (after Rogers, 1960) stimulating the eggs (Table III). The optimum concentration of undissociated carbonic acid plus dissolved gaseous carbon dioxide was about 0.25 to 0.5 $\times$ 10^{-3}M at pH 7.3 for eggs of *Ascaris lumbricoides*. At a given concentration of undissociated carbonic acid plus dissolved gaseous carbon dioxide, hatching of eggs was always greatest at lower hydrogen ion concentrations up to pH 8 (Fig. 17). High concentrations of carbon dioxide always inhibited the hatching of eggs.

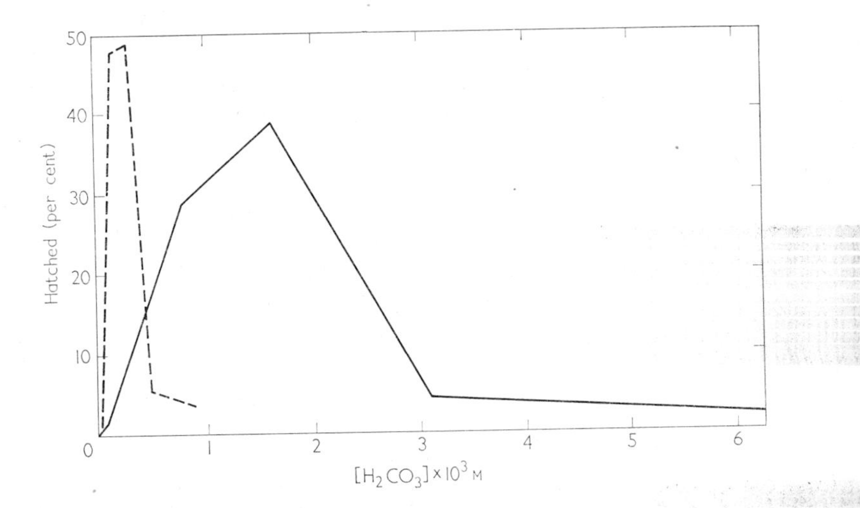

FIG. 17. The hatching of eggs of *Ascaris lumbricoides* at different concentrations of undissociated carbonic acid and hydrogen ions (after Rogers, 1960). The medium was bicarbonate–carbon dioxide buffer at pH 7.3 (broken line) and pH 6.0 (continuous line) containing 0.02M sodium dithionite under different mixtures of nitrogen and carbon dioxide.

Eggs of *Toxocara mystax* were similar to those of *Ascaris lumbricoides;* the eggs of *Ascaridia galli* were more variable. Sometimes they hatched without carbon dioxide in the gas phase; sometimes the optimum concentration of undissociated carbonic acid plus dissolved gaseous carbon dioxide rose to about 0.1 $\times$ 10^{-3}M at pH 7.3. Very often concentrations which stimulated hatching of eggs of *Ascaris lumbricoides* inhibited those of *Ascaridia galli* (Rogers, 1961).

Reducing agents had a pronounced effect on the hatching of eggs of *Ascaris lumbricoides* particularly when the concentration of carbon dioxide was low. The order of activity of three reducing agents was sodium dithionite > cysteine > ascorbic acid. This effect was not generally affected by changes in pH. With *Ascaridia galli* reducing agents were not so effective though they always increased the activity of the stimulus

(Fig. 18). As the reducing agents which increased activity were so different in structure their actions cannot be attributed to any of their individual properties. It seems therefore that it was the oxidation-reduction potential which was the important factor in the stimulus. *Ascaris lumbricoides* evidently needed a lower potential than *Ascaridia galli*. *Toxocara mystax* was more like *Ascaris lumbricoides*.

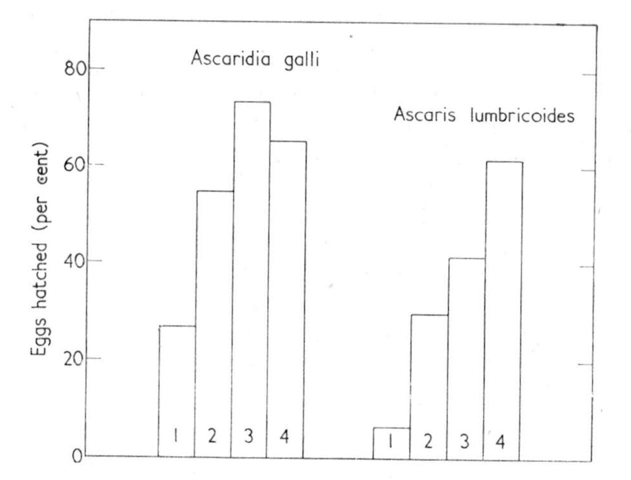

FIG. 18. The hatching of eggs of *Ascaridia galli* and *Ascaris lumbricoides* in media containing different reducing agents (after Rogers, 1960, 1961). The experiments were conducted in bicarbonate–carbon dioxide buffers at pH 8. For *Ascaridia galli* the gas phase was 1% carbon dioxide in nitrogen; for *Ascaris lumbricoides* it was 5% carbon dioxide in nitrogen. The reducing agents were (1) control, (2) ascorbic acid, (3) cysteine, (4) sodium dithionite, all at 0.02M.

It has not been shown that these results which have been obtained from studies *in vitro* fully describe the stimulus provided by the host for infection *in vivo*. Moreover, the eggs that have been studied so far have been obtained directly from female worms and so may differ from eggs which cause infection under natural conditions. Indeed Rogers (1961) has shown that the stimulus for hatching of eggs of *Ascaridia galli in vitro* is variable and eggs which have been dried are more difficult to hatch. On the other hand results obtained *in vitro* are in general accord with some of our knowledge of the host and the parasite. The stimulus for some species, at least, is what might be expected for organisms which infect the host via the alimentary canal (Rogers, 1960) and may even have a bearing on specificity (Chapter 10). And it has been shown that the capacity of infective eggs of *Ascaris lumbricoides* to hatch *in vitro* matched their capacity to hatch *in vivo* (Rogers, 1958). It has also been shown that the stimulus was ineffective with eggs which had not developed to the infective stage (Fig. 19). As *in vivo*, eggs will not hatch *in vitro* until development has passed the first moult (Alicata, 1934).

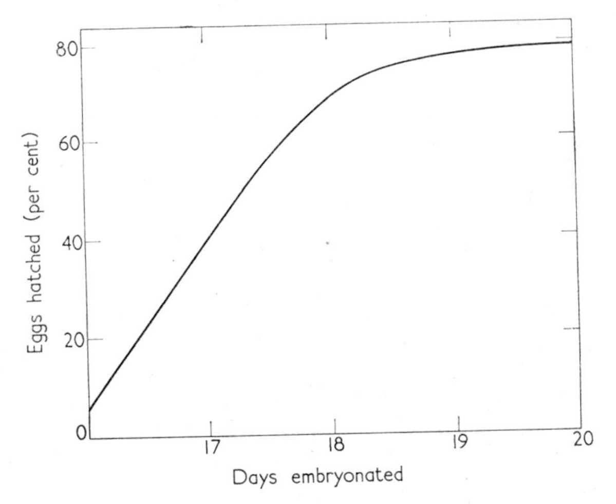

FIG. 19. The development of the hatching response of eggs of *Ascaris lumbricoides* as a function of the age of the embryo. The eggs were incubated at 30°C in 0.1N sulphuric acid. They were stimulated to hatch at 37°C in a buffer of 0.4M bicarbonate under 5% carbon dioxide in nitrogen, containing 0.04M sulphur dioxide (after Fairbairn, 1960).

Hatching fluid produced by infective eggs of nematodes

"Hatching fluid" has been prepared from the eggs of *Ascaris lumbricoides* (Rogers, 1958). Large numbers of eggs were stimulated to hatch under optimal conditions *in vitro*. Larvae and egg-shells were removed by centrifuging and the substances used to stimulate hatching were removed by dialysis. The remaining solution contained a chitinase, lipase and possibly a protease. The chitinase, tested with chitin prepared from arthropods or empty egg-shells as a substrate, showed an optimum at pH 6 which is somewhat higher than that for chitinases from molluscs and arthropods. Proteolytic activity in the hatching fluid was not detected with blood serum as a substrate but nitrogenous material was freed from empty egg-shells by the action of the hatching fluid. However the optimum, pH 6, was so low as to suggest that the nitrogenous material may have been freed by the action of the chitinase. The lipase was detected with tributyrin as a substrate. Its optimum was about pH 7.3 to 7.5.

The hatching fluid, presumably secreted by the embryo after it had been stimulated, acted on the inside of the egg-shell. It seemed that the lipase acted as an esterase and attacked the inner impermeable layer of lipid; after this the chitinase, and possibly the protease, attacked the outer layers of the shell. Evidently the enzymes continued to hydrolyze the shell after hatching had occurred. Thus when the N-acetylglucosamine released during the hatching of a thick suspension of eggs was measured at intervals and related to the number of eggs which had hatched, it was found that the amount freed per egg hatched increased with time (Table IV). Moreover eggs continued to hatch after the stimulus was removed.

TABLE IV

The Amount of N-Acetylglucosamine freed in the Medium in relation to the Hatching of Eggs of Ascaris lumbricoides

Time (min)	Eggs Hatched (%)	Eggs Hatched (wt.†)	N-Acetylglucosamine Liberated total μg	N-Acetylglucosamine Liberated μg per mg of eggs hatched
0	nil	nil	—	—
45	1	0.22	trace	—
90	18	4.03	36	8.9
135	53	11.87	129	10.8
180	75	16.81	214	12.7

† as mg of uterine eggs

Hatching fluid also attacked egg-shells from the outside and it was possible to induce the hatching of unstimulated eggs of *Ascaris lumbricoides* by placing them in hatching fluid obtained from eggs which had been stimulated. Thus, it appears that these results demonstrate quite clearly the indirect action of the host in the process of infection with eggs of nematode parasites. The course of events which link the reception of the stimulus by the infective embryo with the release of the hatching fluid is unknown. It is possible that the stimulus acts directly on the centre which secretes the fluid; but it is also possible that stimulus and secretion are linked by some system of internal secretion which has a general function in developmental physiology of nematodes (Fig. 15).

Infection with eggs of the Acanthocephala and parasitic Platyhelminthes

The eggs of Acanthocephala are infective to arthropods which they enter via the gut. The shells have a layer of chitin (see Chapter 9) and though some insects may on occasions secrete a chitinase in the gut it seems likely that the action of the host, in starting the process of infection, might be indirect.

The eggs of trematodes usually hatch without the intervention of a host. Thus if the fully-developed eggs of *Fasciola hepatica* are exposed to light the embryo produces a "hatching enzyme" which is probably proteolytic in its action. This enzyme attacks, from the inside of the shell, the substance binding the operculum and so permits the egg to open (Rowan, 1956, 1957). In species such as *Halipegus eccentricus* in which the egg is infective it seems reasonable to suppose that hatching is provoked in a similar way, but here the host would provide a stimulus which takes the place of the light needed to provoke the hatching of eggs of *Fasciola hepatica*.

The "egg-shells" or embryophores of cestodes, which lack chitin, are formed largely of protein and hatching takes place chiefly by the direct action of the hosts' digestive juices. The structure of the embryophore varies in different families and this may be correlated with differences in the process of hatching (Silverman, 1954*a*). The eggs of the family Taeniidae have thick, radially striated embryophores, the removal of which requires the hosts' digestive enzymes. It seems that this is brought about by the action of the hosts' proteases on the "cement substances" within the embryophore. Silverman (1954*a*) found that the eggs of *Taenia saginata* required treatment with gastric juice before the embryophore could be broken down by intestinal juice. Treatment with intestinal juice alone was, however, sufficient for eggs of *Taenia pisiformis*. After the dissolution of the embryophore the addition of bile salts to the intestinal juice led to changes in the "oncospheral membrane" (the membrane surrounding the hexacanth embryo) which, in turn, led to the activation of the hexacanth embryo. This then ruptured the oncospheral membrane and became free to attack the tissues of the host. Sodium taurocholate was more effective than sodium glycocholate in activating *Taenia pisiformis;* for *Taenia saginata* hydrochloric acid was more effective. In the presence of bile salts the addition of cholesterol promoted the hatching of eggs of both species.

Two explanations for the action of bile salts have been given (Silverman, 1954*b*): (1) the bile salts activated the pancreatic lipase which attacked the oncospheral membrane; (2) the bile salts acted as they do on some bacterial membranes (Henry and Stacey, 1943) extracting polysaccharide, protein and salts of ribonucleic acid. The physiological changes induced in the hexacanth embryo during hatching are unknown. What is seen in the embryo is the great increase in activity and the secretion of material from the ducts which open to the exterior between each pair of lateral hooks (Silverman, 1954*a*).

The hatching of eggs of cestodes of the family Hymenolepididae is similar to that of davaineid, anoplocephalid and dilepidid eggs, but it differs from that seen in eggs of Taeniidae (Silverman, 1954*b*). This may be correlated with the presence of the thin embryophore which is commonly found in cyclophyllidian cestodes outside the Taeniidae. Digestive juices do not seem to be necessary at least for some of these species and activation of the embryo does not require bile salts or intestinal juice (Taylor, 1926; Stunkard, 1934). Changes in the temperature and the tonicity of the medium are often sufficient to cause activity of the embryo (Venard, 1938).

From these and other results of the infection of animals with eggs of parasites other than nematodes, it seems that in some groups like the Cestoda the components in the environment provided by the host which induce infection act directly on the coverings of the infective agent. In the Acanthocephala, however, and perhaps in the few trematodes which have an infective egg, the action of the host may be indirect.

The Physiology of Infection with Larvae

The first event in the process of infection of animals with trichostrongyle larvae is the completion of the second moult or exsheathment. The physiology of this process has been examined by Sommerville (1957), Rogers and Sommerville (1957, 1960) and Rogers (1960) who used larvae of *Haemonchus contortus, Trichostrongylus axei, Ostertagia circumcincta* and *Trichostrongylus colubriformis.* A stimulus from the host causes the infective larvae to secrete an "exsheathing fluid" which attacks a small area encircling the sheath about 20 μ from the anterior end of the larva. After the area has become weakened, movements of the larva cause the anterior end of the sheath to become detached as a cap (Lapage, 1935; see Chapter 3). Changes in the sheath which take place during exsheathment have been described by Rogers and Sommerville (1960).

Though the whole process of exsheathment took place in about 3 hours at 37°C, the action of the stimulus was complete in about 15 minutes for *Trichostrongylus axei* and about 30 minutes for *Haemonchus contortus* (Fig. 20). It was thus possible to study the stimulus and breakdown of the sheath as separate processes. Indeed, it was possible to collect exsheathing fluid separate from the substances needed for the stimulus. This exsheathing fluid was found to attack from the inside the appropriate parts of sheaths dissected from larvae which had not

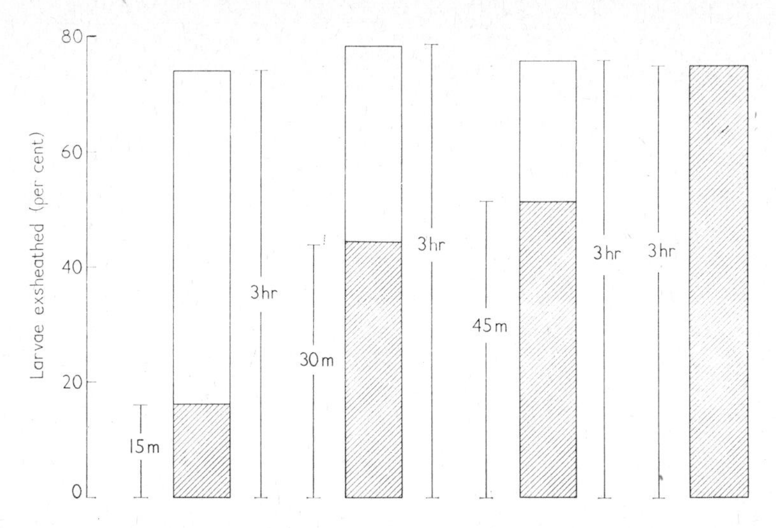

FIG. 20. The time relations of the stimulus for the exsheathment of larvae of *Trichostrongylus axei*. The proportion of larvae which exsheathed when they were incubated in bicarbonate–carbon dioxide buffer at pH 6.9 containing 0.02M sodium dithionite and 0.05M sodium chloride under 100% carbon dioxide is shown by the lengths of the hatched areas. The exsheathment which took place subsequently in 0.001M magnesium chloride in 0.01M phosphate buffer at pH 7.2 is shown by the lengths of the open areas (after Rogers, 1960).

been stimulated. In this way it was possible to examine actions of the stimulus and the exsheathing fluid largely independently of one another.

The stimulus for exsheathment of trichostrongyle larvae

The components of the environment provided by the host which act as a stimulus for exsheathment are similar to those which stimulate the hatching of eggs of ascarids (Table III). However, the differences in the requirements of different species of larvae are more marked than in the different species of eggs.

With larvae of *Trichostrongylus axei* and *Haemonchus contortus*, Rogers (1960) found that the activity of the stimulus increased with increasing concentrations of undissociated carbonic acid plus dissolved gaseous carbon dioxide; even when the gas phase was 100% carbon dioxide the stimulus was effective under the proper conditions. As with the ascarid eggs a given concentration of undissociated carbonic acid plus dissolved gaseous carbon dioxide was always more effective at a higher pH up to pH 8 (Figs. 21, 22). Lower concentrations of carbon dioxide were more effective with *Trichostrongylus axei*. Thus about 70% of the infective larvae of this species exsheathed in 3 hours at pH 7.3, 37°C,

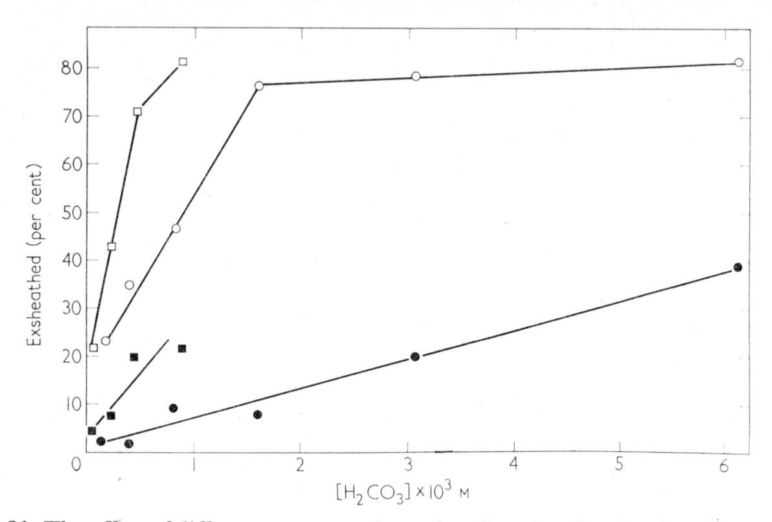

FIG. 21. The effect of different concentrations of undissociated carbonic acid plus dissolved gaseous carbon dioxide on the exsheathment of larvae of *Trichostrongylus axei* (after Rogers, 1960). Bicarbonate-carbon dioxide buffers under nitrogen containing carbon dioxide at different partial pressures were used. Sodium dithionite, 0.02M, was present in experiments which gave the results for the upper curves; 0.05M sodium chloride was present in all experiments. □, ■, pH 7.3; ○, ●, pH 6.0.

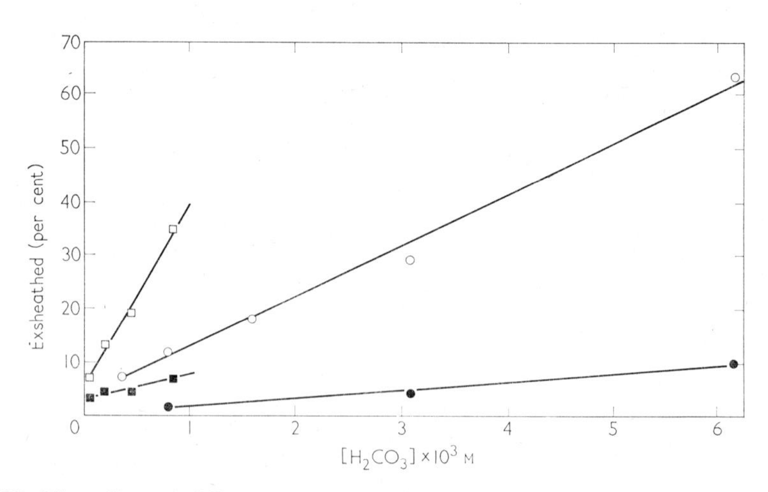

FIG. 22. The effect of different concentrations of undissociated carbonic acid plus dissolved gaseous carbon dioxide on the exsheathment of larvae of *Haemonchus contortus* (after Rogers, 1960). Bicarbonate–carbon dioxide buffers under nitrogen containing carbon dioxide at different partial pressures were used. Sodium dithionite, 0.02M, was present in experiments which gave the results for the upper curves; 0.05M sodium chloride was present in all experiments. □, ■, pH 7.3; ●, ○, pH 6.0.

in 0.02M sodium dithionite when the total concentration of carbonic acid plus dissolved gaseous carbon dioxide was about 0.5×10^{-3}M. More than 1.5×10^{-3}M was necessary to get the same results with *Haemonchus contortus*.

Reducing agents at concentrations of 0.02 to 0.04M often increased the activity of the stimulus when carbon dioxide was present. At pH 6 the activity of reducing agents was sodium dithionite > cysteine > ascorbic acid. At pH 7.3 the activity of cysteine and ascorbic acid was increased relative to the activity of sodium dithionite. This action of pH on the relative activity of the different reducing agents was in accordance with changes in the value of E_0 which would fall as the pH was raised from 6.0 to 7.3 and supports the view that it was the oxidation-reduction potential which was important in the stimulus rather than the individual properties of the reducing agents (Rogers, 1960).

The concentration of salt in the medium affected the stimulus. Concentrations of sodium chloride up to about 0.1M often increased activity but concentrations between 0.3M and 0.4M inhibited. Sodium taurocholate, 0.05M, increased the effect of the stimulus on larvae of *Trichostrongylus axei* and *Haemonchus contortus* by 10 to 15%. Temperature had pronounced effects on the process of exsheathment. Below 30°C exsheathment of larvae of *Trichostrongylus axei* was poor. Activity increased rapidly as the temperature was raised to about 40°C. This effect was due partly to the action of temperature on the stimulus and partly to its action on the exsheathing fluid (Table V), but the effect on the stimulus was more critical. Thus stimulation at 14°C was ineffective even when the larvae were later incubated at 37°C when the exsheathing fluid, if present, would be expected to act. On the other hand, after the stimulus had acted at 37°C, subsequent incubation at 14°C still allowed the exsheathing fluid to act, though slowly.

Infective larvae of *Trichostrongylus colubriformis* normally exsheath in the abomasum and the adults live in the small intestine. Like *Trichostrongylus axei*, this parasite is not restricted to ruminants. It is not surprising therefore that the requirements for stimulating exsheathment are less exacting than for *Haemonchus contortus* (Chapter 10) and depend on components in the environment found in the hydrochloric acid-secreting region of the alimentary canal of mammals. Thus the optimum pH range was 1.5 to 2.5. Carbon dioxide increased the stimulus greatly; the best results were obtained when the concentration of undissociated carbonic acid plus dissolved gaseous carbon dioxide was about 5×10^{-3}M. Reducing agents were not important for this species.

The most important component of the environment needed from the host for restarting the development of infective agents from ascarid eggs and sheathed trichostrongyle larvae seems to be unionized carbonic acid or dissolved gaseous carbon dioxide. It appears that hydrogen ions and reducing agents act largely by enhancing or inhibiting the effect of carbon dioxide. It is not known if the stimulus affects the development of larvae generally, or simply leads to the secretion of the exsheathing fluid.

TABLE V

The Effect of Aeration, Temperature and Hydrogen Ion Concentration on the "Trigger" Mechanism of Trichostrongylus axei

Trigger	Water 2 hr
Effect of aeration	
Trigger 15 min	**Water 2 hr**
Aerated: 0% exsheathed	Aerated: 0% exsheathed
	Reduced: 0% exsheathed
Reduced: 44% exsheathed	Aerated: 82% exsheathed
	Reduced: 98% exsheathed
Effect of temperature	
Trigger 10 min	**Water 2 hr**
38°C: 0% exsheathed	38°C: 71% exsheathed
	14°C: 32% exsheathed
14°C: 0% exsheathed	38°C: 0% exsheathed
	14°C: 0% exsheathed
Effect of pH	
Trigger 10 min	**Water 2 hr**
pH 6: 20% exsheathed	pH 6: 99% exsheathed
	pH 10: 100% exsheathed
pH 10: 0% exsheathed	pH 6: 40% exsheathed
	pH 10: 0% exsheathed

In these experiments the stimulating medium was prepared from the rumen fluid of sheep (from Rogers and Sommerville, 1960).

The actions of exsheathing fluid produced by infective larvae of nematodes

The sheath which encloses the infective larvae of trichostrongyle parasites is the uncast cuticle formed during the incomplete second moult (see Chapter 3). Examination with an electron microscope of thin sections of sheaths of larvae of *Trichostrongylus axei* and *Nippostrongylus muris* which had been fixed in neutral osmium tetroxide showed three layers which were largely structureless. The overall composition of sheaths which had been obtained by treating several species of larvae with dilute sodium hypochlorite has been given by Bird and Rogers (1956). The principal constituents were proteins which were soluble in hot water and which contained the amino acids, proline, hydroxy-proline, aspartic acid, cysteic acid, glutamic acid, alanine, leucine, glycine, and valine. The absence of aromatic amino acids and lysine and argine indicated that the sheaths would not be attacked by trypsin or pepsin so that a direct action of the host in causing exsheathment seemed unlikely. It should be remembered, however, that the completion of the moult takes place by the weakening of the cuticle in a narrow circle at the anterior end of the larvae and that figures for the overall composition for the sheaths do not preclude the presence of small amounts of substances in this region which could be attacked by the hosts' digestive enzymes. However, digestive enzymes do not attack the sheaths *in vitro*, or else they act on them very slowly. And the stimulus which leads to exsheathment has no effect on the sheaths of dead larvae or on sheaths dissected from the living larvae. On the other hand, exsheathing fluid, collected from larvae which had been stimulated, attacked sheaths from larvae which had not been stimulated. The exsheathing fluid clearly corresponded to the hatching fluid of ascarid eggs and contained the substances which completed the second moult by attacking the sheath.

Though the stimulus for the secretion of exsheathing fluid is similar to that required for the secretion of hatching fluid by ascarid eggs, the two fluids are evidently different in composition. Thus the exsheathing fluid from larvae of *Haemonchus contortus* has no obvious action on egg-shells of *Ascaris lumbricoides* and the hatching fluid from this parasite has no obvious effect on sheaths.

The optimum temperature for the action of exsheathing fluid was 40°C; it was inactivated by heating at 60°C for ten minutes. Activity required the presence of a heat-stable co-factor which could be replaced by adding magnesium chloride or manganese chloride. Complete inhibition was obtained with Hg^{++} (0.001M); partial inhibition was obtained with Fe^{+++} (0.001M) and iodoacetic acid (0.05M). The action of exsheathing fluid on sheaths leads to the release of nitrogenous and reducing substances. As yet, the precise nature of the substrate attacked by the fluid and the nature of the active substance in the fluid is unknown.

Exsheathing fluids have some specificity. The material obtained from larvae of *Haemonchus contortus* attacked its own sheaths and those from *Trichostrongylus axei* to about the same degree. Changes it caused in sheaths from larvae of *Trichostrongylus colubriformis* and *Oesophagostomum columbianum* were small. It seems that exsheathing fluid is stored in the region of the larvae of *Trichostrongylus axei* between the base of the œsophagus and the excretory pore. In this region also are probably placed the receptors for the stimulus as well as the mechanism for the release of the fluid.

Infection via the gut of the host with larval stages of parasitic platyhelminths

Platyhelminth parasites have a variety of infective larval stages which infect the host when they are ingested. Thus many metacercariae of the digenetic trematodes are enclosed in a non-living cyst-wall and live outside a host until infection occurs, rather as it does with an infective "egg". Other infective larvae, like the cysticercoids of some cestodes, have no protective coverings which correspond to egg-shells or cyst-walls, though parts of these larvae are often digested during the process of infection. Larval forms like these are not free-living and are protected by the tissues of the intermediate host though they often remain alive long after the host has died (Wykoff, 1959).

The metacercarial stage of the life cycle of trematodes is extremely varied and encystment takes place under a variety of conditions in different species. The cyst-wall is formed by the secretions of "cystogenous" glands and sometimes includes the outer layer of the cuticle of the cercaria (Rothschild, 1936). It seems that protein is the basic component of the cyst-wall because it is generally attacked by digestive proteases. Thus combinations of pepsin-hydrochloric acid and trypsin have caused excystment with several different species (Faust and Khaw, 1925, 1927; Ferguson, 1940, 1943; Hemenway, 1948; Hunter and Chait, 1952; Hoffman, 1958). In some species at least, the cyst-wall was only partly removed in this way, and movements of the larvae, perhaps activated by the entry of substances which penetrated the partly digested cyst-wall, or other mechanical stress, were necessary to free the larvae.

The infective larval stages of cestodes show very different degrees of development and, in some respects, the action of the host in starting development is related to this. Thus for plerocercoids of *Schistocephalus solidus* and *Ligula intestinalis* which reach a degree of development just short of maturity in the cold-blooded intermediate host, a rise in temperature to 40°C acts as a stimulus and sexual maturity is quickly reached (see Smyth, 1947, for references). The plerocercoids of *Diphyllobothrium dendriticum* are relatively poorly developed and the changes which take place in the final host seem to depend on nutrients (Smyth, 1958, 1959). It is not known if any particular nutrient has a specific effect in relation to the developmental changes which occur when infection takes place. When the cysticercoid or cysticercus is the infective stage, excystment and evagination of the scolex is an important part of the process of infection. A number of factors such as temperature, the nature and concentration of bile salts, the presence of digestive proteases and hydrochloric acid affect evagination (Malkani, 1933; de Waele, 1934; Edgar, 1941) and the relative importance of these factors varies with the species (Rothman, 1959; see Chapter 10). With some larvae the actions of the digestive enzymes are obvious enough; they simply remove some of the tissues of the parasite. But the mechanisms by which the other factors stimulate development are not clear.

Infection via the Surface of the Host

The infective stages of many parasites enter the host via the surface of the body or through natural orifices other than the mouth. Penetration of the hosts' tissues may be due to the activity of the infective stage itself, e.g. when miracidia enter the tissues of the snail, or it may be achieved by the activity of the intermediate host, e.g. when microfilariae are introduced into the host by the action of the infected mosquito. As when infection takes place via the gut of the host, the infective larvae which penetrate the surface of the host change in form and activity during this process. Thus the miracidium sheds its cilia when it enters the host and the hookworm larva loses its sheath and secretes substances which aid in the penetration of tissue. Though something is known about changes like these which take place during the process of infection the components in the environment provided by the host which induce these changes are largely unknown.

Though the skin of mammals may have properties and metabolic processes which are unique (Lorincz and Stoughton, 1958), it does not appear that nematodes which enter the mammalian host through the skin obtain specific substances or stimuli there. Infection with *Ancylostoma caninum* or *Nippostrongylus muris* can be achieved almost equally well by placing the larvae on the skin or by subcutaneous or intraperitoneal injection. Also the larvae of many species of parasites will penetrate the skin of a wide variety of hosts so that they show little specificity in this stage of the life cycle. Indeed the action of the larvae in penetrating the skin may be simply the result of random probing movements. The infective larvae of *Nippostrongylus muris*, for instance, will penetrate a variety of living and dead biological tissues as well as some artificial membranes. Infection through the skin of the host involves exsheathment and the secretion of spreading factors in some species of nematodes (Looss, 1911; Lee and Lewert, 1957). Though the conditions which stimulate these changes are not known precisely it is clear that they are not confined to skin; for instance, the exsheathment of *Ancylostoma duodenale* will occur in a variety of viscid media.

The activities of larvae which assist the penetration of tissues of vertebrate hosts have been reviewed by Lewert (1958) and some aspects have been discussed by Millemann and Thonard (1959). Enzymes which affect substances in the connective tissue are commonly produced by a variety of invading larvae. The enzymes include proteases (true collagenases are rare), hyaluronidase-like spreading factors, and even lipases (Thorson, 1953; Mandlowitz *et al.*, 1960). The stimuli which cause the larvae to secrete these substances may be simple; e.g. a rise in temperature or even tactile stimuli may be effective.

The infection of snails with miracidia has been described by Dawes (1959, 1960) who used *Fasciola hepatica* and *Fasciola gigantica.* In the process of infection the miracidium of *Fasciola hepatica* "creates a perforation in the snail's integument by loosening, cytolysis and abstraction of epithelial cells, an action which appears to be chemical rather than mechanical and is probably the result of enzyme activity". Before penetration was completed the miracidium lost its ciliated epithelium and though it retained its eyes, gut and other organs it was clearly as a young sporocyst rather than a miracidium that it entered the host (Dawes, 1959). The metamorphosis from miracidium to sporocyst is a relatively simple one but it must require a mechanism for co-ordinating the variety of processes which take place within the metamorphosing parasite. It is unlikely, therefore, that these processes could be affected by the direct action of substances from the host; probably the host provided a stimulus for the production of substances within the "resting" infective stage which lead to a resumption of development.

Dawes' preliminary results obtained with miracidia of *Schistosoma mansoni* were similar to those obtained with *Fasciola* and he is of the opinion that all digenetic trematodes which have a ciliated miracidium would enter the molluscan host in the same way.

Clear evidence that the host provides a stimulus which initiates the process of infection comes from studies on the relationship between the plant-parasitic nematode, *Heterodera rostochiensis*, and its host. The infection of plants takes place when the infective stage pierces the cuticle and enters the tissue of the plant. But in parasites like *Heterodera rostochiensis* the action of the host in influencing the process of infection starts some time before the infective larvae penetrate the tissues of the plant. In these forms the infective agent is enclosed in the shell of the egg. The eggs, in turn, are enclosed in a "cyst" formed of the outer layer of the body of the parent. The hatching of the egg within the cyst takes place in response to a substance ("root diffusate") secreted by the roots of the host plants—largely species of *Solanum* (Franklin, 1951; Ellenby, 1945, 1954). The second-stage larvae which emerge do not feed until they have entered the host plant and become parasites (Dropkin, 1955). Here again then, the infective stage is a resting stage and the host provides a stimulus for the hatching of the egg. Other developmental changes do not occur until the larvae have actually penetrated the tissue of the host.

The chemistry of the substance from the roots of tomato plants which stimulates the hatching of the eggs of *Heterodera rostochiensis* has been examined by Calam, Todd and Waring (1949) and Marrian, Russel, Todd and Waring (1949). The results suggested that the substance, which has been named eclepic acid, was an unsaturated lactone of molecular weight about 300. In addition to the lactone ring, the presence of one carboxyl group and two hydroxyl groups was postulated. From these data Ellenby (1957) and Ellenby and Gilbert (1957, 1958) considered that the hatching substance might have the cardiotonic properties commonly found even in simple unsaturated lactones. This deduction has been examined in a series of elegant experiments and seems to be correct.

Ellenby regards the hatching factor of root excretion as acting on the embryo rather than on the egg-shell. There is some evidence that it acts, as do the cardiac glycosides on the mammalian heart, by affecting the active transport of cations (Ellenby and Gilbert, 1958). Thus, though eclepic acid is a stimulus for starting the process of infection and acts indirectly, its mode of action is probably different from that of carbon dioxide and other factors which start the process of infection in the infective agents of nematode parasites of the gut. It is possible, however, that substances related to the hatching factor in root excretion have a function in the same mechanism as that which is activated by carbon dioxide (Fig. 23; Rogers, 1958; Fairbairn, 1960) and might even be important in the physiology of nematodes generally. This view is supported by the discovery that root diffusates from susceptible plants induce the moulting of pre-adult larvae of plant parasites such as *Paratylenchus projectus* (Rhoades and Linford, 1959).

The larvae of *Heterodera* and a number of other plant parasites are attracted to substances which diffuse out from the tissues of the host. With some parasites, e.g. *Meloidogyne hapla*, repelling as well as attracting substances are produced by the host. Presumably these substances aid the larvae to reach the right site for penetrating the host (Wieser, 1956). Infective larvae of *Heterodera* adhere to hydrophobic surfaces on the host by the sucking action of their lips and the stylet penetrates the cell walls (Dickinson, 1959). These actions probably result from a purely physical and unspecific stimulus. In addition to the mechanical activities, the process of infection with a number of plant parasitic nematodes probably involves the secretion of cellulases and pectinases which attack substances in the cell walls and spaces between them (Tracey, 1958; Chitwood and Oteifa, 1952).

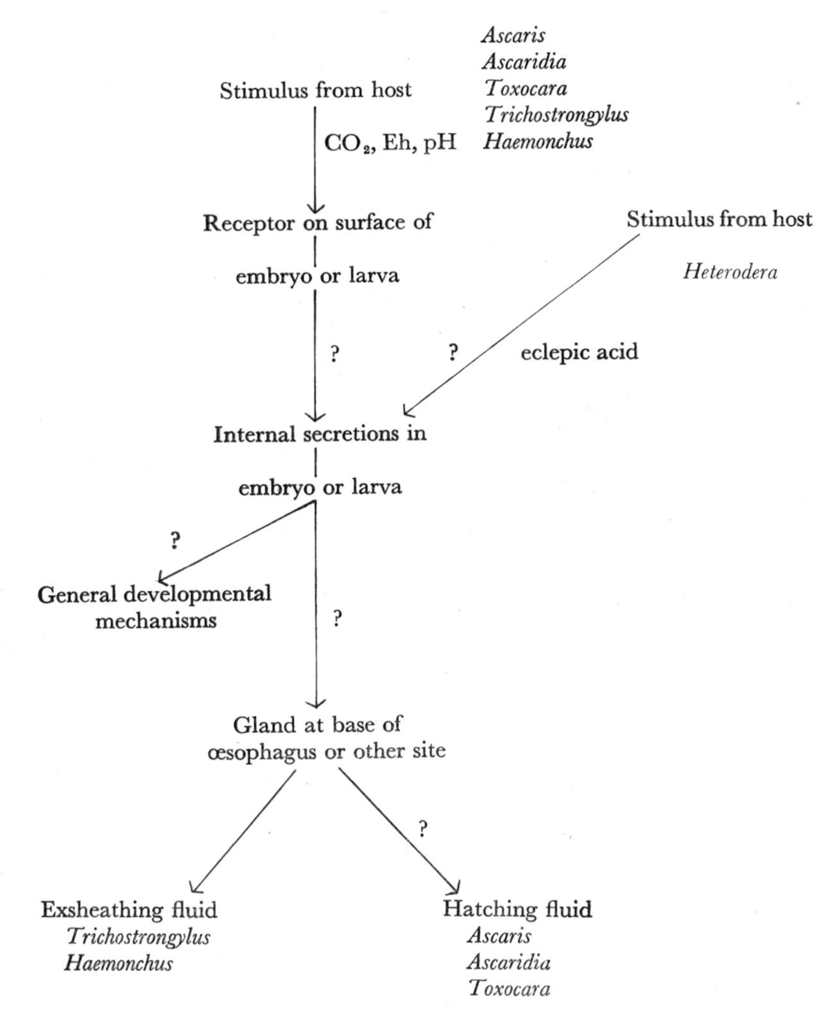

FIG. 23. The possible relationships between some nematode parasites and the host in the process of infection.

Discussion

The clearest evidence that special components in the environment are necessary to start some of the changes which occur when the infective stage develops into a true parasite has been obtained with the eggs of ascarids and the third-stage larvae of trichostrongyles. It is significant that the same factors, carbon dioxide, Eh and pH affect these morphologically different but ecologically similar stages in the life cycle. The same sort of stimulus may be important for infective agents of other sorts of nematodes such as *Trichinella spiralis, Eustrongylides ignotus* and *Enterobius vermicularis* which infect the host via the gut. It is even possible, I suppose, that moulting of later parasitic stages is influenced by stimuli from the host; in species which enter the gut after a histotrophic stage, or after a period in the lungs, carbon dioxide may be an important component of the stimulus.

It is uncertain which component of the bicarbonate–carbon dioxide buffer system is important in the stimulus though there is some evidence that it is the unionized components which are effective. This is supported by the fact that the egg-shell of *Ascaris lumbricoides* is impermeable to some ions; cyanide and azide ions do not affect development or respiration whereas hydrogen cyanide and hydrazoic acid inhibit (Resnitschenko, 1927, 1928; Passey and Fairbairn, 1955). During respiration oxygen passes into the egg and carbon dioxide is produced. Labelled carbon dioxide passes in through the shell in some form or other (Passey and Fairbairn, 1957). The results which suggest that undissociated carbonic acid or dissolved gaseous carbon dioxide rather than bicarbonate or carbonate ions is a component of the stimulus thus seem reasonable. It seems that undissociated carbonic acid or dissolved gaseous carbon dioxide is the principal component of the stimulus and that other factors, chiefly the Eh and pH, simply enhance or decrease its effect.

Dissolved carbon dioxide has a variety of effects on development. It affects the rate of cell division and differentiation in some organisms; it controls sexual differentiation in *Hydra* (Loomis, 1957) and inhibits the emergence of gametocytes of *Plasmodium gallinaceum* from erythrocytes and exflagellation of the male gametocyte (Bishop and McConnachie, 1956). How it affects these processes is unknown.

In the infective stages of some nematodes carbon dioxide may act on a receptor on the surface or it may act directly on the cells storing the hatching or exsheathing fluids (Fig. 23). Whatever the mechanism it seems that the dependence of development upon a stimulus of this sort is an adaptation to parasitism because it ensures that the infective agent does not lose its protective coverings (and perhaps protective physiological mechanisms also) until it reaches an environment which may support its further development. A further adaptation in the process of infection is the capacity of eggs to hatch in dilute solutions of salts which inhibit the process in eggs of *Trichostrongylus retortaeformis* (Wilson, 1958). The eggs of this species hatch outside the host in places where the salt concentration would not be high.

In Fig. 23 it is suggested that substances related to the hatching factor of *Heterodera* may have a role in the general physiology of nematodes. This is entirely speculation of course. But it is attractive because it suggests that the process of infection with these nematodes is an adaptation to parasitism which has been taken one step further than in the process of infection with ascarid eggs and trichostrongyle larvae so giving the process greater specificity (see Chapter 10).

The conditions governing the process of infection at the body surface are even less clear than those governing entry via the gut of the host. It seems, however, that a stimulus from the host triggers the metamorphosis of miracidia to the parasitic form. The changes that occur with other infective agents, exsheathment of some larval nematodes, the casting of the tail of some infective cercariae, and the production of "spreading factors" must also require a stimulus from the host but this could be very simple—a rise in temperature or a tactile stimulus may be sufficient.

Summary

The process of infection of the host with the eggs of ascarids or with the larvae of trichostrongyles is "triggered" by physical and chemical components in the gut contents of the host. Of these, dissolved gaseous carbon dioxide or undissociated carbonic acid is the most important but the oxidation-reduction potential, temperature and hydrogen ion concentration also influence the process. These stimuli lead to the secretion of hatching fluids or exsheathing fluids; it is possible that they also affect more deep-seated developmental mechanisms. It is also suggested that the factor provided by the host which leads to hatching of infective stages of *Heterodera* acts by restoring part of the developmental mechanism of the parasite which has been lost in the "resting" infective agent. This implies that substances allied to the hatching factor in root diffusate may have some physiological function in nematodes generally.

Factors in the gut contents of the host such as digestive enzymes and bile salts start the process of infection with infective agents of many platyhelminths; but here the effect of the host seems to be direct and it does not "trigger" developmental changes in the parasite.

Infection with miracidia involves a metamorphosis of the parasite and here it is again postulated that the host restarts a developmental mechanism which is incomplete in the "resting" infective stage.

REFERENCES

Alicata, J. E. (1934) *Proc. helm. Soc. Wash.* **1**, 12.
Barrington, E. J. W. (1957) *In* "The Physiology of Fishes". (M. E. Brown, ed.), Academic Press, New York.
Bergeim, O., Kleinberg, J. and Kirch, E. R. (1945) *J. Bact.* **49**, 453.
Bird, A. F. and Rogers, W. P. (1956) *Exp. Parasit.* **5**, 449.
Bishop, A. and McConnachie, E. W. (1956) *Parasitology*, **48**, 192.
Calam, C. T., Todd, A. R. and Waring, W. S. (1949) *Biochem. J.* **45**, 520.
Chitwood, B. G. and Oteifa, B. A. (1952) *Annu. Rev. Microbiol.* **6**, 151.
Clarke, A. S. (1953) *Exp. Parasit.* **2**, 223.
Dawes, B. (1959) *Nature, Lond.* **184**, 1334.
—— (1960) *Nature, Lond.* **185**, 51.
Day, M. F. and Waterhouse, D. F. (1953) *In* "Insect Physiology". (K. D. Roeder, ed.), Chapman and Hall, London.
de Waele, A. (1934) *Ann. Parasit. hum. comp.* **12**, 492.
Dewey, D. W., Lee, H. J. and Marston, H. R. (1958) *Nature, Lond.* **181**, 1367.
Dickinson, S. (1959) *Nematologica*, **4**, 60.
Dropkin, V. H. (1955) *Exp. Parasit.* **4**, 282.
Edgar, S. A. (1941) *Trans. Amer. micr. Soc.* **60**, 121.
Ellenby, C. (1945) *Emp. J. exp. Agric.* **13**, 158.
—— (1954) *Euphytica*, **3**, 195.
—— (1957) *In* "Insect and Foodplant". E. J. Brill, Leiden.
—— and Gilbert, A. B. (1957) *Nature, Lond.* **180**, 1105.
—— (1958) *Nature, Lond.* **182**, 925.
Evans, A. S. and Stirewalt, M. A. (1951) *Exp. Parasit.* **1**, 19.
Fairbairn, D. (1960) *In* "Host Influence on Parasite Physiology". (L. A. Stauber, ed.), Rutgers University Press, New Brunswick.
Faust, E. C. and Khaw, K. (1925) *Proc. Soc. exp. Biol. Med.* **23**, 245.
—— (1927) *Amer. J. Hyg. Monog. Series 8.*
Ferguson, M. S. (1940) *J. Parasit.* **26**, 359.
—— (1943) *J. Parasit.* **29**, 319.
Follansbee, R. (1945) *Amer. J. Physiol.* **144**, 355.
Franklin, M. T. (1951) "The Cyst-forming Species of *Heterodera*". Commonwealth Bureau of Agricultural Parasitology (Helminthology), St. Albans.
Hansen, M. F., Terhaar, C. J. and Turner, D. S. (1956) *J. Parasit.* **42**, 122.
Hemenway, M. (1948) *Proc. Iowa Acad. Sci.* **55**, 375.
Henry, H. and Stacey, M. (1943) *Nature, Lond.* **151**, 671.
Hobson, A. D. (1948) *Parasitology*, **38**, 183.
Hoffman, G. L. (1958) *Exp. Parasit.* **7**, 23.
Hunter, W. S. and Chait, D. C. (1952) *J. Parasit.* **38**, 87.
Lapage, G. (1935) *Parasitology*, **27**, 186.
Larsh, J. E. (1947) *J. Parasit.* **33**, 79.
—— (1950) *Science*, **111**, 62.
Lee, C. L. and Lewert, R. M. (1957) *J. infect. Dis.* **101**, 287.
Lewert, R. M. (1958) *Rice Inst. Pamphl.* **45**, 97.
Loomis, W. F. (1957) *Science*, **126**, 735.
Looss, A. (1911) *Rec. Sch. Med. Cairo*, **4**, 450.
Lorincz, A. C. and Stoughton, R. B. (1958) *Physiol. Rev.* **38**, 481.
Malkani, P. G. (1933) *Indian vet. J.* **9**, 193.
Mandlowitz, D., Dusanic, D. and Lewert, R. M. (1960) *J. Parasit.* **46**, 89.
Marrian, D. H., Russel, P. B., Todd, A. R. and Waring, W. S. (1949) *Biochem. J.* **45**, 524.

Millemann, R. E. and Thonard, J. C. (1959) *Exp. Parasit.* **8**, 129.
Passey, R. F. and Fairbairn, D. (1955) *Canad. J. Biochem. Physiol.* **33**, 1033.
—— (1957) *Canad. J. Biochem. Physiol.* **35**, 511.
Payne, F. K. (1923) *Amer. J. Hyg.* **3**, 584.
Read, C. P. (1950) *Rice Inst. Pamphl.* **37**, 1.
Resnitschenko, M. S. (1927) *Biochem. Z.* **191**, 345.
—— (1928) *Biochem. Z.* **201**, 110.
Rhoades, H. L. and Linford, M. B. (1959) *Science,* **130**, 1476.
Rogers, W. P. (1940) *J. Helminth.* **18**, 183.
—— (1949) *Aust. J. sci. Res.* **B2**, 157.
—— (1958) *Nature, Lond.* **181**, 1410.
—— (1960) *Proc. roy. Soc.* **B152**, 367
—— (1961) *J. Helminth. R. T. Leiper Supplement,* 151.
—— and Sommerville, R. I. (1957) *Nature, Lond.* **179**, 619.
—— (1960) *Parasitology*, **50**, 1.
Rothman, A. H. (1959) *Exp. Parasit.* **8**, 336.
Rothschild, M. (1936) *J. Mar. biol. Ass.* **20**, 537.
Rowan, W. B. (1956) *Exp. Parasit.* **5**, 118.
—— (1957) *Exp. Parasit.* **6**, 131.
Silverman, P. H. (1954*a*) *Ann. trop. Med. Parasit.* **48**, 207.
—— (1954*b*) *Ann. trop. Med. Parasit.* **48**, 356.
Smyth, J. D. (1947) *Biol. Rev.* **22**, 214.
—— (1958) *Nature, Lond.* **181**, 1119.
—— (1959) *Ann. N. Y. Acad. Sci.* **77**, 102.
Sommerville, R. I. (1957) *Exp. Parasit.* **6**, 18.
Spector, W. S. (1956) "Handbook of Biological Data". W. B. Saunders, Philadelphia.
Stunkard, H. W. (1934) *Z. Parasitenk.* **6**, 481.
Sturkie, P. O. (1954) "Avian Physiology". Baillière, Tindall and Cox, London.
Taylor, E. L. (1926) *Ann. trop. Med. Parasit.* **20**, 220.
Thorson, R. E. (1953) *Amer. J. Hyg.* **58**, 1.
Tracey, M. V. (1958) *Nematologica*, **3**, 179.
Turner, A. W. and Hodgetts, V. E. (1955) *Aust. J. agric. Res.* **6**, 115.
Venard, C. E. (1938) *Ann. N. Y. Acad. Sci.* **37**, 273.
von Brand, T. (1946) "Anaerobiosis in Invertebrates". Biodynamica, Normandy, Missouri.
von Brand, T. and Weise, W. (1932) *Z. vergl. Physiol.* **18**, 339.
Vonk, H. J., Mansour-Bek, J. J. and Slijper, E. J. (1946) *Tabul. biol., The Hague,* **21**, 1.
Wieser, W. (1956) *Proc. helm. Soc. Wash.* **23**, 59.
Wilson, P. A. G. (1958) *J. exp. Biol.* **35**, 584.
Wykoff, D. E. (1959) *Diss. Abstr.* **19**, 3285.

PART III

The Life of Parasites

General Introduction

IT has been argued that the infective stage of nematode parasites is a resting stage, which, on entering the proper host, is stimulated to resume its development. It is the relationship between the parasite and its final host from this time, when development is resumed, to the time when the parasite reaches sexual maturity, which will be discussed here.

The period which follows shortly after the parasite has emerged from the infective stage must be hazardous, especially when the infective stage has not been protected within an intermediate host. The free-living infective stage can maintain itself in a variable environment but it does not grow; growth, it seems, is resumed only in the relatively stable environment on or within the proper host. If the infective agent is free-living it will be able to withstand variations in temperature, in salt concentration and in the availability of water. But as soon as the development of the parasitic stage starts most of the morphological and physical characters which protect the infective agent from unfavourable features of the environment are lost. The parasite, newly developed from the infective stage, needs in its environment the basic nutrients for its energy-providing mechanisms as well as specific nutrients for certain metabolic and structural purposes. The basic medium must have the proper physico-chemical and physical properties; the dissolved gases must have the right concentrations; and substances which have specific stimulating actions on the development and behaviour of the parasites may be needed. The young parasites must be adapted to meet the deleterious components of the environment. Of these the most important are the substances and conditions—the enzymes, antibodies and non-specific tissue reactions—by means of which the host "attacks" the parasite.

With our present knowledge we cannot select from these features of the medium any one component which may be of over-riding importance in determining the survival of the parasite. In fact, as discussed earlier, no single feature of the environment needed for parasitism may be unique; rather it might be the requirement of a pattern of components in the medium which commits an organism to a parasitic mode of life. In this part of the book some aspects of these subjects, as far as they affect the parasite as it grows to maturity, will be briefly reviewed. As the overall aim of this discussion is to try to assess the nature of the dependence of the parasite on the host in this stage of the life cycle, emphasis will be given to those systems in which the role of the host is most clearly understood. Unfortunately there is little precise information of this sort available at present so that even in the restricted discussion which follows, the host–parasite relationship can be seen only in vague terms.

CHAPTER 6

Physiology of Parasitic Stages

MOST of the work on the physiology of invertebrates has been carried out with arthropods and especially with insects. This is because these animals have considerable economic importance. Probably for this reason also, the physiology of protozoan and metazoan parasites has also been widely studied though not as much as the physiology of the Insecta. Studies with insects cover a wide field; studies on the developmental physiology, physiology of the nervous system and other "organ-systems" are as common as more biochemical work on such subjects as intermediary metabolism and nitrogen catabolism. With the metazoan parasites, however, a large part of the work has been devoted to biochemical subjects whereas organ-system physiology is a relatively neglected field.

There are several reasons for this. (1) Many organ-systems of the Arthropoda bear a superficial resemblance to those of the vertebrates with which much of "classical physiology" has been carried out so that well-established techniques are often more easily applied to these animals than to parasites. (2) It is usually easier to isolate for special study the organs of the Arthropoda. For example, the isolated Malphigian tubules can be studied physiologically outside the body of the insect; but the excretory system of a nematode or platyhelminth cannot be studied in this way. (3) Parasites are usually small and difficult to obtain in large numbers. As a result much of the best work on the physiology of parasites has been carried out with an atypical nematode parasite, *Ascaris lumbricoides*, simply because it is a large parasite that can be conveniently obtained in large numbers and kept alive outside the host for several days without much trouble.

For these reasons there are large gaps in our knowledge of the general physiology of helminths. And unfortunately these gaps occur largely in fields where we might expect to gain an understanding of the relationships between parasites and their hosts. We have little knowledge of developmental physiology of parasites or of what governs their movements in the host during the complex migrations which frequently occur, or even of how parasites retain their final positions within the host. Sensory physiology and neuro-muscular transmission have hardly been examined. Above all we have little knowledge of the physiological processes by which the parasite can establish itself within the host and resist its damaging chemical and physical actions.

Though this information is not yet available much of the background knowledge of intermediary metabolism which is fundamental to these studies is known and many of the biochemical processes by which the energy is obtained by parasites have been established. In this Chapter intermediary metabolism and some other aspects of the physiology of adult and larval parasites will be briefly discussed. Data on the chemical composition of parasites which has been discussed in detail elsewhere (von Brand, 1952; Fairbairn, 1957) will not be included, and those aspects of the physiology of parasites which relate more closely to substances in the environment provided by the host—nutrition and oxygen relationships—will be discussed separately in later chapters.

Intermediary Metabolism of Parasitic Nematodes

Metabolism of Carbohydrates and Lipids

Though lactic acid is not commonly excreted by parasitic nematodes even under anaerobic conditions, there is sufficient evidence to suggest that the Embden-Myerhof system of phosphorylating glycolysis is present in the tissues of parasitic adults and larvae (for example see Rogers and Lazarus, 1949*a*; Bueding and Yale, 1951; Rathbone and Rees, 1954; Agosin and Aravena, 1959*a*). In some details, of course, glycolytic systems in different parasites differ from those of their vertebrate hosts. For instance, the addition of diphosphopyridine nucleotide (DPN) to dialysed extracts of acetone powder of muscle of *Ascaris lumbricoides* did not increase the rate of glycolysis, and dialysis never led to the complete removal of the coenzyme (Bueding and Yale, 1951). Differences of this sort do not affect the overall character of the glycolytic system though they may affect such features as the rate of reaction.

Phosphorylation occurs during glycolysis as in vertebrate tissues, and in fluoride-poisoned preparations adenosine triphosphate accumulates (Fig. 24). Neither arginine phosphate nor creatine phosphate has been detected in parasitic stages (Rogers and Lazarus, 1949*a*; Savel, 1955*a*) though arginine phosphate has been found in free-living infective larvae (Jones, 1955).

It has been shown that the synthesis of glycogen in the muscle of *Ascaris lumbricoides* is promoted when glucose-1-phosphate is added (Rogers and Lazarus, 1949*a*; Cavier and Savel, 1953) though detailed studies have not been carried out.

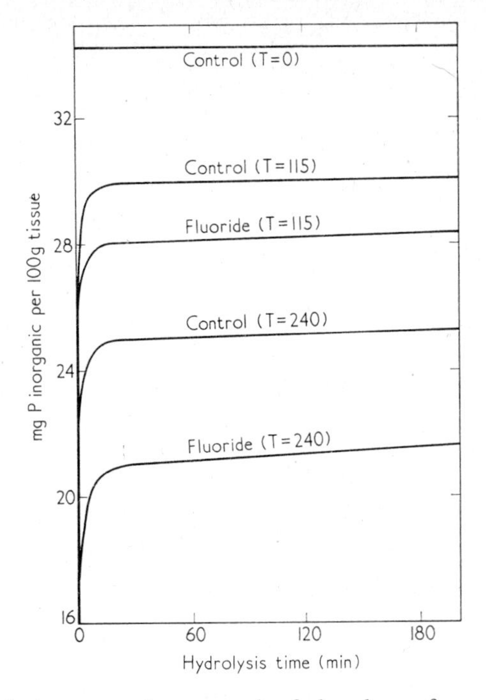

FIG. 24. The hydrolysis curves of compounds of phosphorus formed during the incubation of muscle *brei* of *Ascaris lumbricoides* with and without fluoride (after Rogers and Lazarus, 1949*a*). The time of incubation is shown by T (in minutes). Hydrolysis was carried out in 1 N hydrochloric acid at 100°C.

Only small amounts of lactic acid are formed in homogenates of muscle of *Ascaris lumbricoides* or in whole homogenized *Ascaridia galli* unless pyruvate is added. In cell-free preparations of muscle, testis and ovary of *Ascaris lumbricoides*, the production of pyruvic acid is not sufficient to maintain DPN in an oxidized state. In muscle the limiting step appears to lie at phosphoglyceromutase or at enolase and causes the accumulation of a phosphoglyceric acid (Rathbone and Rees, 1954). These results lead Fairbairn (1957) to suggest that in intact worms the formation of C_2 to C_6 acids might be due to a diversion at some point in the glycolytic reaction sequence. Rathbone and Rees (1954) found no changes in the steam volatile fatty acids in tissue preparations undergoing glycolysis. Entner (1957) and Entner and Gonzalez (1959), who showed that part of the pentose phosphate pathway was present in the muscle of *Ascaris lumbricoides*, found that ether-extractable acid was formed from added ribose-5-phosphate. As in mammalian muscle the pentose phosphate pathway is probably relatively unimportant as a source of energy.

The metabolism of pyruvate may follow a number of routes in nematode parasites. In some the route of metabolism is similar to the Krebs tricarboxylic acid cycle of vertebrate tissues. Thus Massey and Rogers (1950) showed that substrates of the cycle were metabolized aerobically by the tissues of *Nematodirus* spp., *Neoaplectana glaseri* and *Ascaridia galli*. The formation of citrate by the condensation of "acetate" and oxaloacetic acid was demonstrated and inhibition of respiration by fluoroacetic acid was shown to take place by processes similar to those which occur in mammalian tissues (Massey and Rogers, 1951). Goldberg (1957) has shown that larval and adult *Trichinella spiralis* contain components of the classical cytochrome system and showed the presence of aconitase, isocitric dehydrogenase, fumarase and malic dehydrogenase. Thus, although larvae of *Trichinella spiralis* consume about the same amount of glycogen anaerobically and aerobically (von Brand *et al.*, 1952), this parasite appears to have an efficient system for the metabolism of pyruvate. It is not known as yet whether these enzyme systems are organized in particles which have the morphology of classical mitochondria.

Although a nematode parasite may have a pronounced aerobic respiration which is cyanide-sensitive, it does not necessarily follow that the cytochrome–cytochrome oxidase system will be present. Thus a high rate of oxidative metabolism is essential for the survival of *Litomosoides carinii*, and although this respiration is almost completely inhibited by 0.002 M potassium cyanide, no cytochrome *c* or cytochrome oxidase can be detected by the most sensitive metabolic tests (Bueding and Charms, 1951, 1952). Somewhat similar results have been obtained with *Trichuris vulpis* (Bueding, 1960*a*).

The virtual absence of cytochrome *c* and cytochrome oxidase from the muscle of *Ascaris lumbricoides* is less unexpected. This is because the respiration of this tissue is not inhibited by cyanide; hydrogen peroxide is the end-product instead of water (Laser, 1944) and many intermediates of the tricarboxylic acid cycle fail to stimulate respiration (Rathbone, 1955). It is generally considered that electron transport by the conventional mechanisms associated with the tricarboxylic acid cycle has no physiological importance in the muscle of this parasite. Some workers, however, have suggested that cytochrome *c* and other components of the system may be present in sufficient amounts to give activity in intact cells (Kikuchi *et al.*, 1959).

Chin and Bueding (1954) found that washed homogenates of the muscle had an oxygen uptake which was associated with esterification of inorganic phosphate and P/O ratios ranging from 1.3 to 3.5 were obtained without added substrate when catalase was present to destroy the hydrogen peroxide. Washed particles prepared from the muscle oxidized pyruvic acid when dialysed perienteric fluid was also added, though the P/O ratios became very low. When succinate was the added substrate the oxidative phosphorylation was reduced even further. Undialysed perienteric fluid gave the same results without adding succinate. A partial explanation of these results was obtained when it was shown that the perienteric fluid of *Ascaris lumbricoides* contains succinate at an average concentration of 8.4 mM (Bueding and Farrow, 1956). Apparently there was no direct coupling between oxidative phosphorylation and the oxidation of succinate.

Intact mitochondria have not been obtained from the muscle of *Ascaris lumbricoides* by conventional methods using sucrose solutions. But particles with the appearance of mitochondria have been obtained from muscle which has been homogenized in dialysed body fluid (Kmetec, Miller and Swartzwelder, personal communication, 1961). The biochemical characteristics of these particles are as yet unknown.

A soluble succinic dehydrogenase has been prepared from the succinic oxidase complex of *Ascaris lumbricoides*. There is evidence that the complex contains flavine adenine dinucleotide and DPN (Bueding *et al.*, 1955). The muscle also contains lactic dehydrogenase, fumarase and a "malic enzyme". The malic enzyme reacted with DPN but was also about half as active with TPN. It showed no activity as an oxalo-acetic decarboxylase over a wide range of hydrogen ion concentrations and so differed in several respects from the "malic enzyme" of mammalian tissue (Saz and Hubbard, 1957). The significance of the succinic oxidase complex has been discussed by Bueding (1960*a*). Under physiological conditions in the gut of the host the pO_2 is very low and this system would be expected to catalyse the reduction of fumarate to succinate rather than the reverse reaction. Moreover the complex contains a DPNH oxidase which under anaerobic conditions in the presence of fumarate leads to the formation of succinate and oxidized DPN. Presumably, in the intact cell the reduction of fumarate would be coupled through the coenzyme with oxidative processes.

Volatile fatty acids excreted by *Ascaris lumbricoides* include propionic acid, α-methylcrotonic (tiglic) acid and α-methylbutyric acid (Bueding, 1953; see Chapter 7) as end-products of carbohydrate metabolism. A major advance in the biochemistry of *Ascaris* is the elucidation of probable mechanisms of the syntheses of these substances (Bueding, 1960*a*). As might be expected pyruvate is a basic component in the syntheses. Thus the results of Saz and Vidrine (1959) indicated that the fixation of carbon dioxide into pyruvate was followed by successive reduction of the malate to fumarate and succinate. In muscle much of the succinate was decarboxylated to propionate.

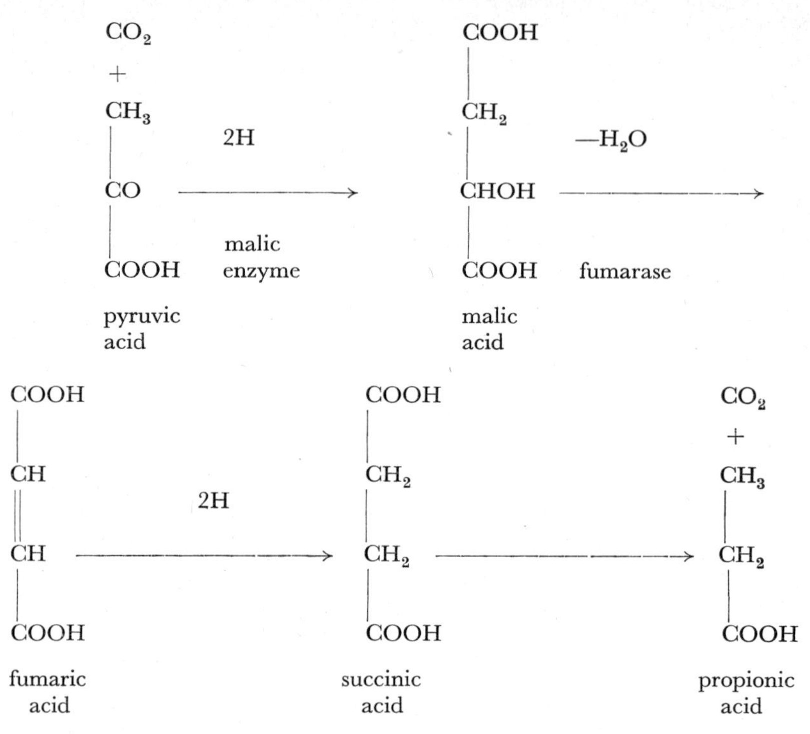

The major product of fermentation of *Ascaris*, α-methylbutyric acid, has for its precursors acetate and propionate (Saz and Weil, 1960). The route of synthesis, for which considerable evidence has been produced (Saz *et al.*, 1958; Saz and Weil, 1960), probably involves the formation of methylacetoacetate by the condensation of the carboxyl carbon of acetate with carbon 2 of propionate. This, it has been suggested, is followed by the reduction of the methylacetoacetate to β-hydroxy-α-methylbutyric acid which is dehydrated to give tiglic acid which may be reduced to α-methylbutyric acid or excreted.

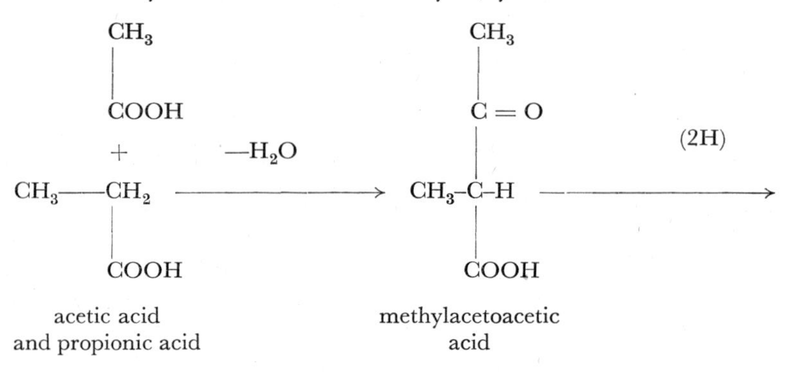

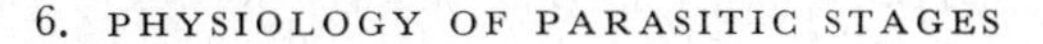

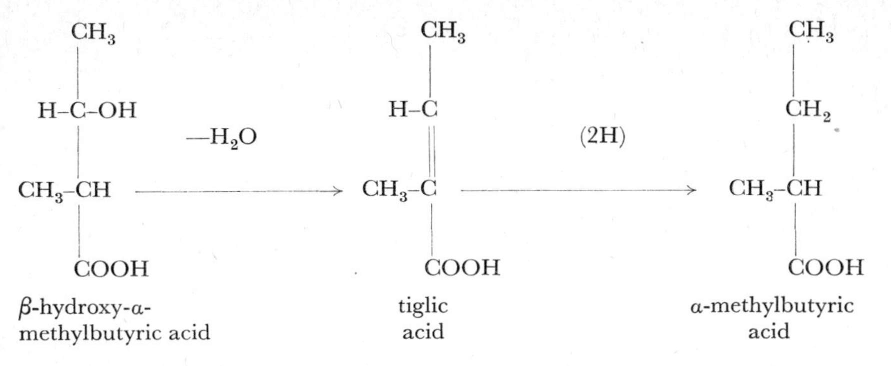

The synthesis of volatile fatty acids by *Heterakis gallinae*, a small nematode parasite which lives in the caeca of chickens, has been examined by Fairbairn (1954). Under anaerobic conditions this parasite excretes acetic and propionic acids, and carbon dioxide has a pronounced sparing effect on the use of endogenous reducing substances (Glocklin and Fairbairn, 1952). By following the metabolism of labelled carbon dioxide Fairbairn found that fatty acid production in the parasite showed some similarities to *Propionibacterium*. In this organism carbon dioxide is fixed to form oxaloacetic acid which is reduced via the conventional dicarboxylic acid route to succinic acid. As in *Ascaris lumbricoides* the succinate is decarboxylated to give propionate and carbon dioxide. The route by which acetate is formed is still unknown.

The metabolism of pyruvate in the filarial worm *Litomosoides carinii* also takes unusual routes. Bueding (1949) and Berl and Bueding (1951) found that anaerobically 80% of the carbohydrate used appeared as lactic acid, and 20% appeared as acetic acid. Aerobically 20 to 25% formed polysaccharide. The remainder of the glucose used was completely oxidized or appeared as acetylmethylcarbinol. The complete oxidation of pyruvate in *Litomosoides carinii* cannot take place in the conventional tricarboxylic acid cycle because the cytochrome system is absent (Bueding and Charms, 1952). Nevertheless heavy-metal-containing catalysts are involved and the inhibition obtained with low concentrations of fluoroacetate suggests that a system which is similar to part of the tricarboxylic acid cycle may be present (Bueding, 1949).

The oxidation of pyruvate to acetylmethylcarbinol in *Litomosoides carinii* has been studied by Berl and Bueding (1951). It seems that two distinct mechanisms may have been operating. In one, acetylmethylcarbinol was synthesized from acetaldehyde alone, in the other acetaldehyde and pyruvate might have been concerned. The actual role of acetylmethylcarbinol in the economy of the parasite is unknown; (−)-acetoin is actively used by the filariae especially under aerobic conditions and this process is not inhibited by antabuse. Moreover, the strong inhibition obtained with the anthelmintic drug hexachlorophene, at concentrations as low as 2.7×10^{-5} M, suggests that it may play an important part in the metabolism of some helminths.

Acetylmethylcarbinol is also synthesized by *Ascaris lumbricoides*. As in *Litomosoides carinii* it results from the condensation of acetaldehyde-diphosphothiamine-magnesium complex, formed by the pyruvic oxidase, with free acetaldehyde. Condensation of the complex with pyruvate gives α-acetolactic acid but the absence of the appropriate decarboxylase prevents the synthesis of acetylmethylcarbinol by this route (Saz *et al.*, 1958).

Though the structure of the high molecular weight lipids of nematodes has been studied (see von Brand, 1952; Fairbairn, 1957, for references) little is known about the metabolism of these compounds. Histological work carried out by Hirsch and Bretschneider (1937) showed that fat in the intestinal cells of *Ascaris lumbricoides* decreased markedly during the 6 days the animals were kept in a non-nutrient medium. However, the lipids in the reproductive systems, muscle and hypodermis cannot be used by starving parasites *in vitro*. Thus the chemical analyses carried out by von Brand (1934) showed that there was no significant decrease in fat in worms kept *in vitro* for 24 hours under aerobic conditions, and even after 5 days the losses in the bodies of the parasites could be accounted for by the fat in the eggs which had been laid. The synthesis of lipids, especially in the ovaries of *Ascaris lumbricoides* must proceed rapidly *in vivo*. As Fairbairn (1957) has pointed out, the daily output of lipid in the eggs laid *in vivo* accounts for about 1.6% of the total solids of the female parasite.

The only clear-cut evidence showing the catabolism of fat in the parasitic stages of nematodes has been obtained in experiments with larvae of *Trichinella spiralis* (von Brand, 1952). Under anaerobic conditions in a non-nutrient medium no lipid was consumed; aerobically, however, lipids were used and this seemed to be independent of the consumption of carbohydrate. Von Brand *et al.* (1952) suggested that the oxidation of lipids might be an important source of energy for the parasites, especially for motility.

Metabolism of Compounds of Nitrogen

Aspects of the metabolism of nitrogenous compounds have been reviewed by Savel (1955*a*, 1955*b*) and Fairbairn (1957).

Studies on the nature of nitrogenous end-products have been carried out *in vitro*, and, as a rule, antibiotics or other substances have been added to the non-nutrient media to limit bacterial growth. The results of experiments with several larval and adult helminths are shown in Table VI. The total amount of soluble compounds of nitrogen

TABLE VI

The Partition of Nitrogenous Compounds excreted by Nematode Parasites

Species	N Total mg/g/hr	Percentage partition of N compounds "polypeptide" /N	ammonia /N	urea /N	uric acid /N	Reference
Ascaris lumbricoides (adults)						
aerobic	0.39	21	69	7	0	Savel (1955*a*)
anaerobic	0.41	17.9	71	6.6	0	
Ascaridia galli (adults)						
aerobic	0.35	15	56	12	0	Rogers (1952)
anaerobic	0.37	15	59	15	0	
Nematodirus spp. (adults)						
aerobic	1.36	35	42	14	5	Rogers (1952)
anaerobic	1.72	35	29	4	4	
Trichinella spiralis (larvae)						
aerobic	2.9†	21	33	0	0	Haskins & Weinstein (1957*b*)

†Calculated on the basis, 100,000 larvae = 3.5 mg dry wt. (Stannard *et al.*, 1938) and water forms 80% of the wet wt.

excreted by nematode parasites is large compared with some free-living invertebrates. Thus the nitrogen excreted by fasting Crustacea examined by Dresel and Moyle (1950) ranged from the low level of the terrestrial *Oniscus asellus*, 0.03 mg per g wet wt. per 24 hours, to that of the estuarine *Gammarus zaddachi*, 0.60 mg per g wet wt. per 24 hours. As might be expected the amounts of nitrogen excreted were greater in the smaller species.

The ammonotelic character of the nitrogen catabolism of nematode parasites of the alimentary canal would be expected if water is freely available. But the osmotic pressure of the fluids of the parasites is probably the same as, or a little less than, that of the environment (Schopfer, 1932; Hobson *et al.*, 1952*a*). Ammonia is highly toxic to some nematode parasites (von Brand and Simpson, 1947) and it is probable that a lowering of the rate of water exchange between the parasites and the environment would lead to an accumulation of toxic amounts of ammonia in the tissues. Under conditions of stress, however, it appears that some nematode parasites may switch from a predominantly ammonotelic catabolism to a less toxic mechanism. Thus the experiments of Cavier and Savel (1954*a*) and Savel (1955*b*) showed that, under conditions in which the intake of water through the cuticle of *Ascaris lumbricoides* was limited, the parasite became ureotelic. When the anterior and posterior extremities of the worms were placed in saline and the bodies confined in U-tubes without saline, the total amount of nitrogen which was excreted was the same as in worms wholly immersed in saline. But the proportion of nitrogen excreted as ammonia fell to 27%, and the urea nitrogen rose to 51.5% (compare Table VI). All the nitrogen was excreted at the tail; the saline in which the mouth and excretory pore were immersed contained no nitrogen. During these experiments large amounts of water, about 10 ml, were ingested at the anterior end and excreted at the tail so considerable amounts must have passed along the gut of the parasite. To explain these results Fairbairn (1957) suggested that ammonia might normally be excreted through the cuticle and intestine of *Ascaris lumbricoides*. When the supply of water to the cuticle limited the excretion of ammonia via this route, the concentration in the intestine may have been raised considerably, and this may have led to an increased detoxication of ammonia to urea. There is some evidence (Delaunay, 1934; Bahl, 1945) that a change from ammonotelic to ureotelic metabolism occurs as an adaptation to water shortage in earthworms; more classical examples of this phenomenon have been reported from vertebrates such as the lungfish, *Protopterus aethiopicus* (Smith, 1930).

As in many invertebrates and even some vertebrates, nematode parasites excrete appreciable amounts of amino acids. Whether this is due simply to a leakage from the cells caused by the conditions under which the parasites were examined *in vitro* or whether it is due to deficiencies in the organization of these animals is not known. If losses in amino acids do occur *in vivo* as *in vitro* where 28.5% of the soluble excreted nitrogen may be due to amino acids (Haskins and Weinstein, 1957*a*) this may place a stress on the economy of the organisms. Adult *Ascaris lumbricoides, Ascaridia galli* and *Nematodirus* spp. were found to excrete the following amino acids: leucine, phenylalanine, alanine, valine, proline, aspartic acid and glutamic acid (Rogers, 1955); larval *Trichinella spiralis* excreted similar amino acids though glycine, serine and methionine were present and aspartic acid was absent (Haskins and Weinstein, 1957*a*). "Polypeptides", or material which was precipitated by phosphotungstic acid but not by trichloracetic acid (Godfried, 1939), formed an appreciable part of the soluble nitrogenous material produced by both small and large nematodes (Rogers, 1952; Savel, 1955*b*). The peptides in the excretions of *Ascaris lumbricoides, Nematodirus* spp. and *Ascaridia galli* were examined by paper chromatography (Rogers, 1955). At least three peptides were produced by each species. The R_F values in two solvents and the colour reactions with ninhydrin indicated that the three substances were similar for the three types of parasites examined. But the most interesting end-products of nitrogen metabolism are the amines examined by Haskins and Weinstein (1957*b*, 1957*c*). Larvae of *Trichinella spiralis* were found to produce methyl, ethyl, propyl, butyl, amyl and heptyl amines, ethylene diamine, cadaverine, ethanolamine, 1-amino-2-propanol and probably allyl amine. These amines, with the exception of amyl and heptyl amine and ethylene diamine, were also produced by larvae of *Ascaris lumbricoides*. As these substances were found to be present in the vitelline fluid of the eggs of *Ascaris lumbricoides* it seems probable that they were products of normal metabolism and were not produced as the result of pathological changes caused by the methods used for culturing the parasites *in vitro*.

The metabolic processes which lead to the production of this variety of amines are not known. Decarboxylation of amino acids could lead to the formation of a number of these substances but ethylene diamine, amyl, heptyl and allyl amines could not arise directly in this way (Haskins and Weinstein, 1957*c*). Though amines are produced by a number of micro-organisms they are not commonly excreted by vertebrates or invertebrates so this aspect of the metabolism of nematodes is of especial interest. Moreover, many amines are toxic and even small amounts produced by parasites in the gut or muscles of the host could cause disease.

Amines are strongly basic and they are sometimes produced in large amounts when micro-organisms are incubated in acid media. The chief end-products of metabolism of nematode parasites are acidic, and it is possible that the production of amines keeps the environment nearer neutrality and so aids the survival of some species. This might be important when the organism is enclosed in an egg-shell for long periods as in *Ascaris lumbricoides*.

Processes leading to the excretion of ammonia, urea, and uric acid have been examined in adult nematode parasites. In the tissues of *Nematodirus* spp. and *Ascaridia galli* ammonia was produced by the deamination of amino acids; urease was present also. Urea was formed by the citrulline cycle of Krebs and Henseleit (1932) and the arginase was similar in some respects to the enzyme found in vertebrate tissues. Muscle adenylic acid and, to a less extent, adenine stimulated ammonia formation. Young adult *Ascaridia galli* formed large quantities of ammonia and urea from added xanthine, uric acid, and allantoin, but guanase activity was absent (Rogers, 1952). Similar results have been obtained with tissues of young specimens of *Ascaris lumbricoides* (Cavier and Savel, 1954*b*, 1954*c*). It is probable then that the route of breakdown of purines in the tissues of young *Ascaris* and *Ascaridia* is similar to that outlined by Florkin and Duchateau (1943), and involves the successive action of urico-oxidase, allantoinase, and allantoicase. The conversion of small amounts of xanthine to uric acid by the action of xanthine oxidase would account for the urea formed from this substrate in the tissues of *Ascaridia*. The loss of enzymes concerned in the breakdown of purines in older worms (Rogers, 1952; Cavier and Savel, 1954*c*) may represent a simplification of metabolism which took place as the parasitic mode of life became more firmly established.

The metabolism of amino acids and proteins in the tissues of nematodes has not been studied extensively. Transaminases, arginase, *l*-amino acid oxidases, proteases and peptidases have been found in the tissues of the intestine (Rogers, 1952; Cavier and Savel, 1954*d*; also see Chapter 8). In ovaries of *Ascaris lumbricoides* the activity of arginase and *l*-amino acid oxidase is low but the metabolism of amino acids, generally, is highly active. Thus Pollak and Fairbairn (1955) found that specific alanine-glutamic acid and aspartic acid-glutamic acid transaminases were active and were freely reversible. Of the other 18 amino acids tested, however, only glycine and serine reacted as donors of amino groups in the presence of α-ketoglutarate and pyruvate, and then only weakly. The weak glutamic dehydrogenase in the ovaries could be coupled with the active transaminases to give a trans-deamination system. The synthesis of alanine, aspartic and glutamic acids by reductive amination of pyruvate and α-ketoglutarate took place readily when ammonium chloride and sodium bicarbonate were added to the homogenates. As Pollak and Fairbairn (1955) pointed out, an emphasis on anabolic reactions is to be expected in organs which produce the protein necessary for the large output of eggs of this species.

The uptake of alanine, glycine, tyrosine and tryptophane labelled with ^{14}C at the 2 positions, by larvae of *Trichinella spiralis* has been examined *in vivo* and *in vitro* (Stoner and Hankes, 1955, 1958; Hankes and Stoner, 1956, 1958). *In vivo* the ^{14}C from these amino acids appeared in the protein of the parasites even when the cyst-wall was well developed. *In vitro* the labelled amino acids were taken up and considerable amounts of the ^{14}C were incorporated into the protein.

It has been shown (Rogers, 1945) that the protein nitrogen of the body fluid of *Ascaris lumbricoides* fell when the worms were kept 4 days in non-nutrient medium; this was partly due to increases in the volume of the body fluid. Cavier and Savel (1954*e*) found that if glycine, alanine, glutamic acid and tyrosine were added to the medium after the worms had been starved for 6 days, the protein concentration in the body fluid was steadily increased during the following 6 days. The addition of the amino acids also prevented the rise in the non-protein nitrogen of the body fluid of starving worms. The mechanism by which the protein content of the body fluid was raised is not clear. It seems unlikely that the excretion of amino acids which takes place if the worms are kept in saline media would have been reduced unspecifically by the addition of the four amino acids to the medium.

Though some studies on the changes in the nucleic acids during fertilization and the early stages of segmentation of eggs have been carried out (Pasteels, 1948; Nigon and Bovet, 1955; Panijel and Pasteels, 1951) the role of nucleic acids in protein synthesis in nematodes has not been examined.

Nerve-Muscle Physiology

The general organization of the body and the mechanism of movement of nematodes shows unusual features (Harris and Crofton, 1957), as does the histological structure of muscle and nerve cells (Chitwood and Chitwood, 1940). The peculiarities of neuro-muscular physiology of the worms have not been explored however, and little is known beyond the fact that acetylcholine is probably involved as a transmitter. And even if acetylcholine is involved the matter is obscure because conventional neuro-muscular junctions do not occur in these animals, and this may apply to synapses also.

Some work has been done on the electrophysiology of *Ascaris lumbricoides*. With potassium chloride microelectrodes simple and complex

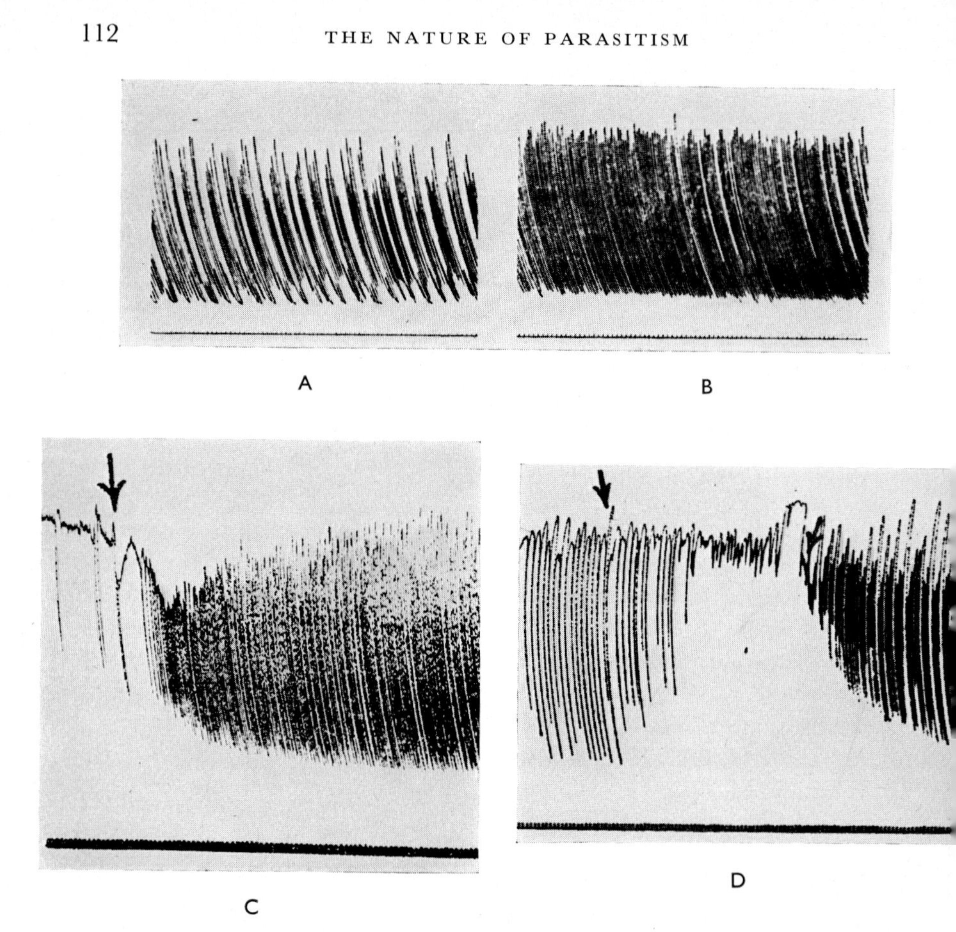

FIG. 25. A and B are kymograph records of the movements of isolated nerve-dorsal muscle strips of *Ascaris lumbricoides*. Some preparations become contracted; the addition of thiamine, C, encouraged relaxation. Osmotic pressure also affected activity, D; changes in the concentration of salts in the medium from 120 mM to 150 mM (first arrow) and 150 mM to 120 mM (second arrow) affected activity. The time-marker intervals are in minutes (after Baldwin and Moyle, 1946).

spikes which normally did not completely discharge the resting potential were recorded from the "protoplasmic bulbs" of the muscle cells (Jarman, 1959). There was evidence that the nerve cord in each field served to co-ordinate the activity of associated muscle cells.

Whole *Ascaris lumbricoides* and ligated fragments from the anterior end and middle of the worm often show a slow spontaneous rhythmical activity which has been recorded kymographically and used for the assay of anthelmintics and pharmacologically active substances (Baldwin, 1943; Krotov, 1953, 1956*a*, 1956*b*; Norton and de Beer, 1957).

The regularity and form of movement made by the whole or tied-off tubular fragments of *Ascaris* may be modified by loading the specimen with weights of about 0.25 to 1.5 g (Rico, 1926; Baldwin, 1943) or by applying an electrical stimulus (Krotov, 1953, 1956*a*). The movements made by the whole worms *in vitro* have been described by Krotov (1953). Baldwin (1943) studied tied-off tubular fragments about 2.5 cm long, taken just posterior to the lips, or just anterior to the genital pore. The anterior preparation which contained the nerve ring showed complex movements. The preparation bent in arcs from one side to another but not necessarily alternately; there was also some twisting movement. Preparations taken just anterior to the genital pore showed simple contractions which alternated on the ventral and dorsal side. Strips of muscle containing either the dorsal or ventral nerve cord from this part of the worm have been used as nerve-muscle preparations (Baldwin and Moyle, 1946; Fig. 25). They consistently showed different patterns of activity; it seems from the tracings published by Baldwin and Moyle that the ventral strips took longer to recover from a contraction or relaxation than the dorsal strips.

Baldwin (1943) found that a number of compounds such as atropine, eserine, nicotine, muscarine, pilocarpine, strychnine, acetylcholine, adrenaline and tyramine, which normally affect the activity of nerve-muscle preparations, had no action on the tied-off tubular fragments of *Ascaris lumbricoides*. This was partly due to the impermeability of the cuticle which was intact except at the ligatured ends of the preparations. With nerve-muscle preparations from strips of body wall, permeability was not a limiting factor and different results were obtained. The activity of these strips often could be maintained for long periods in a "balanced salt solution" buffered with bicarbonate under a gas phase of carbon dioxide in nitrogen. These preparations were stimulated by acetylcholine but eserine had no effect. The effects of acetylcholine were imitated by choline and nicotine and were antagonized by strychnine and tubocurarine but not by an excess of nicotine. Adrenaline, atropine, histamine, pilocarpine, strychnine and a number of substances which have an effect on conventional nerve-muscle preparations had no action on the muscle from *Ascaris* (Baldwin and Moyle, 1949).

Krotov, who repeated and extended much of Baldwin's work, has summarized most of his results in two papers, one dealing with motor responses of *Ascaris lumbricoides* and the other dealing with the pharmacology (Krotov, 1956*a*, 1956*b*). Results were obtained largely with whole *Ascaris* though some nerve-muscle strips were used. The medium—Locke's solution—was also different from that used by Baldwin and reactions to electrical stimulation as well as spontaneous movements were recorded. The most important of Krotov's results came from the observation that the anterior and posterior ends of whole *Ascaris* were more sensitive to most pharmacologically active substances than other regions. Thus acetylcholine 10^{-11} affected the whole worms whereas 10^{-6} was the lowest concentration at which Baldwin and Moyle (1949) obtained activity with nerve-muscle strips. Moreover, prostigmine potentiated the action of acetylcholine on the whole worms. Nicotine at concentrations from 10^{-5} to 10^{-7} stimulated spontaneous activity; at higher concentrations it caused irreversible contraction of the body and loss of electrical excitability. Adrenaline at 10^{-8} and muscarine and pilocarpine at 10^{-6} to 10^{-7} stimulated activity. From these and other results Krotov concluded that the neuro-muscular physiology of *Ascaris* was similar to that in most other animals. He suggested that his results differed from those of Baldwin and Moyle largely because he had used whole *Ascaris* rather than fragments of the worm for his tests. Norton and de Beer (1957) who used a nerve-muscle preparation somewhat different from that used by Baldwin and Moyle (1949) also found that *Ascaris* was similar to vertebrate skeletal muscle in its response to several pharmacologically active substances.

The presence of acetylcholine in the tissues of nematodes has been shown by Mellanby (1955). Microfilaria of *Dirofilaria repens*, taken from the blood of the host, contained as much as 2.4 μg of acetylcholine per g of fresh tissue. Male *Litomosoides carinii* contained 0.92 μg/g, slightly more than in the females. The acetylcholine content of the anterior 4 mm of *Ascaris lumbricoides* which contained the nerve ring and associated ganglia was about 0.39 μg/g; this was about 15 times as much as was found in the body wall. Acetylcholine esterase has also been found in small amounts in the tissues of *Ascaris* and *Litomosoides* (Bueding, 1952).

It is probable that the co-ordination of movements of different parts of the body of nematodes is achieved by the movement of perienteric fluid caused by local changes in volume. Co-ordination could thus be brought about without elaborate reflex networks and with the relatively simple nervous system of the typical nematode (Harris and Crofton, 1957).

Indirect evidence obtained by Bueding *et al.* (1959) suggests that the production of succinate has a function in the chemistry of muscular contraction of *Ascaris lumbricoides*. Piperazine, a secondary amine which blocks the response of nerve-muscle preparations of *Ascaris* to the stimulating actions of acetylcholine (Norton and de Beer, 1957), reduced the production of succinate in paralysed worms, though it did not inhibit the incorporation of 2-^{14}C lactate into succinate.

OSMOREGULATION

The permeability of nematodes to water and salts has been examined in some detail, partly to provide data for designing culture media and partly for work on chemotherapy. Though much of the work has been done with *Ascaris lumbricoides* or *Parascaris equorum* some data from free-living nematodes and other parasites are available. Unfortunately, little is known about the mechanism of osmoregulation; even the information on the structure of the cuticle is largely morphological and is restricted to a few species.

The Structure of the Cuticle

As far as is known the cuticle of all nematodes originates as a secretion of the underlying hypodermis. Before each moult the new cuticle is formed below the old one which is later shed at the end of the moult. As the cuticle is secreted it is non-cellular, but it does have a complex structure in those species which have been examined. The cuticle of adult *Ascaris lumbricoides* and *Parascaris equorum* has been examined in most detail; the results have been reviewed by Fairbairn (1957).

In many adult nematodes nine separate layers can be identified morphologically in the cuticle (Chitwood and Chitwood, 1940; Bird and Deutsch, 1957; Bird, 1958). These are: two cortical layers, a "fibrillar" layer, a "homogeneous" layer, a boundary layer, three layers of fibres and a basal lamella. All these layers seem to be composed largely of protein. The protein of the cortical layers of *Ascaris* which contains more than 4% sulphur has been regarded as a keratin (Flury, 1912). Also the proportion of amino acids present in the protein suggests keratin (Savel, 1955*a*); and ficin and papain attack the cortex (Robbins and Lamson, 1934; Berger and Asenjo, 1940) whereas trypsin and pepsin do not (Chitwood, 1936). However the X-ray diffraction pattern obtained from the cortex indicates the presence of a collagen rather than keratin (Fauré-Fremiet and Garrault, 1944). But the issue is still confused because hydroxyproline is not present in this part of the cuticle (Savel, 1955*b*; Bird, 1957). Brown (1950) and Bird (1957), on evidence which was based largely on histochemical tests, regarded the external cortical layer as quinone-tanned protein.

The albumen-like proteins from the cuticle of *Ascaris lumbricoides* (Chitwood, 1936; Bird, 1957) may have come largely from the matrix or "homogeneous" layer. The most clearly-defined proteins in the cuticle are those taken from the three layers of fibres. Thus these layers give gelatin when heated under the appropriate conditions (Chitwood, 1936); the X-ray diffraction patterns are typical of collagen (Fauré-Fremiet and Garrault, 1944; Picken *et al.*, 1947), and hydroxyproline is found in the hydrolysates (Bird, 1957).

In addition to protein and water, the cuticle of *Ascaris lumbricoides* contains carbohydrate and lipid (Fairbairn, 1956; Fairbairn and Passey, 1957; Bird, 1957). Some of the lipid forms a layer on the outside of the cuticle which is important in determining the entry of some compounds into the worm (Trim, 1944, 1949).

The three basic layers of the cuticle, cortex, matrix and fibre layer, have been tentatively identified in a plant parasitic nematode, *Heterodera glycines*, and a free-living form, *Hoplolaimus tylenchiformis* (Hirschmann, 1959).

The composition of the cuticle of the fourth-stage larvae of *Nippostrongylus muris* has been examined by Simmonds (1958) who obtained material for analysis by allowing the larvae to moult *in vitro*. Protein, lipid and carbohydrate were present. The composition of the protein resembled that of collagen except that the tyrosine content was higher.

Permeability

There is evidence that *Parascaris equorum, Ascaris lumbricoides* and several related species normally live in a slightly hypertonic medium within the host. Thus the osmotic pressure of the body fluid of these parasites, measured soon after they were taken from the host, was lower than that of the host's intestinal fluids (Duval and Courtois, 1928; Schopfer, 1932; Hobson *et al.*, 1952*a*). Fairbairn (1957) has pointed out that the difference between the fluids of the parasites and their hosts could have been due to the loss of volatile substances from the body fluid, or to the decomposition of intestinal fluid. It is known, for instance, that the pH of freshly collected body fluid is about 6.9, but this increases rapidly in air to about 7.1 (Hobson *et al.*, 1952*a*). On the other hand, it appears that Schopfer and Hobson *et al.* were aware of the instability of intestinal fluid and took some precautions to combat it. Nevertheless, the points made by Fairbairn (1957) on these matters are important and they should be examined further.

Ascaris lumbricoides and *Parascaris equorum* swell or shrink in saline media which are too dilute or too concentrated (Hobson *et al.*, 1952*a*; Schopfer, 1925; Fig. 26). This is due to the passage of water through the body wall and through the intestinal wall. Somewhat similar results have been obtained with other ascarids (Schopfer, 1932) and with *Angusticaecum* spp. from the colon of the tortoise (Panikkar and Sproston, 1941). In the range 20 to 40% sea water, the osmotic pressure of the body fluid of *Ascaris lumbricoides* was always slightly *above* that of the medium (Hobson *et al.*, 1952*a*), rather than below as *in vivo*. In *Angusticaecum* this property was most pronounced in very dilute media. Thus worms placed in tap water maintained an osmotic pressure equivalent to 1.16 to 1.3% sodium chloride even after 4 days (Panikkar and Sproston, 1941). It appears, then, that these worms were euryhaline to about the same extent as the polychaete *Nereis diversicolor* (Fig. 27)

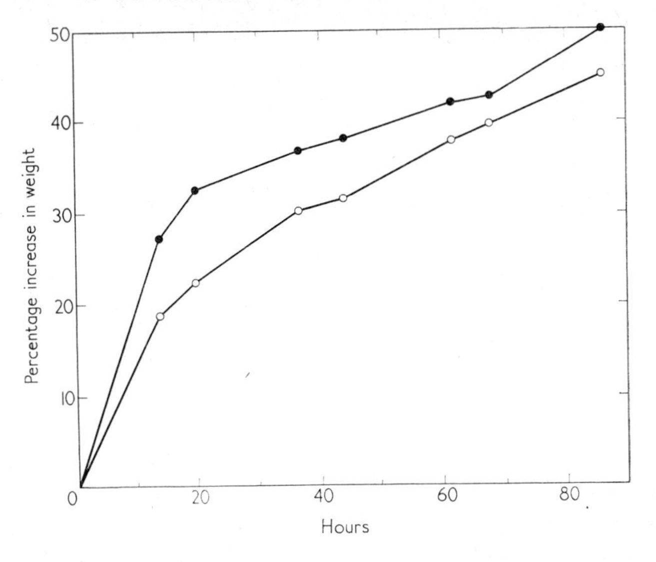

FIG. 26. The increase in weight of normal (●) and ligatured (O) females of *Ascaris lumbricoides* in 20% sea water (after Hobson *et al.*, 1952*a*).

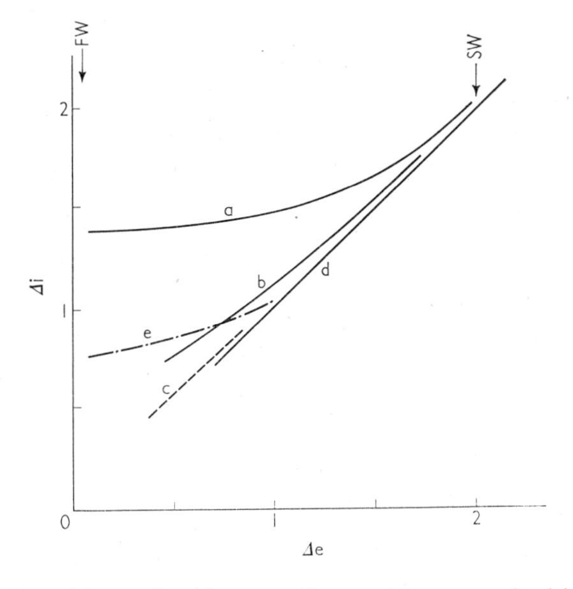

FIG. 27. Variation of internal with external osmotic pressure in (a) *Carcinus*, (b) *Nereis*, (c) *Ascaris*, (d) *Maia*, and (e) *Angusticaecum;* (a), (b) and (d) after Baldwin (1940); (c) from figures of Hobson *et al.* (1952*a*); (e) from figures of Panikkar and Sproston (1941).

and they survived under conditions which caused *Parascaris equorum* to burst (Schopfer, 1925).

In 30% sea water there was little change in the weight of *Ascaris lumbricoides* even after many days. Though the osmotic pressure of the body fluid did not change under these circumstances, and the ionic conductivity fell only slightly, there was about a 50% increase in the concentration of chloride. Even so the chloride content of the body fluid was well below that in the external medium. This result was also obtained at other dilutions of sea water between 20 and 40% (Hobson *et al.*, 1952*b*).

It seems that water enters or leaves nematodes through the cuticle very largely in relation to the relative concentrations of the internal and external media, though the high turgor pressure of the body fluids which may average 70 mm of mercury in *Ascaris lumbricoides* (Harris and Crofton, 1957) must influence the passage of water especially from hypotonic media. Some inorganic ions pass through the cuticle and body wall of at least some species (Panikkar and Sproston, 1941) but phosphate ions do not pass through the cuticle of living *Ascaris lumbricoides* (Rogers and Lazarus, 1949*b*). However, after treatment with a cationic detergent (cetyltrimethyl ammonium bromide) inorganic phosphate leaks out through the cuticle of living worms; this detergent also affects the permeability of the isolated cuticle to dyes (Trim, 1949). The capacity of this species to maintain the concentration of chloride in the body fluid below that in the external medium lies in the body wall; the cuticle is freely permeable to this ion (Hobson *et al.*, 1952*a*).

The isolated cuticle of *Ascaris lumbricoides* is permeable to "glucose and to a wide range of other non-electrolytes" (Hobson, 1948). When the body wall is intact, however, glucose does not pass, though urea and potassium iodide do (Mueller, 1928). Trim (1949) stated that the kinetics of the penetration of a number of anthelmintics *in vitro* indicated the presence of an outer, thin homogeneous layer of lipid which was the main barrier against the entry of a number of compounds into the worm. Moreover, Alexander and Trim (1946) found that naturally occurring and synthetic surface-active substances, at concentrations which gave minimum tensions at an oil–water interface, accelerated the entry of hexylresorcinol into the parasite through its cuticle. The surface-active substances were not absorbed in appreciable amounts. Bird and Deutsch (1957), who studied the cuticle by electron microscopy, found an outer osmiophilic layer about 100 mμ thick which they regarded as the lipid to which Trim referred. Bird (1958) also found that material which stains with Sudan Black when it is placed on filter paper can be obtained from the surface of *Ascaris lumbricoides* by washing the worms in light petroleum for a few seconds.

Though there is little doubt that lipids are present on the surface and that they facilitate the entry of fat-soluble substances, the layer is clearly incomplete and does not act as a "permeability barrier" against the entry of water *in vitro*. *In vivo* many nematode parasites in the gut are thickly covered with mucinous material. Whether this affects the penetration of normal substances into the parasites is unknown; it certainly affects the entry of drugs like hexylresorcinol (Rogers, 1944).

Definite evidence about osmoregulatory mechanisms in adult nematodes is lacking though the possibility that the excretory system, as in larval nematodes, and the alimentary canal may aid in the removal of water has been suggested by several authors. But even if there are such mechanisms they are largely ineffective in some species, and in others function only in hypotonic media. What is perhaps surprising is the remarkable capacity of these animals to remain alive when the composition of their body fluid has been altered by exposing them to hypotonic or hypertonic media. Thus *Angusticaecum graeca* remained alive for at least five days under conditions in which the osmotic pressure of the body fluid ranged in concentrations equivalent to 0.978 to 3.535 % sodium chloride (Panikkar and Sproston, 1941).

Davey (1938) found that the survival of *Ostertagia circumcincta in vitro* was not much affected over a range of concentrations of sodium chloride from 0.4 to 1.3 %; but, as the survival of these nematodes even under the best conditions was for a short period only, these results may not be significant. The results obtained with parasitic larvae, *Eustrongylides ignotus* (von Brand and Simpson, 1942), were more definite. This parasite was kept alive for several months in media in which the concentration of organic and inorganic materials varied greatly. Survival was reduced to 16 days, however, when the content of sodium chloride in the medium was raised to 3 %. In these experiments with *Ostertagia* and *Eustrongylides* the change in the composition of the body fluids was not examined, but if these species are poikilosmotic as are *Ascaris lumbricoides* and *Parascaris equorum*, their tissues must be adapted to function in a wide range of concentrations.

Intermediary Metabolism in the Acanthocephala and Parasitic Platyhelminthes

The metabolism of metazoan parasites generally, as far as is known, conforms with what we know about parasitic nematodes. Certainly there is clear evidence that glycolysis occurs in the tissues of cestodes and trematodes. There is also evidence that mechanisms similar to the tricarboxylic acid cycle are concerned in the oxidation of pyruvic acid in several species. Just how far these mechanisms which are part of the "ground plan" of all cells are essential in the economy of these organisms is unknown. It certainly seems that glycolysis is the major route for the formation of pyruvic acid; but, as in the parasitic nematodes, there are in many cestodes and trematodes other routes, often specialized and differing even from genus to genus, by which carbohydrates and lipids are catabolized.

Anaerobic Respiration

Under anaerobic conditions lactic acid is the major end-product of carbohydrate metabolism of a number of species of parasitic platyhelminths. For example, the amounts excreted by scolices of *Echinococcus granulosus* from hydatid cysts, or by adult *Hymenolepis diminuta*, *Oochoristica symmetrica*, and *Schistosoma mansoni* may account for 50 to 80% of the carbohydrate used (Agosin, 1957; Read, 1956; Bueding, 1949). In *Moniezia expansa*, however, lactic acid accounts for only 16% of the glycogen used by worms in non-nutritive media (von Brand, 1933) and for *Fasciola hepatica* the figure is even less than this (Weinland and von Brand, 1926; Stephenson, 1947*a*; Mansour, 1959*a*).

The route by which lactic acid is formed has been examined in detail in several species; in general the route is similar to the classical scheme of Embden and Meyerhof. Thus many of the substrates and enzymes of the glycolytic pathway have been found in the tissues of *Hymenolepis diminuta* (Read, 1949, 1951*a*, 1951*b*), *Echinococcus granulosus* (Agosin and Aravena, 1959*b*) and *Schistosoma mansoni* (Bueding and Most, 1953; Bueding, 1955). As might be expected, however, some of the enzymes differ from those which carry out similar reactions in other organisms. Thus the lactic dehydrogenase and phosphoglucose isomerase of *Schistosoma mansoni* differ in their reaction kinetics and response to specific antibodies from comparable enzymes in rat or rabbit muscle (Mansour and Bueding, 1953; Mansour, Bueding and Stavitsky, 1954; Bueding and MacKinnon, 1955*a*). Moreover, the parasite contains four hexokinases which specifically catalyse the phosphorylation of glucose, fructose, mannose and glucosamine, whereas the comparable reactions are carried out by the one enzyme in mammalian brain or yeast (Bueding, Ruppender and MacKinnon, 1954; Bueding and MacKinnon, 1955*b*). Distinctive properties have been found in enzymes of other parasites; e.g. aldolase in larvae of *Taenia crassiceps* may differ from the aldolase of the host (Phifer, 1958).

The metabolism of phosphorus associated with glycolysis in *Hymenolepis diminuta* has been studied by Read (1951*a*). As well as demonstrating the esterification of phosphate in substrates of enzymes of the glycolytic pathway, Read examined the phosphorus compounds in the resting tissue of the parasite. Compounds identical with or similar to adenosine triphosphate, adenosine diphosphate and DPN were present but neither arginine phosphate nor creatine phosphate was detected. Generalizing on the absence of the classical phosphagens from the tissues of adult parasites, Read suggested that the sheltered existence which these animals lead does not need the sudden expenditure of energy frequently required by free-living animals so that "the phosphagen energy storage mechanism" may have been lost.

Though lactic acid may not appear as a major end-product of anaerobic carbohydrate metabolism in some species of parasites, it does not follow that glycolysis is not an active feature of their metabolism. It is probable, for instance, that pyruvate or other intermediates might be diverted to routes giving end-products other than lactic acid as in muscle of *Ascaris lumbricoides*. The routes of synthesis of the wide range of fatty acids and other organic acids (von Brand, 1952; Bueding and Most, 1953; Read, 1956; Mansour, 1959*a*, 1959*b*) which are excreted by parasitic helminths are not known but it seems reasonable to suppose that the formation of pyruvic acid by glycolysis is basic to many of them.

There is evidence that the pentose phosphate pathway may serve as a route for the catabolism of glucose in some parasitic platyhelminths (De Ley and Vercruysse, 1955; Agosin and Aravena, 1959*c*) though the importance of this route relative to glycolysis is not known.

No carbon dioxide is produced as a result of anaerobic metabolism in *Hymenolepis diminuta, Oochoristica symmetrica* or *Moniliformis dubius* (Read, 1956; Laurie, 1957). Other species, such as *Moniezia expansa, Paramphistomum cervi* and *Echinococcus granulosus* produce considerable amounts (von Brand, 1933; Lazarus, 1950; Agosin *et al.*, 1957). The origin of the carbon dioxide is unknown.

Anaerobic production of acid by adult *Hymenolepis diminuta* and *Oochoristica symmetrica* is reversibly inhibited by about 20 to 30% by bile salts at a physiological concentration (0.1%). Though the feeding of bile salts to infected hosts did not appreciably affect the tapeworms *in vivo* the possibility that bile salts influence the distribution of the parasite in the small intestine of the hosts needs consideration (Rothman, 1958).

Aerobic Respiration

As in the nematodes, the Pasteur effect is shown to various degrees by the parasitic Platyhelminthes and Acanthocephala. The availability of oxygen to *Schistosoma mansoni* makes little difference in the rate at which glycogen is used or in the production of lactic acid (Bueding, 1950). In *Moniezia expansa* the total amount of acid formed under anaerobic and aerobic conditions is similar but succinic acid is produced in addition to higher fatty acids when oxygen is withheld (Alt and Tischer, 1931; von Brand, 1933). The amount of glycogen used by

Macracanthorhyncus hirudinaceus under aerobic and anaerobic conditions shows the ratio of 1 : 1.3 (Ward, 1952). For the scolices of *Echinococcus granulosus* the ratio is about 1 : 1.1. And pyruvic acid is excreted as well as lactic, acetic and succinic acids and ethyl alcohol under anaerobic conditions (Agosin, 1957). The Pasteur effect is a little more marked in *Hymenolepis diminuta.* More polysaccharide is stored per unit of glucose used from the medium when oxygen is available and lactic acid production decreases by about 30 %. But even in this species the efficiency of oxidation is low. The oxygen uptake accounts for the complete oxidation of less than 5 % of the glucose removed from the medium (Read, 1956). Comparable details are not available for Acanthocephala but Laurie (1959) has shown that respiration is accompanied by a pronounced aerobic fermentation in *Moniliformis dubius* which leads to the excretion of acetic, formic and lactic acids (see Chapter 7).

Oxidative pathways in cestodes and trematodes involve some substrates and enzymes of the tricarboxylic acid cycle, but, as might be expected, the respiratory quotients are generally low (Read, 1953, 1956; Agosin *et al.*, 1957; van Grembergen, 1949). There is also evidence that part at least of the cytochrome system is present (Friedheim and Baer, 1933; van Grembergen, 1944, 1949; Read, 1952). Read (1952) showed that cytochrome oxidase is present in one species of the Acanthocephala. It seems unlikely, however, that the cytochrome–cytochrome oxidase system and the organized tricarboxylic acid cycle of mitochondria have an important role in the economy of parasitic platyhelminths and Acanthocephala as they have in vertebrate animals. Even *Schistosoma mansoni*, which, from its size and site in the host, might be expected to have an important aerobic metabolism, is largely anaerobic (Bueding, 1950). Read (1956) has suggested that the products of anaerobic metabolism formed in the inner tissues of tapeworms might diffuse to the periphery where some oxidative metabolism might take place. In this way energy from aerobic respiration would be available for the peripheral nerve trunks and muscular system, and for the absorptive surface. Support for this suggestion comes from histochemical studies on the distribution of succinic dehydrogenase (Hedrick, 1956) and from electron micrographs which indicate that mitochondria might be present in the peripheral tissues of tapeworms (Read, 1955). It seems, however, that mitochondria are not generally important in the economy of most parasites. Cytoplasmic particles with the biochemical and morphological characteristics of mitochondria are found even in the Protozoa, and the particles must have been present in the ancestral stocks of the parasites. As mitochondria would have little selective value to parasites living in sites where food was plentiful and oxygen was in short supply, losses of varying degrees may have occurred leaving biochemical fragments of mitochondrial mechanisms which are relatively unimportant in the energy metabolism of the modern platyhelminth parasite.

Metabolism of Nitrogen Compounds

Analysis of fluids from the tissues of adult parasites and from the cysts of larval stages has shown that ammonia, urea and uric acid are frequently present (see von Brand, 1952, p. 141). Quantitatively, ammonia is the most important nitrogenous end-product excreted by *Fasciola hepatica, Fasciola gigantica, Paramphistomum explanatum,* and larvae of *Taenia taeniaeformis* (van Grembergen and Pennoit-DeCooman, 1944; Goil, 1958; Haskins and Olivier, 1958). Urea was excreted only by the tapeworm for which it accounted for 33 % of the total nitrogen excreted; the other important components were amines (15 % of the total nitrogen), amino acids (12 %) and peptides (27 %). In addition to ammonia, *Fasciola hepatica* produced amino acids; the other trematodes may excrete some uric acid. Present knowledge of the distribution of enzymes concerned in the formation of these end-products is fragmentary. Urease is absent from *Fasciola hepatica, Moniezia benedini* and *Taenia pisiformis,* though all these parasites have high arginase activity (Florkin and Duchateau, 1943; van Grembergen and Pennoit-DeCooman, 1944).

Some enzymes concerned in the metabolism of amino acids have been examined in platyhelminths and Acanthocephala. Thus transaminases have been examined in *Fasciola hepatica, Hymenolepis diminuta, Raillietina cesticillus* and *Macracanthorhyncus hirudinaceus* (Daugherty, 1952*a*, 1952*b*; Aldrich, Chandler and Daugherty, 1954; Foster, 1955) and several *l*-amino oxidases have been examined in *Hymenolepis diminuta* (Daugherty, 1955). The activity of these enzymes has been shown to vary greatly between individual parasites of the same species. In most instances no satisfactory explanation of these variable results has been given, though Aldrich *et al.* (1954) showed that the activity of the four transaminase systems in *Hymenolepis diminuta* was greatly reduced if the male rats used as hosts were castrated. The decrease in activity of the transaminases was associated with a decreased deposition of fat in the tapeworms.

Daugherty (1957*a*, 1957*b*) and Daugherty and Foster (1958) have shown that the absorption of *l*-cystine and *l*-methionine takes place, at least in part, by active transport in *Hymenolepis diminuta* and *Raillietina cesticillus.* Analyses of the amino acids of protein hydrolysates from adult and larval *Hymenolepis diminuta* have been compared with those from the tissues of the intestine of the final host and those from the intermediate host. The results showed that there was a similarity in the relative abundance of the different amino acids in the adult parasite and vertebrate host, and in the larval parasite and the invertebrate host (Goodchild and Wells, 1957).

Kent (1948, 1957*a*, 1957*b*) has examined proteins from the tissues of *Taenia saginata, Moniezia expansa, Hymenolepis diminuta* and *Raillietina cesticillus*. All these parasites contained proteins conjugated with cerebrosides, or glycogen, or both these substances, and Kent suggested that complexes of this sort may be characteristic of cestodes. Some general requirements for the synthesis of proteins by cestodes *in vitro* have been discussed by Smyth (1958).

Nerve-Muscle Physiology in Parasitic Platyhelminthes

The parasitic platyhelminths have well-defined muscle cells in the sub-cuticular layers and in the parenchyma; the most complex organization of the muscle cells is found in the suckers, bothridia and acetabula. In cestodes the longitudinal and transverse musculature is responsible for the contractions and expansions which take place most vigorously in the neck region, especially *in vitro* but probably also *in vivo* (Wardle and McLeod, 1952, p. 110). A similar organization of the musculature is found in the Trematoda. There is also a well-developed nervous system in the Platyhelminthes though detailed information on the innervation of the muscles is not available except for some adhesive organs.

The waves of contraction which move backward in the body of *Catenotaenia pusilla* are not interrupted by cutting the main nerve trunks or the excretory canals (Rietschel, 1935). The stimulus for contraction probably arises and is conducted in the musculature itself which is continuous in the parenchyma even at the junctions between the proglottids (Rietschel, 1935; Hyman, 1951, p. 321).

The movements of cestodes *in vivo* and *in vitro* and the environmental factors which may influence them have been described by Wardle (1934) and Wardle and McLeod (1952, p. 110). Dawes (1946, p. 512) has summarized work on the movements of larval trematodes. This information, though aiding the understanding of the penetration of the host's tissues by larval cestodes and expulsion from the host of eggs and fragments of the strobila, does not tell us much about the nerve-muscle physiology.

Pharmacologically active substances such as serotonin and lysergic acid affect the metabolism of some parasites. Thus Mansour (1959*b*) found that serotonin and lysergic acid diethylamide stimulated the movements of *Fasciola hepatica* which was incubated in a saline medium containing serum and glucose. The quantities and proportion of propionic acid and acetic acid (3 : 1) excreted into the medium were not affected by the drugs but lactic acid production was increased greatly.

Bromolysergic acid diethylamide which inhibited the stimulatory action of serotonin and lysergic acid diethylamide on the parasite also inhibited the increased lactic acid production. These results have interesting implications both in the neurophysiology and in the nature of the metabolic processes which supply energy for muscular contraction in flukes, and further research in this field may be most profitable.

Histochemical tests have shown that acetylcholine esterase is present in the small central area of nervous tissue in the miracidium of *Schistosoma mansoni* (Pepler, 1958). And Bueding (1952) found that the adult parasite contains an acetylcholine esterase at concentrations similar to those in the central nervous systems of vertebrates. Moreover, the enzyme from the parasite showed a substrate specificity and anomalous behaviour in relation to substrate concentration as is found with the enzyme which is important in neuro-muscular transmission (Fig. 28).

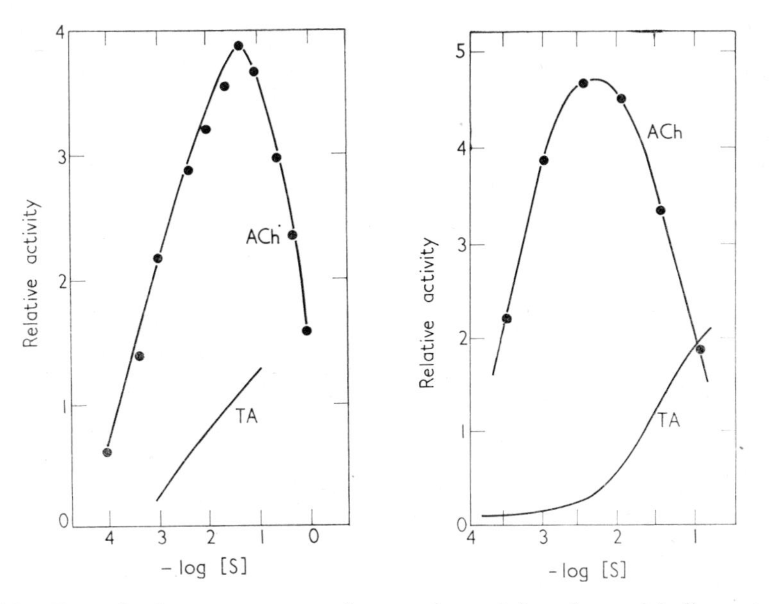

FIG. 28. Effect of substrate concentration on the activity of acetylcholine esterase from *Schistosoma mansoni* (left: after Bueding 1952) and electric tissue of *Electrophorus electricus* (right: after Augustinsson and Nachmansohn, 1949). The substrates were acetylcholine (ACh) and triacetin (TA).

The probability that the enzyme plays a functional role in the parasite is supported by the finding that schistosomes also contain a choline acetylase. A substance with the pharmacological properties of acetylcholine has been extracted from *Taenia crassicollis* and *Dipylidium caninum* (Artemov and Lure, 1941) and choline esterase activity has been demonstrated in *Fasciola hepatica*, *Taenia pisiformis* and its larval stage (Bacq and Oury, 1937; Pennoit-DeCooman, 1940; Pennoit-DeCooman and van Grembergen, 1942).

Osmoregulation in Parasitic Platyhelminthes and Acanthocephala

Water and salts must be taken up with nutrients through the body surface of cestodes and Acanthocephala. This may also occur in the Trematoda; but these animals, though they have a body surface through which gas exchange takes place, have an alimentary canal which lessens greatly the necessity for a permeable outer covering. A number of views on the nature and origin of the cuticle of platyhelminths have been expressed. Hyman (1951, pp. 223, 320) favoured the suggestion that the cuticle of both the Trematoda and Cestoda is secreted by the general mesenchyme or by special cells in that tissue. The cuticle of the Acanthocephala is a thin structureless layer on the top of a thick epidermis of fibrous syncytial construction. In all these groups it seems that the cuticle is largely protein and contains no chitin.

Electron micrographs of sections of *Hymenolepis diminuta* show that the cuticle is covered by large numbers of villus-like extensions (Read, 1955). It is not known if similar structures occur in the Acanthocephala.

There seems to be little control over the osmotic entry or loss of water in larval or adult cestodes. Thus these parasites gain or lose water very much in accordance with the concentrations of the medium (Wardle, 1937; Schopfer, 1929, 1932; Chandler, Read and Nicholas, 1950; Read, Douglas and Simmons, 1959). The minimum changes in the weight of species from mammals occurred when they were incubated in Tyrode's solution rather than in diluted or concentrated solutions of the same medium. Three-fourths Locke's solution was most suitable for plerocercoids of *Schistocephalus solidus* from teleosts (Smyth, 1946). Wherever measurements have been made it has been found that the osmotic pressure of tissue fluids of cestodes has been less than that of the normal environment. Thus the depression of the freezing point (Δ) for tissue extracts of *Moniezia expansa* and *Anoplocephala perfoliata* was found to be −0.669°C and −0.69°C respectively whereas Δ for the intestinal fluid of the sheep is −0.825°C, and for the horse, the host of *Anoplocephala perfoliata*, −0.74°C (Schopfer, 1932). This is a similar result to that obtained with parasitic nematodes.

Smyth (1946) obtained results with plerocercoids of *Schistocephalus solidus* which showed that a change in weight occurred when the parasites were kept in sodium chloride solution of Δ −0.44°C. This result agreed with the finding that a high degree of viability and natural behaviour was obtained in a diluted Locke's solution of Δ −0.42°C.

On the other hand the Δ of tissue fluids of the teleost host is about $-0.54°C$, and *in vitro* survival in a medium containing large molecules (peptone broth) was high when Δ was about $-0.56°C$. Read *et al.* (1959), discussing these results, suggested that the discrepancy might be due to the partial permeability of the parasite to the solute so that the difference in the initial absolute osmotic pressures of the medium and tissue fluids might be greater than the osmotic pressure exerted across the outer membrane of the parasite.

Special features in the osmotic properties of cestodes from cartilagenous fish have been studied by Read *et al.* (1959). For the strobilate phase of the Tetraphyllidea, and perhaps for Trypanorhyncha also, urea is an important osmotically active component of the tissues and of the environment (Fig. 39). Urea is retained in bodies of both marine and fresh-water Chondrichthyes (Smith, 1936). In marine forms it raises the osmotic pressure of the body fluids above that of the sea and is of considerable selective advantage; in fresh-water forms, the concentration of urea in the blood, though much reduced, is osmotically disadvantageous. Apparently the retention of urea was characteristic of the early marine Chondrichthyes stock. It is not surprising, therefore, to find that the parasites of marine cartilagenous fish living in the spiral valve fluid, in which the concentration of urea may reach 500 mM, are not only tolerant to this normally toxic substance but are able to take advantage of its presence.

Read *et al.* (1959) worked chiefly with *Calliobothrium verticillatum* from the dogfish, *Mustelus canis*, but related parasites from other cartilagenous fish were also examined. Free-living platyhelminths and parasites of vertebrates other than Chondrichthyes were used for comparison. When *Calliobothrium verticillatum* was incubated in solutions containing constant amounts of calcium chloride, magnesium chloride and potassium chloride, but with varying amounts of sodium chloride, it was found that the change in weight of the parasite and the movement of chloride in or out of the tissues were related to the concentration of the sodium chloride in the medium. In all but the most concentrated media, however, there was during the first few minutes of incubation a consistent increase in the wet weight of the worms which was followed by a decline. It was found that this initial uptake of water was due to the presence of urea, in amounts up to 1.6% of the wet weight, in the tissues of the parasites. When urea was added to the medium the changes in weight of the parasites were decreased, and the rise in chloride and the fall in urea in the tissues were also decreased. Concentrations of urea (200 mM) which had a favourable effect on the parasites of cartilagenous fish had toxic actions on platyhelminths from other vertebrates. The tissues of these parasites became irreversibly hydrated and movement ceased. The cestodes in Chondrichthyes are clearly well adapted to the urea in the fluids of the host.

The poikilosmotic behaviour of cestodes probably applies to trematodes also though in some larvae and ectoparasitic species the elimination of water may be a more active process (Osborn, 1905). In some cercariae at least there seems to be some correlation between the rate of pulsation of the excretory bladder and the dilution of the medium (Herfs, 1922). Some adult trematodes can withstand large changes in the osmotic pressure of the medium. Thus Stephenson (1945, 1947*b*) found that the survival of *Fasciola hepatica in vitro* was not greatly affected by changes in salt concentration (58 to 230 mM for sodium chloride). In these experiments, however, the maximum time of survival was only about 60 hours. Bueding (1950) found that glycolysis and activity of *Schistosoma mansoni* were not affected by changes of the concentration of sodium chloride from 68 to 680 mM.

Of the Acanthocephala, *Neoechinorhynchus emydis* has been examined (Gettier, 1942; Van Cleave and Ross, 1944). The flattened form of this parasite, in which it is usually found inside the host, is maintained *in vitro* in 137 to 145 mM solutions of sodium chloride. At lower concentrations they become turgid but can be restored to the flattened shape in 145 mM salt solution. The changes in shape could be induced *in vivo* by injecting suitable solutions into the intestine of the host turtles (Van Cleave and Ross, 1944). Optimum survival in salt solutions occurs at concentrations of 85 to 125 mM.

The function ascribed to the excretory systems of platyhelminths and Acanthocephala, though based largely on anatomical considerations, is perhaps more firmly established than in the Nematoda. At least it has been shown that flame cells which are normally associated with excretory or osmoregulatory functions, are commonly found in the excretory systems of these animals.

Summary

The course of breakdown of glycogen in parasitic nematodes and platyhelminths follows the classical Embden-Myerhof route of phosphorylating glycolysis. However, lactic acid is not necessarily the end-product of anaerobic metabolism. Pyruvic acid, and perhaps other intermediates of the glycolytic reaction sequence as well, may be metabolized further by other routes which may differ even between closely related genera. Evidence is available which suggests that pyruvic acid may be closely involved in the synthesis of lower fatty acids which are excreted by a number of parasites, especially by many of the parasitic nematodes. Carbohydrate may be metabolized via the pentose phosphate shunt in the muscle of *Ascaris lumbricoides* and in some platyhelminths. The importance of this pathway relative to glycolysis is probably small.

Glycolysis in helminths leads to the synthesis of adenosinetriphosphate but it appears that phosphagens of the classical types are not formed. Except in glycolysis, the coupling of anaerobic carbohydrate metabolism with the production of "high-energy phosphate bonds" has not been demonstrated. The transfer of energy via thiol compounds also awaits investigation.

The aerobic metabolism of carbohydrate in metazoan parasites embraces the tricarboxylic acid cycle, the fixation of carbon dioxide, and the cytochrome–cytochrome oxidase system. No detailed investigation of fatty acid oxidation has yet been carried out. So far, the completely integrated mechanism of the mitochondria of many vertebrate and invertebrate tissues has not been demonstrated. Indeed, in many helminths it is clear that only fragments of the classical mechanism exist though these may be supplemented or replaced by other aerobic processes of unknown importance in the general economy of parasites. A high degree of specialization seems to have occurred in the processes of aerobic metabolism of carbohydrates and lipids in many helminths.

The general interpretation of the evidence on intermediary metabolism of metazoan parasites which is accumulating suggests that the basic mechanisms of cellular respiration of the ancestral forms were those of phosphorylating glycolysis followed by the oxidation of pyruvic acid via the tricarboxylic acid cycle and the cytochrome–cytochrome oxidase system. It is clear, however, that there is no homogeneity in the processes of cellular respiration of modern helminths. There is here no feature which could be regarded as truly characteristic of parasitism; nor do the parasites of different phyla or classes show characteristic differences in their cellular respiration (see Chapter 7).

Ammonia is the chief excretory product of nitrogen metabolism in parasitic nematodes and platyhelminths but urea is often excreted in appreciable amounts, especially, it appears, under conditions of water shortage in one species. The water relations of parasites *in vivo* are not clearly understood. Thus the osmotic pressures of fluids from parasites may be somewhat lower than those of the environment *in vivo*. On the other hand, helminths are poikilosmotic *in vitro*. Water would not be freely available, except under special circumstances, in either of these two conditions and facultative ureotelism would often aid survival.

The excretion of a large variety of amines by several species of helminths indicates an unusual feature of nitrogen catabolism in these animals. It is not yet known if this is a common feature in helminths generally.

REFERENCES

Agosin, M. (1957) *Exp. Parasit.* **6**, 586.
—— and Aravena, L. C. (1959*a*) *Exp. Parasit.* **8**, 10.
—— (1959*b*) *Biochim. biophys. Acta,* **34**, 90.
—— (1959*c*) *Bol. Soc. chileno Parasit.* **14**, 30.
——, von Brand, T., Rivera, G. F. and McMahon, P. (1957) *Exp. Parasit.* **6**, 37.
Aldrich, D. V., Chandler, A. C. and Daugherty, J. W. (1954) *Exp. Parasit.* **3**, 173.
Alexander, A. E. and Trim, A. R. (1946) *Proc. roy. Soc.* **B133**, 220.
Alt, H. L. and Tischer, D. A. (1931) *Proc. Soc. exp. Biol. Med.* **29**, 222.
Artemov, N. M. and Lure, R. N. (1941) *Bull. Acad. Sci. U. R. S. S. Ser. Biol.* **2**, 278.
Augustinsson, K. B. and Nachmansohn, D. (1949) *Science,* **110**, 98.
Bacq, Z. M. and Oury, A. (1937) *Bull. Acad. Belg. Cl. Sci.* **23**, 891.
Bahl, K. N. (1945) *Quart. J. micr. Sci.* **85**, 343.
Baldwin, E. (1940) "An Introduction to Comparative Biochemistry". Cambridge University Press, Cambridge.
—— (1943) *Parasitology,* **35**, 89.
—— and Moyle, V. (1946) *J. exp. Biol.* **23**, 277.
—— (1949) *Brit. J. Pharmacol.* **4**, 145.
Berger, J. and Asenjo, C. F. (1940) *Science,* **91**, 387.
Berl, S. and Bueding, E. (1951) *J. biol. Chem.* **191**, 401.
Bird, A. F. (1957) *Exp. Parasit.* **6**, 383.
—— (1958) *Parasitology,* **48**, 32.
—— and Deutsch, K. (1957) *Parasitology,* **47**, 319.
Brown, C. H. (1950) *Nature, Lond.* **165**, 275.
Bueding, E. (1949) *J. exp. Med.* **89**, 107.
—— (1950) *J. gen. Physiol.* **33**, 475.
—— (1952) *Brit. J. Pharmacol.* **7**, 563.
—— (1953) *J. biol. Chem.* **202**, 505.
—— (1955) *In* "Some Physiological Aspects and Consequences of Parasitism". (W. H. Cole, ed.), Rutgers University Press, New Brunswick.
—— (1960*a*) *In* "Host Influence on Parasite Physiology". (L. A. Stauber, ed.), Rutgers University Press, New Brunswick.
—— and Charms, B. (1951) *Nature, Lond.* **167**, 149.
—— and Charms, B. (1952) *J. biol. Chem.* **196**, 615.
——, Entner, N. and Farber, E. (1955) *Biochim. biophys. Acta,* **18**, 305.
—— and Farrow, G. W. (1956) *Exp. Parasit.* **4**, 345.
—— and MacKinnon, J. A. (1955*a*) *J. biol. Chem.* **215**, 507.
—— (1955*b*) *J. biol. Chem.* **215**, 495.
—— and Most, H. (1953) *Ann. Rev. Microbiol.* **7**, 295.
——, Ruppender, H. and MacKinnon, J. A. (1954) *Proc. nat. Acad. Sci., Wash.* **40**, 773.
——, Saz, H. J. and Farrow, G. W. (1959) *Brit. J. Pharmacol.* **14**, 497.
—— and Yale, H. W. (1951) *J. biol. Chem.* **193**, 411.
Cavier, R. and Savel, J. (1953) *C. R. Soc. Biol., Paris,* **237**, 99.
—— (1954*a*) *C. R. Soc. Biol., Paris,* **238**, 2448.
—— (1954*b*) *Bull. Soc. Chim. biol., Paris,* **36**, 1433.
—— (1954*c*) *C. R. Soc. Biol., Paris,* **239**, 205.
—— (1954*d*) *Bull. Soc. Chim. biol., Paris,* **36**, 1631.
—— (1954*e*) *C. R. Acad. Sci., Paris,* **238**, 2035.
Chandler, A. C., Read, C. P. and Nicholas, H. O. (1950) *J. Parasit.* **36**, 523.
Chin, C. and Bueding, E. (1954) *Biochim. biophys. Acta,* **13**, 331.

Chitwood, B. G. (1936) *Proc. helm. Soc. Wash.* **5**, 18.
—— and Chitwood, M. B. (1940) *In* "Introduction to Nematology". (B. G. Chitwood and M. B. Chitwood, eds.), M. B. Chitwood, Babylon, New York.
Daugherty, J. W. (1952*a*) *Exp. Parasit.* **1**, 331.
—— (1952*b*) *J. Parasit.* **38**, Suppl. 32.
—— (1955) *Exp. Parasit.* **4**, 455.
—— (1957*a*) *Exp. Parasit.* **6**, 60.
—— (1957*b*) *Amer. J. trop. Med. Hyg.* **6**, 464.
—— and Foster, W. B. (1958) *Exp. Parasit.* **7**, 99.
Davey, D. G. (1938) *Parasitology*, **30**, 278.
Dawes, B. (1946) "The Trematoda". Cambridge University Press, Cambridge.
Delaunay, H. (1934) *Ann. Rev. Physiol. Physicochem. Biol.* **10**, 695.
De Ley, J. and Vercruysse, R. (1955) *Biochim. biophys. Acta,* **13**, 331.
Dresel, E. I. B. and Moyle, V. (1950) *J. exp. Biol.* **27**, 210.
Duval, M. and Courtois, A. (1928) *C. R. Soc. Biol., Paris,* **99**, 1952.
Entner, N. (1957) *Arch. Biochem. Biophys.* **71**, 52.
—— and Gonzalez, C. (1959) *Exp. Parasit.* **8**, 471.
Fairbairn, D. (1954) *Exp. Parasit.* **3**, 52.
—— (1956) *Canad. J. Biochem. Physiol.* **34**, 39.
—— (1957) *Exp. Parasit.* **6**, 491.
—— and Passey, R. F. (1957) *Exp. Parasit.* **6**, 566.
Fauré-Fremiet, E. and Garrault, H. (1944) *Bull. Biol., Woods Hole,* **78**, 206.
Florkin, M. and Duchateau, G. (1943) *Arch. int. Physiol.* **53**, 267.
Flury, F. (1912) *Arch. exp. Path. Pharmak.* **67**, 275.
Foster, W. B. (1955) *J. Parasit.* **41**, Suppl. 30.
Friedheim, E. A. H. and Baer, J. G. (1933) *Biochem. Z.* **265**, 329.
Gettier, A. (1942) *Proc. helm. Soc. Wash.* **9**, 75.
Glocklin, V. C. and Fairbairn, D. (1952) *J. cell. comp. Physiol.* **39**, 341.
Goil, M. M. (1958) *J. Helminth.* **32**, 119.
Goldberg, E. (1957) *Exp. Parasit.* **6**, 367.
Goodchild, C. G. and Wells, O. C. (1957) *Exp. Parasit.* **6**, 575.
Godfried, E. G. (1939) *Biochem. J.* **33**, 955.
Hankes, L. V. and Stoner, R. D. (1956) *Proc. Soc. exp. Biol. Med.* **91**, 443.
—— (1958) *Exp. Parasit.* **7**, 92.
Harris, J. E. and Crofton, H. D. (1957) *J. exp. Biol.* **34**, 116.
Haskins, W. T. and Weinstein, P. P. (1957*a*) *J. Parasit.* **43**, 25.
—— (1957*b*) *J. Parasit.* **43**, 19.
—— (1957*c*) *J. Parasit.* **43**, 28.
—— and Olivier, L. (1958) *J. Parasit.* **44**, 569.
Hedrick, R. M. (1956) *J. Parasit.* **42**, Suppl. 34.
Herfs, A. (1922) *Arch. Protistenk.* **44**, 227.
Hirsch, G. C. and Bretschneider, L. H. (1937) *Cytologia, Tokyo, Fujii Jub. Vol.* 424.
Hirschmann, H. (1959) *Proc. helm. Soc. Wash.* **26**, 73.
Hobson, A. D. (1948) *Parasitology*, **38**, 183.
——, Stephenson, W. and Eden, A. (1952*a*) *J. exp. Biol.* **29**, 1.
—— (1952*b*) *J. exp. Biol.* **29**, 22.
Hyman, L. H. (1951) "The Invertebrates" Vol. II. McGraw-Hill Book Co., New York.
Jarman, M. (1959) *Nature, Lond.* **184**, 1244.
Jones, C. A. (1955) *J. Parasit.* **41**, Suppl. 48.
Kent, H. N. (1948) *Experientia*, **4**, 1.
—— (1957*a*) *Exp. Parasit.* **6**, 351.

—— (1957*b*) *Exp. Parasit.* **6**, 486.
Kikuchi, G., Ramirez, J. and Guzman Barron, E. S. (1959) *Biochim. biophys Acta,* **36**, 335.
Krebs, H. A. and Henseleit, K. (1932). *Hoppe-Seyl. Z.* **210**, 33.
Krotov, A. I (1953) *Med. Parazit.* Year 1953, 387.
—— (1956*a*) *Med. Parazit.* **25**, 58.
—— (1956*b*) *Med. Parazit.* **25**, 60.
Laser, H. (1944) *Biochem. J.* **38**, 333.
Laurie, J. S. (1957) *Exp. Parasit.* **6**, 245.
—— (1959) *Exp. Parasit.* **8**, 188.
Lazarus, M. (1950) *Aust. J. sci. Res.* **B3**, 245.
Mansour, T. E. (1959*a*) *Biochim. biophys. Acta,* **34**, 456.
—— (1959*b*) *J. Pharmacol.* **126**, 212.
—— and Bueding, E. (1953) *Brit. J. Pharmacol.* **8**, 567.
——, Bueding, E. and Stavitsky, A. B. (1954) *Brit. J. Pharmacol.* **9**, 182.
Massey, V. and Rogers, W. P. (1950) *Aust. J. sci. Res.* **B3**, 251.
—— (1951) *Aust. J. sci. Res.* **B4**, 561.
Mellanby, H. (1955) *Parasitology,* **45**, 287.
Mueller, J. F. (1928) *Z. Zellforsch.* **8**, 361.
Nigon, V. and Bovet, P. (1955) *C. R. Soc. Biol., Paris,* **149**, 129.
Norton, S. and de Beer, E. J. (1957) *Amer. J. trop. Med. Hyg.* **6**, 898.
Osborn, H. L. (1905) *Zool. Jb. Abt.* 2, **21**, 401.
Panijel, J. and Pasteels, J. (1951) *Arch. Biol. Liège,* **62**, 353.
Panikkar, N. K. and Sproston, N. G. (1941) *Parasitology,* **33**, 214.
Pasteels, J. (1948) *Arch. Biol., Liège,* **59**, 405.
Pennoit-DeCooman, E. (1940) *Ann. Soc. zool. Belg.* **71**, 76.
—— and van Grembergen, G. (1942) *Verh. vlaam. Acad. Wet.* **4**, 7.
Pepler, W. J. (1958) *J. Histochem. Cytochem.* **6**, 139.
Phifer, K. (1958) *Exp. Parasit.* **7**, 269.
Picken, L. E., Pryor, M. G. M. and Swann, M. M. (1947) *Nature, Lond.* **159**, 434.
Pollak, J. K. and Fairbairn, D. (1955) *Canad. J. Biochem. Physiol.* **33**, 307.
Rathbone, L. (1955) *Biochem. J.* **61**, 574.
—— and Rees, K. R. (1954) *Biochim. biophys. Acta,* **15**, 126.
Read, C. P. (1949) *J. Parasit.* **35**, Suppl. 26.
—— (1951*a*) *Exp. Parasit.* **1**, 1.
—— (1951*b*) *Proc. Soc. exp. Biol. Med.* **76**, 861.
—— (1952) *Exp. Parasit.* **1**, 353.
—— (1953) *Exp. Parasit.* **2**, 341.
—— (1955) *In* "Some Physiological Aspects and Consequences of Parasitism". (W. H. Cole, ed.), Rutgers University Press, New Brunswick.
—— (1956) *Exp. Parasit.* **5**, 325.
——, Douglas, L. T. and Simmons, J. E. (1959) *Exp. Parasit.* **8**, 58.
Rico, J. T. (1926) *C. R. Soc. Biol., Paris,* **94**, 718.
Rietschel, P. E. (1935) *Zool. Anz.* **111**, 109.
Robbins, B. H. and Lamson, P. D. (1934) *J. biol. Chem.* **106**, 725.
Rogers, W. P. (1944) *Parasitology,* **36**, 98.
—— (1945) *Parasitology,* **36**, 211.
—— (1952) *Aust. J. sci. Res.* **B5**, 210.
—— (1955) *Exp. Parasit.* **4**, 21.
—— and Lazarus, M. (1949*a*) *Parasitology,* **39**, 302.
—— (1949*b*) *Parasitology,* **39**, 245.

Rothman, A. H. (1958) *Exp. Parasit.* **7**, 328.
Savel, J. (1955*a*) *Rev. Path. comp.* **55**, 52.
—— (1955*b*) *Rev. Path. comp.* **55**, 213.
Saz, H. J. and Hubbard, J. A. (1957) *J. biol. Chem.* **225**, 921.
—— and Vidrine, A. (1959) *J. biol. Chem.* **234**, 2001.
——, Vidrine, A. and Hubbard, J. A. (1958) *Exp. Parasit.* **7**, 477.
—— and Weil, A. (1960) *J. biol. Chem.* **235**, 914.
Schopfer, W. H. (1925) *Parasitology*, **17**, 221.
—— (1929) *Rev. suisse Zool.* **36**, 221.
—— (1932) *Rev. suisse Zool.* **39**, 59.
Simmonds, R. A. (1958) *Exp. Parasit.* **7**, 14.
Smith, H. W. (1930) *J. biol. Chem.* **88**, 97.
—— (1936) *Biol. Rev.* **11**, 49.
Smyth, J. D. (1946) *J. exp. Biol.* **23**, 47.
—— (1958) *Nature, Lond.* **181**, 1119.
Stannard, J. N., McCoy, O. R. and Latchford, W. B. (1938) *Amer. J. Hyg.*, **27** 666.
Stephenson, W. (1945) *Nature, Lond.* **155**, 240.
—— (1947*a*) *Parasitology*, **38**, 140.
—— (1947*b*) *Parasitology*, **38**, 116.
Stoner, R. D. and Hankes, L. V. (1955) *Exp. Parasit.* **7**, 99.
—— (1958) *Exp. Parasit.* **7**, 145.
Trim, A. R. (1944) *Parasitology*, **35**, 209.
—— (1949) *Parasitology*, **39**, 281.
Van Cleave, H. J. and Ross, E. (1944) *J. Parasit.* **30**, 369.
van Grembergen, G. (1944) *Enzymologia*, **11**, 268.
—— (1949) *Enzymologia*, **13**, 16.
—— and Pennoit-DeCooman, E. (1944) *Natuurwet. Tijdschr.* **26**, 91.
von Brand, T. (1933) *Z. vergl. Physiol.* **18**, 562.
—— (1934) *Z. vergl. Physiol.* **21**, 220.
—— (1952) "Chemical Physiology of Endoparasitic Animals". Academic Press, New York.
—— and Simpson, W. F. (1942) *Proc. Soc. exp. Biol. Med.* **49**, 245.
—— (1947) *J. Parasit.* **33**, 71.
——, Weinstein, P. P., Mehlman, B. and Weinbach, E. C. (1952) *Exp. Parasit.* **1**, 245.
Ward, H. L. (1952) *J. Parasit.* **38**, 493.
Wardle, R. A. (1934) *Physiol. Zool.* **7**, 36.
—— (1937) *Canad. J. Res.* **D15**, 117.
—— and McLeod, J. A. (1952) "The Zoology of Tapeworms". University of Minnesota Press, Minneapolis.
Weinland, E. and von Brand, T. (1926) *Z. vergl. Physiol.* **4**, 212.

CHAPTER 7

The Oxygen Requirements of Parasites

THERE are several reasons why oxygen is the most efficient final electron acceptor in the processes by which organisms obtain energy. But chiefly it is (a) because more energy can be obtained from the substrate when it is fully oxidized, and (b) because the end-products of metabolism, carbon dioxide and water, have a low toxicity and are usually freely diffusible. In addition, these end-products are of value to most organisms.

Do these considerations apply to internal parasites as they do for free-living organisms?

Clearly, the more efficiently the parasite gets its energy from the substrate it metabolizes, the less the demand it makes on the host. This would be of advantage for many species which survive best in a healthy host. But the inability of a parasite to oxidize completely the energy-yielding substrates may not increase the demand on the host greatly. For instance, a parasite which can metabolize glucose anaerobically only and excretes lactic acid as the end-product obtains 36,000 cal per g mol. of glucose instead of the 686,000 cal from complete oxidation. But the lactic acid is not wasted. The host may use it for the synthesis of glycogen and finally oxidize it to carbon dioxide and water. Some energy is wasted in this process but it is small compared with that lost by the excretion of lactic acid in a free-living organism. It would be highly inefficient if a parasite used only part of the energy in the substrate and then excreted the end-products in a form which could not be oxidized further by the host.

Under some circumstances parasites may be more favourably placed than free-living organisms for getting rid of toxic end-products. This occurs when the host carries out the detoxication. For example, small amounts of amines produced by a parasite could be safely removed by most hosts but, if allowed to accumulate in the environment of the parasite, they could reach toxic concentrations.

Many parasites also have advantages over free-living organisms in the type of substrate they use as a source of energy. Thus those which have access to the glucose distributed from the liver of the vertebrate host can depend almost entirely upon this substrate for their energy needs. On the other hand, the host, in the interests of economy, must use all the available substrates for maintaining its glycogen reserves. The use of glycogenic amino acids for this purpose gives rise to ammonia which is highly toxic to the host and to at least some parasites (von Brand and Simpson, 1947). But ammonia from this source need not be formed in the tissues of the parasite; the task of synthesizing glycogen and detoxicating the ammonia is the function of the host.

These points about the obtaining and use of energy by the parasite should not be over-emphasized. They have been raised not because they are necessarily important in themselves but because they illustrate the complexity of the relationship between the parasite and its host in what may be thought to be a relatively simple matter. The relationship between the parasite and the host is usually so complex that it would be unwise to give too much importance to any single factor which might affect the efficiency of the parasite. This should be kept in mind especially when interpreting the results of experiments on the oxygen requirements of parasites.

The possibility that oxidative processes may be important in parasites because the products so formed are required for some synthetic mechanisms has been put forward by Read (1956) who based his views on those of Clifton (1947) and van Niel (1949). This hypothesis that the products formed during oxidative metabolism may, under some circumstances, be more important than the energy produced, is an attractive one because it could explain some of the anomalies, such as the small Pasteur effect, in the metabolism of parasites. Unfortunately there is as yet little factual evidence, from micro-organisms or metazoan parasites, to support the suggestion. Some of the processes by which basic substances, needed for many syntheses, are formed in micro-organisms without molecular oxygen as a final hydrogen acceptor are discussed by Nisman (1954).

The direct measurement of the oxygen used by parasites *in vivo* is difficult so this problem has usually been examined indirectly by asking the questions:

(1) What is the pressure of oxygen (pO_2) in the environment of the parasite *in vivo*?

(2) Can the parasite respire aerobically in oxygen at this partial pressure?

(3) Can the parasite use the energy obtained from the use of oxygen for work under the conditions in which it lives in the host?

Oxygen in the Environments of Parasites

Information about the amounts of oxygen present in a wide variety of habitats has been collected and discussed by von Brand (1946, pp. 23–38) who has also summarized this information especially in relation to the oxygen available to internal parasites (von Brand, 1938*a*, 1952). Read (1950) has also reviewed information on the oxygen tensions in the small intestine.

In the tissues of vertebrate animals, whenever the blood supply is adequate and the diffusion barrier is not great, it seems that oxygen must be generally available at pressures above 20 mm of mercury. Even in the intestine close to the mucosa the pressure may be greater than this in animals such as rats in which the diameter of the intestine is less than about 0.5 cm (Rogers, 1949*a*; Fig. 29). In the gut, where the ratio

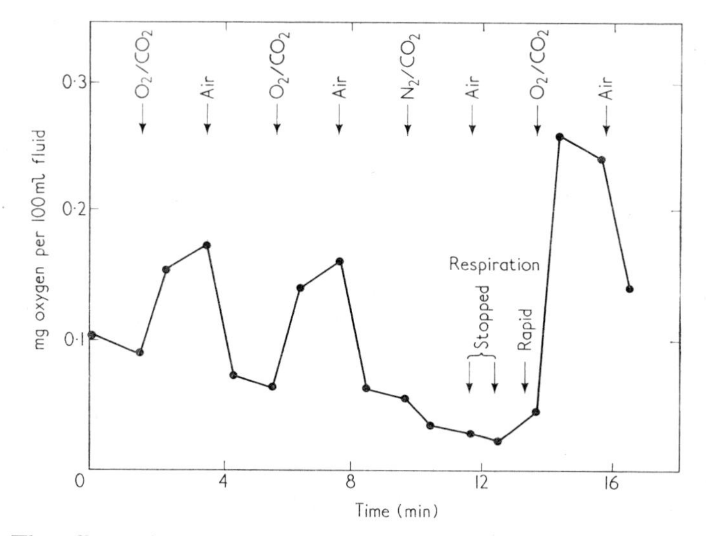

Fig. 29. The effects of the nature of inspired gas mixtures on the oxygen content of the fluid close to the mucosa of the small intestine of the rat (after Rogers, 1949*a*). Measurements were made with an "oxygen electrode" under nembutal anaesthesia.

of the surface area of the mucosa to the volume enclosed is small, pressures of oxygen are much lower. Close to the mucosa of the intestine of sheep, for instance, the pO_2 may be as low as 4 mm (Rogers, 1949*a*).

In vertebrates the lowest oxygen pressures normally occur in the contents of the alimentary canal and perhaps in the bile. Analysis of the bulk intestinal contents has shown that the oxygen tension ranges from 0 to about 0.6 mm of mercury in a variety of large warm-blooded vertebrates (von Brand, 1946, p. 32). In the small intestine of man and the pig much higher pressures have sometimes been measured. This may have been caused by gas which had been swallowed.

The end-products formed by micro-organisms in the gut contents suggest that their metabolism is largely anaerobic. Moreover, the oxidation-reduction potential of the gut contents suggests a low pO_2. It is generally accepted, therefore, that though the material in the lumen of the gut of warm-blooded vertebrates may not be entirely anaerobic, the pO_2 must be very low. It seems that similar conditions may prevail in poikilothermic vertebrates where the lower venous pressure would be partly compensated by the lower oxygen uptake of the tissues.

Generally speaking, then, most regions of warm-blooded vertebrates outside the alimentary canal receive adequate supplies of oxygen. However, in some cold-blooded vertebrates, which lack an effective oxygen-transporting system (Ruud, 1954) or which live temporarily in environments low in oxygen, such as mud or stagnant water, there must be regions where the pO_2 is very low.

Under certain circumstances the tissues of vertebrates which are normally well supplied with oxygen become deficient in oxygen. The growth of fibrous tissue, necrosis, and other pathological changes which lead to a decreased supply of blood cause a fall in the pO_2. The reaction of the host in surrounding a parasite with a fibrous cyst-wall may reduce the oxygen available to a parasite.

The oxygen tensions in the tissues of the many invertebrate animals are probably lower than in vertebrates. But it is impossible to generalize about the amounts of oxygen which would be available to parasites in the tissues of invertebrates. Compare for instance two molluscs, *Loligo*, with its efficient ventilation and circulatory systems, and *Mytilus*, which, with its shell closed, must become anaerobic.

Oxygen tensions in the tissues of plants have not been measured extensively (Goddard and Meeuse, 1950). Scott (1949) showed that the low respiration of sections of plant organs was not due to a failure in the diffusion of oxygen. He found, however, that the oxygen pressure in beetroot fell to 13.6% at 1 cm. It appears, then, that appreciable amounts of oxygen would be available to parasites in the more superficial regions of plants if the oxygen tension of the environment was normal (von Brand, 1946, p. 37).

The Oxygen Requirements of Nematode Parasites

The Consumption of Oxygen

The capacity of nematode parasites to use oxygen has been reviewed by a number of writers (Hobson, 1948; Mendes, 1949; Bueding, 1949*a*; von Brand, 1952, p. 150; Bueding and Most, 1953) and it is clear that all the metazoan parasites which have been examined so far respire aerobically when oxygen is present at partial pressures above 160 mm of mercury. Moreover, oxygen at these pressures is not toxic. These organisms, then, are not obligate anaerobes.

The QO_2 values (μl of oxygen per mg dry wt. per hr) for endogenous respiration of different species of nematode parasites vary greatly—from about 0.3 for large *Ascaris lumbricoides* to 12.6 for the small *Neoaplectana glaseri* (von Brand, 1952, p. 150). When the oxygen uptake is calculated on a surface area basis results are consistent for specimens of different sizes of a given species (Krüger, 1940) and indeed the differences between species are often reduced with this method of calculation (Rogers, 1948; Lazarus, 1950). It is clear, however, that even on this basis differences in respiratory rates are so great for many species (von Brand, 1942) that factors other than purely passive penetration of oxygen in the tissues of the parasites are needed as an explanation. These are obvious enough; the actual metabolic routes involving oxygen differ somewhat in different species, and some parasites have oxygen-transporting pigments. And probably there are differences in the way oxygen enters and is distributed to the tissues of different species.

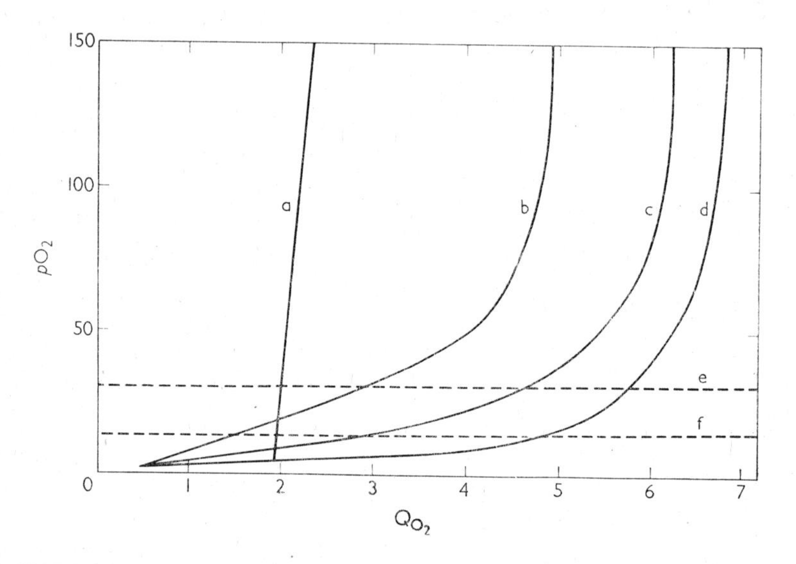

FIG. 30. The relation between oxygen pressure in the environment and the oxygen uptake of larvae (μl per mg dry wt. per hr) of (a) larvae of *Trichinella spiralis* (after Stannard *et al.*, 1938) and adult (b) *Haemonchus contortus*, (c) *Nematodirus* spp. and (d) *Nippostrongylus muris* (after Rogers, 1949*b*). The broken lines (e) and (f) represent the oxygen pressure close to the mucosa of the small intestine of the rat and the sheep (after Rogers, 1949*a*).

Though the respiration of a number of species of nematodes has been measured at the partial pressure of atmospheric oxygen, measurements have seldom been made at other tensions. In many adult and larval forms that have been examined (Fig. 30) the consumption of oxygen of the parasite varies with the oxygen tension, e.g. in adult *Ascaris lumbricoides* (Krüger, 1937), *Haemonchus contortus, Nematodirus* spp., *Nippostrongylus muris* (Rogers, 1949*b*), *Heterakis gallinae* (Glocklin and Fairbairn, 1952), and in larval *Eustrongylides ignotus* (von Brand, 1947). On the other hand there are some species of nematodes, relatively few in number, in which respiration is not affected by changes in the pressure of the oxygen (e.g. see Stannard *et al.*, 1938; Fig. 30). It is not clear what these differences in oxygen consumption in relation to oxygen pressure really mean. As Bueding (1949*a*) has pointed out, Harnish's argument that organisms in which the QO_2 is proportional to the pO_2 have a predominantly anaerobic type of metabolism under natural conditions does not meet all the facts.

With the information about the pressures of oxygen in the environment of the parasite and the relationship between pO_2 and QO_2 *in vitro* it is possible to make some estimates of the rate of oxygen consumption of parasites *in vivo*. This cannot be taken as an exact guide, of course; there are many factors, pCO_2, ionic concentrations, pH, etc. which might affect the QO_2 and which cannot yet be duplicated exactly *in vitro*. Nevertheless it seems reasonable to accept estimates based on this sort of knowledge as at least indicating whether a parasite may respire actively or slowly *in vivo*. For example, the larvae of *Trichinella spiralis* which can still respire at a maximum rate *in vitro* when the oxygen pressure is 7 to 8 mm of mercury (Stannard *et al.*, 1938) must be able to respire actively *in vivo* except when the muscle in which they live is working violently. With the adult parasites examined by Rogers (1949*a*, 1949*b*), however, the position is not so clear. *Nippostrongylus muris*, a parasite in the small intestine of the rat where the pO_2 close to the mucosa varied from 7.9 to 30.2 mm of mercury, could probably approach its maximum rate of respiration *in vivo* if it was not moving actively. With *Nematodirus* spp. from the small intestine of the sheep and *Haemonchus contortus* from the abomasum it appears that the rate of respiration *in vivo* might be about one-half to one-quarter of the rate at which oxygen was freely available.

Can any generalizations be made from these results? It seems reasonable to suppose that nematodes similar in size and metabolism to *Nippostrongylus muris* and to *Nematodirus spathiger* could respire actively in tissues of the host outside the alimentary canal except perhaps in regions of relatively low oxygen tensions such as in the bile duct or the pelvis or the kidney. Within the alimentary canal, away from the mucosa, aerobic respiration would be expected to be small, probably accounting for less than 10% of the energy requirements of the parasite. Close to the mucosa it would be appreciable but respiration might be below the maximum rate except in small animals like rats where the ratio of the surface area of the intestinal mucosa to the volume enclosed in the intestine was large. Under such conditions the maximum rate of respiration might sometimes be achieved.

With large parasites like *Ascaris lumbricoides* or even like *Ascaridia galli* which live in the fluid contents of the small intestine away from the mucosa, aerobic respiration would probably be low and could account for only a small part of the energy required by the parasite. The presence of cytoplasmic granules with the appearance of mitochondria in the muscle and in the rachis of the ovary of *Ascaris lumbricoides* (Kmetec *et al.*, pers. comm.; Prestage, 1960) is therefore surprising.

Much of this discussion has been speculative. Can these conclusions be supported or contradicted by other information? The other features which might be considered are: the occurrence of an "oxygen debt", the persistence of fermentative metabolism under aerobic conditions, the toxicity of oxygen, the penetration and transport of oxygen in the tissues of different species, the ability to obtain useful energy from aerobic mechanisms, and survival under anaerobic conditions.

The Oxygen Debt

The temporarily increased oxygen consumption of many animals which have been exposed to anaerobic conditions is often called an "oxygen debt". The origin and significance of this phenomenon has been discussed generally by Mendes (1949) and Prosser (1950, pp. 308, 309) and in detail by von Brand (1946, 1952, pp. 171, 172). Zimmerman and Berry (1949) have given a theoretical consideration of this matter, which, however, has been questioned by Goddard and Meeuse (1950).

Some explanation of the processes involved in the development and repayment of an oxygen debt can be attempted though experimental evidence is still meagre.

It is generally suggested that, when oxygen is not available, incompletely oxidized products of metabolism such as pyruvic acid or lactic acid are formed and may be excreted or accumulated to varying degrees in the tissues. When oxygen becomes available the increased concentrations of intermediates lead to a more rapid use of oxygen for a period until the substrates reach normal concentrations again. Though some points can be questioned in this reasoning, on the whole it seems an acceptable hypothesis; but difficulties arise when the significance of an oxygen debt is considered.

May a tissue which develops an oxygen debt under anaerobic conditions justifiably be regarded as a tissue which is normally aerobic? Or, in another way, is the failure to accumulate the products of fermentation characteristic of a tissue which is normally anaerobic? These questions have been considered by von Brand (1946) who concluded that it was questionable whether *all* products of anaerobic metabolism are excreted in any invertebrate capable of consuming oxygen. The development of an oxygen debt, therefore, suggests that an animal is at least partly aerobic. The capacity of animals to accumulate the end-products of anaerobic metabolism varies almost over a complete range (Bishop, 1950, p. 274; von Brand, 1946) and it is clear that the significance of the oxygen debt can only be interpreted in general terms.

But even this is doubtful when some nematode parasites are considered. Thus *Litomosoides carinii* does not develop an oxygen debt and the carbohydrate consumed anaerobically is almost equivalent to the acetic acid excreted in the medium (Bueding, 1949*b*). This small parasite, which lives in the pleural cavity of the cotton rat where oxygen pressures are probably high (they range from 12 to 39 mm of mercury in the monkey, man and dog), is certainly dependent upon aerobic metabolism for survival (Bueding, 1949*a*).

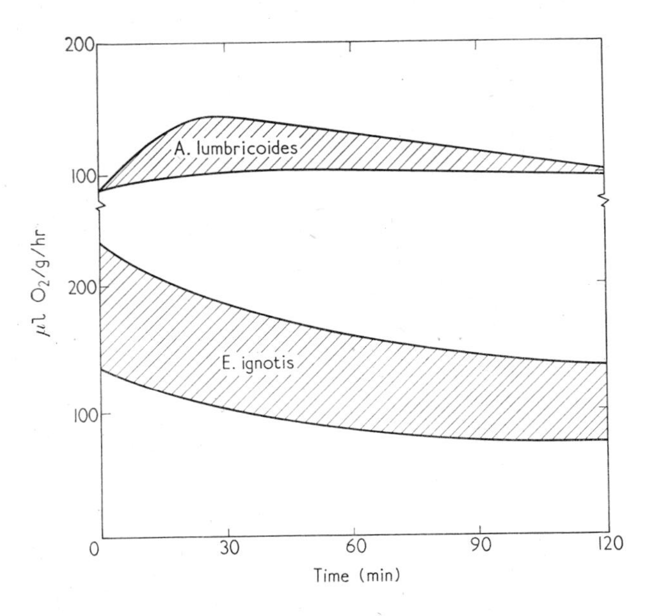

FIG. 31. The "oxygen debt" in *Ascaris lumbricoides* and larvae of *Eustrongylides ignotus* (after Laser, 1944; von Brand, 1942). The upper curve for each species was obtained from the parasites which had been kept under anaerobic conditions for 17 to 20 hr. The lower curves show the respiration of parasites which had been kept for a similar time under aerobic conditions.

The results obtained with the larvae of *Eustrongylides ignotus* and adult *Ascaris lumbricoides* are more in harmony with the general hypothesis. Von Brand (1942) found that the larvae of *Eustrongylides ignotus*, after prolonged anaerobiosis, showed a marked increase in oxygen consumption which accounted for 30% of the oxygen debt they had incurred (Fig. 31). These parasites, from the mesenteries of the fish *Fundulus*, survive at relatively low oxygen pressures in a nutrient medium, but they die quickly in the absence of oxygen (von Brand and Simpson, 1945). With *Ascaris lumbricoides* the uptake of oxygen is increased by 60 to 100% after 17 to 20 hours under anaerobic conditions (Laser, 1944). The increased respiration lasts for less than 2 hours at this level, however, and the oxygen debt is evidently small (Fig. 31). These results are in line with the frequently accepted view that this parasite may have a small aerobic respiration *in vivo*.

The Persistence of Fermentation under Aerobic Conditions

Under certain circumstances a comparison of the amount of food reserves used up in the presence and absence of oxygen may give an overall indication of the relative importance of aerobic and anaerobic metabolism of an animal. Ideally the total amount of substrate used when the animal is doing the same amount of work with and without oxygen would be most informative. Unfortunately it is seldom possible to get this information. For instance, the muscular movement of many parasites stops when oxygen is not available, so results must be interpreted with caution.

The consumption of glycogen has been measured under aerobic and anaerobic conditions in a number of parasites and some of these results are summarized in Table VII. The experiments with the different species which have been listed were carried out under slightly different conditions and the authors have not all used the same basis for calculating change in glycogen content. The results from some species, therefore, are not strictly comparable, though the general implications are quite clear.

Among the nematodes listed in Table VII *Eustrongylides ignotus* is the only one which shows an appreciable Pasteur effect (Dixon, 1937) as judged by the consumption of glycogen. In the others, oxygen does not lead to the conservation of carbohydrate to any appreciable degree. Evidently fermentation persists in the presence of oxygen in most nematode parasites. With a knowledge of the amounts of oxygen consumed by the parasites the amounts of glucose which would be completely oxidized can be calculated. For *Eustrongylides ignotus* the oxygen taken up (von Brand, 1942) accounts for most of the substrate used; with *Ascaris lumbricoides* only a small part of the glycogen is completely oxi-

TABLE VII

The Consumption of Glycogen by Nematode Parasites under Aerobic and Anaerobic Conditions

The results are given as g glycogen used per 100 g wet tissue per 24 hr at 37° to 41°C

Species	Anaerobic	Aerobic	Ratio	Experimental conditions	References
Trichinella spiralis (larvae)	1.4	1.4	1:1	axenic; non-nutritive balanced saline; 23 hours	von Brand *et al.* (1952)
Eustrongylides ignotus (larvae)	0.7	0.2	1:0.3	axenic; non-nutritive balanced saline; mean for 6-day experiment	von Brand and Simpson (1945)
Eustrongylides ignotus (larvae)	0.7	0.5	1:0.7	axenic; balanced saline with 0.2% glucose; mean for 6-day experiment	von Brand and Simpson (1945)
Ascaris lumbricoides (adult females)	1.4	1.2	1:0.9	non-nutritive saline; 24 hours	von Brand (1934)
Parascaris equorum (adults)	1.4	1.6	1:1.1	non-nutritive saline; 24 hours	Toryu (1936)
Heterakis gallinae (adults)	3.7	3.2	1:0.9	non-nutritive Ringer-phosphate; 21 hours	Glocklin and Fairbairn (1952)
Dracunculus insignis (adults)	58	55	1:1	axenic; balanced saline with glucose	Bueding and Oliver-Gonzalez (1950)
Litomosoides carinii (adults)	34–41	42–45	1:1.1	in nutritive sugar-containing media	Bueding (reported by von Brand, 1952, p. 105)

dized. *Heterakis gallinae* falls somewhere between these extremes. In this species about 35% of glucose used over a period of 4 hours was completely oxidized (Glocklin and Fairbairn, 1952).

Studies on the end-products of metabolism excreted into the medium by worms under aerobic and anaerobic conditions generally support these results. Thus the larvae of *Eustrongylides ignotus* produce appreciable amounts of organic acids when oxygen is lacking; no acidic products are formed by aerobic respiration (von Brand, 1938*b*). *Ascaris lumbricoides* produces a mixture of volatile fatty acids containing acetic, propionic, *n*-valeric, α-methylbutyric, *cis* α-methylcrotonic acids (Epps *et al.*, 1950; Bueding and Yale, 1951; Bueding, 1953); von Brand's earlier (1934) experiments with this species suggested that the total production of acid might be doubled under anaerobic conditions. These experiments, like those of Toryu (1935, 1936), who showed that acid production of *Parascaris equorum* was not greatly different in the presence or absence of oxygen, were not carried out with axenic worms. *Heterakis gallinae* produces acidic end-products, which include acetic, propionic, lactic and pyruvic acids, in considerable amounts both under aerobic and anaerobic conditions (Glocklin and Fairbairn, 1952). Little or no evidence for a Pasteur effect was obtained.

Bueding (1949*b*) and Bueding and Oliver-Gonzalez (1950) examined the production of end-products of carbohydrate metabolism of *Litomosoides carinii* and *Dracunculus insignis*. The consumption of total sugar, exogenous from the medium, and endogenous from reserve polysaccharide, by both these parasites was not greatly affected by the presence or absence of oxygen (von Brand, 1952, p. 105). Lactic acid formed a large proportion of the end-products of fermentation of *Dracunculus insignis* and the amount excreted was not much influenced by the presence of oxygen. With *Litomosoides carinii* the process was more complex. Under anaerobic conditions insufficient glucose was taken up from the medium to maintain the polysaccharide reserves. Of the total endogenous and exogenous carbohydrate used, 80% appeared in the medium as lactic acid, and 20% as acetic acid. Under aerobic conditions 10 to 20% of the glucose taken up from the medium was converted to polysaccharide reserve material. Of the rest, 30 to 45% appeared as lactic acid, and 25 to 30% appeared as acetic acid. Considerable amounts of acetylmethylcarbinol were also excreted, but this was not an end-product. When the concentration of acetoin in the medium was about 4 mM, 20 mM was used per g wet weight of filariae per hour when oxygen was present; under anaerobic conditions it was used at about one-third this rate (Berl and Bueding, 1951). Thus the changes which take place in the metabolism of *Litomosoides carinii* when oxygen is removed from the medium are far-reaching and, in fact, oxidative metabolism is essential for the survival of this parasite (Bueding, 1949*b*).

The end-products of fermentative and respiratory metabolism of larvae of *Trichinella spiralis* have been examined by von Brand *et al.* (1952). In this parasite the extent and nature of carbohydrate fermentation was hardly affected by the presence or absence of oxygen. Volatile fatty acids of a similar nature were produced under both conditions, though in somewhat different proportions. Thus, *n*-valeric acid formed about 85% of the total acid which was formed as the result of the fermentative processes; when oxygen was present *n*-valeric acid formed 48%. In addition to *n*-valeric acid, C_6 and C_2 acids were certainly present, and C_4 and C_3 acids were probably present. Lactic acid was found in traces only.

The importance of fat as a substrate for respiration in nematodes has not been extensively examined, though von Brand (1934) showed that loss of lipid in *Ascaris lumbricoides* maintained *in vitro* could be accounted for in the eggs expelled in the medium. In the larvae of *Trichinella spiralis*, however, it appears that lipid is the major substrate used for aerobic respiration (von Brand *et al.*, 1952). Under anaerobic conditions the fat content of the larvae did not change. In air the total lipid in the larvae was decreased by about 20% in 24 hours, or about 0.4 mg per 100,000 larvae in 24 hours. On the assumption that the lipids in *Trichinella spiralis* have the same composition as "average fat" von Brand *et al.* (1952) calculated that the oxygen consumed by the larvae was sufficient to oxidize completely about 64% of this substrate.

The Toxicity of Oxygen

High partial pressures of oxygen are toxic to some nematodes both *in vitro* and *in vivo*. Thus Laser (1944) found that *Ascaris lumbricoides* died in about an hour in an atmosphere of oxygen. This was due to the accumulation of hydrogen peroxide in the tissues of the parasite which contain very little catalase. Although appreciable amounts of catalase are present in *Heterakis gallinae* high partial pressures of oxygen are toxic (Glocklin and Fairbairn, 1952). There is some evidence also that oxygen at high partial pressures is toxic *in vivo* to *Ascaris lumbricoides* and *Trichuris* in man (Vora, 1955; Mishchenko, 1956*a*; Berkhina, 1955).

Oxygen at partial pressures up to at least 160 mm of mercury is not toxic to nematodes; in fact at these pressures it frequently aids their survival *in vitro*.

Survival under Anaerobic Conditions in vitro

Although a large number of experiments have been carried out to examine the effect of lowered pO_2 on the survival of nematodes, few results which allow unequivocal interpretation have been obtained.

The difficulties of lowering the oxygen tension in the environments of nematodes *in vivo* without causing other changes which would have adverse effects on the nematodes is obvious. And there are so many unknown factors which limit the survival of nematodes *in vitro* that it is sometimes uncertain whether the effects of lowering the oxygen tension have arisen directly or indirectly.

It is possible, for instance, that changes in the oxygen tension could affect parasites *in vitro* by affecting the nature and degree of bacterial contamination. Early work on the survival of nematodes was carried out under non-sterile conditions, though efforts were made to limit bacterial growth as much as possible. Davey (1938*a*, 1938*b*) attempted to overcome this problem by allowing the medium to flow slowly over the worms. Moreover, he used a non-nutrient medium in which bacterial growth was largely dependent upon the excretory products of the nematodes as a source of nitrogen and carbon.

Davey studied a number of short, slender parasites from the small intestine of the sheep (Table VIII). In Ringer's solution exposed to air the parasites survived for 4 to 12 days; in the absence of oxygen this period was reduced to less than 48 hours. The experiments showed that these parasites can use their food reserves more effectively for prolonging life in the presence of oxygen. It does not necessarily follow that oxygen is essential for the parasites *in vivo*.

The survival of *Ascaris lumbricoides in vitro* in non-nutrient media is not greatly affected by the presence or absence of oxygen. However, if the animals are kept in continuous activity by repeated electrical stimulation the time of survival is considerably reduced and they die in about 48 hours, whereas control animals in a solution saturated with oxygen at atmospheric pressure remain alive much longer (Slater, 1925).

These results may be interpreted in different ways. For example, it is probable that the continued activity of the parasites may have taxed their capacity to eliminate the products of metabolism from their tissues. Then, if the accumulation of excretory substances became a critical factor in the life of the parasites, the increased production of acids which probably occurs under anaerobic conditions (von Brand, 1934, and Krüger, 1936, 1937, found that there was a definite increase but bacteria were present in their cultures) would shorten the period of survival. There is no reason to believe, moreover, that the parasites are highly active *in vivo* (Makidono, 1956) so that these results cannot be taken to indicate a necessity for aerobic metabolism under such conditions.

Alternatively Slater's results could simply indicate that the food reserves of the parasites were used up more rapidly under anaerobic

TABLE VIII

The Survival of some Parasitic Nematodes under Aerobic and Anaerobic Conditions in vitro *at 37° to 38°C*

Species	Survival time in days Anaerobic	Aerobic	Composition of the medium	References
Eustrongylides ignotus (larvae)	3	19	salt solution	von Brand (1938*b*)
Eustrongylides ignotus (larvae)	18	96	Brewer's thioglycollate medium; axenic	von Brand and Simpson (1945)
Ascaris lumbricoides	9	6	salt solution	Weinland (1901)
Parascaris equorum	5	2	salt solution	Toryu (1935)
Litomosoides carinii	1	7	ox serum; axenic	Ross and Bueding (1950)
Trichostrongylus vitrinus	1	4 – 12	Ringer's solution	Davey (1938*b*)
Ostertagia circumcincta	1	4 – 12	Ringer's solution	Davey (1938*b*)
Cooperia oncophora	1	4 – 12	Ringer's solution	Davey (1938*b*)
Nematodirus filicollis	1	4 – 12	Ringer's solution	Davey (1938*b*)

conditions. Indeed, von Brand (1934) has shown that the use of glycogen by *Ascaris lumbricoides* in non-nutrient media is increased by about 15% when oxygen is not present. This margin of difference might be increased in the actively moving animals of Slater's experiments. Again, it does not follow from this explanation of the results that oxygen is necessary for the survival of *Ascaris in vivo*.

The experiments of von Brand and Simpson (1945) with larval *Eustrongylides ignotus* gave more positive conclusions. In the nutrient media under axenic conditions these parasites remained alive at 37°C for an average period of 98 days; without oxygen the period was reduced to 18 days. However, relatively little oxygen was needed for survival; on a number of occasions larvae were still alive when the pO_2 was less than 8 mm of mercury. There is little doubt, then, that this parasite is an obligate aerobe in its larval stage; but low pressures of oxygen are sufficient.

The results obtained with *Litomosoides carinii* (Ross and Bueding, 1950), though not as unequivocal as with *Eustrongylides ignotus*, clearly indicated that this parasite requires oxygen for its survival *in vivo*. Though no attempts have been made to examine the effects of oxygen on the survival of the larvae of *Trichinella spiralis in vitro*, von Brand *et al.* (1952) showed that anaerobic metabolism, which seemed to be confined largely to substrates of carbohydrate, apparently did not provide energy for the movement of the larvae. When oxygen was present, however, lipids were used and movement of the larvae became possible.

As discussed earlier, high oxygen tensions have a toxic action on some nematodes and Toryu (1935) claimed that even moderate amounts of oxygen reduced the survival of *Parascaris equorum* in non-nutrient media. Under most circumstances, however, it appears that oxygen has a beneficial effect on nematodes *in vitro*. With *Ascaris lumbricoides* this beneficial effect has been clearly demonstrated only under extreme unphysiological conditions and a general statement that oxygen is necessary for *all* nematode parasites *in vivo* is unwarranted.

The Ability of Nematode Parasites to use Aerobic Mechanisms

All nematodes can respire in oxygen, but does this respiration give rise to energy which is useful in the economy of the parasites *in vivo*? The answer to this question is certainly *yes* with parasites like *Eustrongylides ignotus* and *Litomosoides carinii* which not only show a marked Pasteur effect but which also require oxygen for survival *in vitro*. With *Ascaris lumbricoides* the earlier work suggested that oxidative metabolism might be concerned largely with muscular activity. Von Brand (1937) showed that a re-synthesis of glycogen occurred in worms when oxygen was made available after 20 hours' anaerobiosis, and oxidative phosphorylation has been demonstrated in particulate fractions from the muscle (Chin and Bueding, 1954).

For larvae of *Trichinella spiralis* the energy from oxidative metabolism is necessary for motility (von Brand *et al.*, 1952) and perhaps can be used for this function only. There is some evidence, for instance, that oxidative processes, which use lipids as substrates, are to some degree independent of anaerobic processes, and do not lead to the conservation of carbohydrate. It seems possible, therefore, that the oxidation of fats may be necessary for the migration of the larvae *in vivo*, but when they lie quiescent in the muscular tissue of the host the anaerobic catabolism of carbohydrates probably provides sufficient energy for survival.

The Transport of Oxygen in Nematode Parasites

The Diffusion of Oxygen

There are no specialized respiratory surfaces in nematodes. If oxygen is used it must enter through the general body surface, and in some species such as *Ancylostoma caninum*, perhaps through the wall of the intestine also.

The adequacy of simple diffusion to supply oxygen to the central region of respiring cells and tissues has been discussed by Fenn (1927), Hill (1929), and Gerard (1931). The formula which gives the relationship between external and internal oxygen pressures in a cylindrical piece of tissue is

$$y = y_0 - a(r_0^2 - r^2)4k$$

where a is the oxygen uptake in ml per hour per g wet weight, y is the concentration of oxygen in atmospheres at a distance r from the centre of the cylinder, y_0 is the concentration at the surface, r_0 is the radius of the cylinder and k is the diffusion constant in ml of oxygen per cm^2 per hour under a diffusion gradient of 1 atmosphere. If k is taken as that given by Krogh (1919), 8.4×10^{-4}, for the diffusion of oxygen in muscle, and if y and r are taken as 0, y_0 gives the pressure of oxygen on the surface which is just large enough to allow oxygen to diffuse to the centre.

The value of y_0 has been calculated for a number of nematode parasites (Table IX). It should be emphasized, however, that these figures can give only a rough indication of the pressures needed for the supply of oxygen by diffusion. The factors which make this calculation unreliable are: (a) in diffusing from the outer surface of a nematode to the inner tissues oxygen must pass through several different tissues for which the values of k are unknown; (b) nematodes do not have a true cylindrical shape, and (c) (a) is taken as though it is not influenced by changes in pO_2. Because the Q_{O_2} of most nematodes falls as the pO_2 is reduced it is probable that the figures for the pO_2 required on the

TABLE IX

The Relationship between the Radius of the Parasite, its Oxygen Uptake, and the pO_2 *at the Surface which is just Sufficient to Allow the Penetration of Oxygen to Central Tissues by Diffusion Alone*

Species	Radius of parasite (mm)	Oxygen uptake (μl/hr/g wet wt.)	pO_2 at surface (giving $pO_2 = 0$ at the centre, mm Hg)	Probable pO_2 of the environment (mm Hg)
Nippostrongylus muris	0.05	1450	10	8 – 30
Nematodirus filicollis	0.08	1050	15	4 – 13
Haemonchus contortus	0.15	900	40	4 – 13
Litomosoides carinii	0.20	800	70	12 – 39
Ascaridia galli	0.55	525	>760	very low
Ascaris lumbricoides	2.25	60	>760	very low

surface given in Table IX are too high. For these reasons the values given in the table are approximations only.

In spite of these limitations, however, the information in Table IX is of some value. Thus it is clear that *Nippostrongylus muris* could have an active aerobic metabolism even without an efficient oxygen-transporting system. For *Nematodirus filicollis* and *Haemonchus contortus* some sort of mechanism for transporting oxygen to central tissues would be needed. And even if oxygen was available in appreciable amounts in the environment of *Ascaridia galli* and *Ascaris lumbricoides* an efficient circulatory system would be essential for oxygen to reach the central tissues.

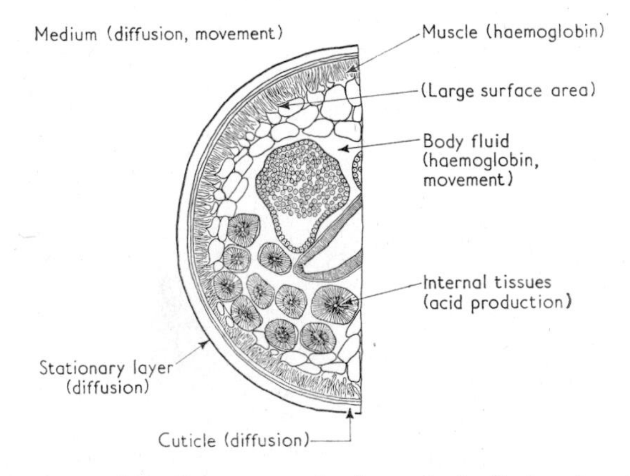

FIG. 32. Transverse section of a nematode (hypothetical) showing features which might influence oxygen transport thus: in the medium, gross movement and diffusion; in the stationary layer and cuticle, diffusion; in hypodermis and muscle, diffusion and haemoglobin; in body fluid in contact with the muscle over a large surface area, movement, diffusion and haemoglobin. Acid production by internal tissues might influence oxygen transport via the Bohr effect.

Figure 32 shows diagrammatically part of a cross-section of a nematode. In it are shown the features which would influence the penetration of oxygen into the animal and its transport to the central tissues.

The thickness of the cuticle, its relative surface area, and the thickness of the "stationary layer" of medium close to the cuticle are the first features which would affect the entry of oxygen into a nematode. In structure the cuticle is complex and it has 9 layers in *Ascaris lumbricoides* (Bird and Deutsch, 1957). The thickness varies greatly in different species—from 10μ in *Oxyuris equi*, to 80μ in *Ascaris lumbricoides* and 100μ in *Strongylus equinus* (Bird, 1958). The evidence at present available indicates that the cuticle is freely permeable to oxygen, even when it is present in a relatively thick layer as in *Ascaris lumbricoides*. The surface area of the cuticle in relation to the total volume is small in large nematodes.

A thick "stationary layer" on the respiratory surface may severely reduce the entry of oxygen into an organism (Carter, 1931). In the small and large intestines of the host where parasites are often coated with mucus this factor may limit respiration. In less viscid media even slight movements of the parasites or organs of the host would serve to reduce the thickness of the stationary layer. In the absence of results from critical experiments, however, detailed discussion of these matters is not warranted. And, though experiments carried out *in vitro* suggest that oxygen in the environment freely enters the parasites, it seems that studies on respiratory exchange on the surface of the worms under conditions similar to those that prevail *in vivo*, especially in relation to the "stationary layer", are needed.

After penetrating the cuticle of nematodes, oxygen must pass through the hypodermis and somatic musculature to reach the internal organs. Except in the dorsal and lateral lines, where the cell bodies are located, the hypodermis is thin. And there is only one layer of spindle-shaped muscle cells which present a large surface area to the fluid in the pseudocoel. These conditions would generally make for an efficient transport of oxygen to the interior of the parasites. Moreover haemoglobins of loading tension (T_L, the pO_2 of 95 % saturation) somewhat lower than that of the pO_2 of the environment are often found in the somatic muscles and possibly in the hypodermis (see Table X).

The Circulation of the Body Fluid

Nematodes have no specialized circulatory system but if the organization of the body did allow some movement of the internal fluid and organs this would greatly aid the transport of oxygen. The fluid in the pseudocoel which makes contact with the tissue of the body wall over a large area has lying in it the alimentary canal and the reproductive system. Into this fluid protrude the "sarcoplasmic" bulbs of the muscle cells and it is traversed by the delicate mesenteries and "innervation processes". There are, however, no anatomical barriers which would prevent movement of the fluid between the body wall and the internal organs. If this movement did take place oxygen transport would be greatly facilitated, especially if the oxygen capacity of the fluid was increased by the presence of a respiratory pigment with the proper physical characteristics.

Harris and Crofton (1957) have studied the function of the cuticle and the fluid of the pseudocoel of *Ascaris lumbricoides* in relation to the general structural organization of these animals. They found that the hydrostatic pressure of the fluid showed wide and often rhythmical variations from 16 mm to as high as 225 mm of mercury. These changes were largely the outcome of contractions of the longitudinal somatic muscles which acted against forces exerted by the internal pressures on the cuticle rather than against antagonistic muscles. Contraction of muscles in a particular region brought about local shortenings in length which were reflected by similar extensions in other parts. All these processes would involve displacement of the fluids in the pseudocoelomic space. Though *Ascaris lumbricoides* cannot be regarded as a typical nematode, Harris and Crofton (1957) pointed out that the physical and mechanical forces which determine its structure would be a common feature of all nematodes and this would account for the uniform structure of the group. It follows then that the movements in the body fluid which are an outcome of this organization would occur throughout the phylum. The bending movements of nematodes which displace the internal organs relative to one another, and the pumping action of the pharynx, especially in small nematodes, would also serve to move the fluid over the surface of the tissues of the body wall and around the internal organs.

The circulation of fluid in the body cavity would improve oxygen transport considerably even if the oxygen capacity of the fluid was that of the primitive circulatory fluid, sea-water. But in many nematodes haemoglobin is present; in some species such as *Ascaris lumbricoides, Strongylus* spp., *Nippostrongylus muris* and *Eustrongylides ignotus* (Keilin, 1925; von Brand, 1938*b*; Davenport, 1949*a*, 1949*b*) the presence of the pigment in the body fluid has been established. But in most nematodes the distribution of the pigment has not been examined and it is uncertain whether the pigment occurs in the body wall, the internal fluid, or in both these regions.

If the pigment was present in the internal fluid, what properties should it have in order to function effectively as an oxygen carrier? Clearly the T_L should be lower than that of the pigment of the body wall. This may not necessitate a pigment which is different from that of the body wall; a small difference in the hydrogen ion concentration in the fluid and body wall might be sufficient to lower the T_L in the fluid. In fact a pigment with a strong Bohr effect such that an increase in the hydrogen ion concentration would decrease the affinity of the pigment for oxygen, so raising the unloading tension (T_U, the pO_2 of half-saturation), would be most effective as an oxygen carrier.

This is because the excretion of acid is likely to be greater on the surface of the internal organs than on the internal surface of the body wall. There are several reasons for this: (1) the tissues of the body wall would have first access to the supply of oxygen so that the acid

TABLE X

The Properties of Oxyhaemoglobins prepared from Nematode Parasites

Species	α–band (mμ)	β–band (mμ)	Pressure of half-saturation (mm Hg)	References
Ascaris lumbricoides (body wall)	599.8	542.5	very low; probably < 0.01	Keilin (1925); Davenport (1949*a*)
Ascaris lumbricoides (body fluid)	578.4	541.5	very low; probably $\ll 0.01$	Keilin (1945); Davenport (1949*a*)
Strongylus spp. (body fluid)	578.1	540.0	very low; probably $\ll 0.01$	Davenport (1949*b*)
Nippostrongylus muris	577.7	540.5	0.1 – 0.2	Davenport (1949*b*); Rogers (1949*c*)
Nematodirus spathiger and *N. filicollis*	576	542	0.05	Davey (1938*b*); Rogers (1949*c*)
Haemonchus contortus	576	541	0.05	Rogers (1949*c*)
Heterakis gallinae	578.3	542.0	—	van Grembergen (1954)
Camallanus trispinosus	575 (about)	540 (about)	7	Wharton (1941)
Trichinella spiralis	580–590	540–550	7.6	Stannard *et al.* (1938)

production, which is lower in aerobic metabolism, would be less than in the internal organs; (2) acidic end-products from the hypodermis and somatic musculature would be excreted, at least partly, to the exterior through the cuticle, whereas end-products from the internal organs must be excreted into the pseudocoel; (3) the reproductive organs in adult parasites use large amounts of energy for the synthesis of eggs and sperm and consequently the acidic products of catabolism are likely to be greater than those produced by the muscle in the body wall which does not seem to be very active *in vivo*.

The Properties of Haemoglobins in Nematodes

Haemoglobin is found in a number of nematodes e.g. *Dioctophyme*, *Toxocara*, *Spirocera*, *Tetrameres*, *Eustrongylides*, (Janicki, 1939; Davey, 1938*b*; Hsü, 1938; Ribeiro and Villela, 1956; Villela and Ribeiro, 1955; von Brand, 1937) and species listed in Table X. Except in one or two species (the pigment in *Parascaris equorum* is said to be "definitely identical with that in the horse"; Hurlaux, quoted by Hyman, 1951, p. 425) the haemoglobins of nematodes differ from those of the host both in their spectroscopic properties and in their affinity for oxygen. This does not imply that the haemoglobins of nematodes have any special common characteristics. In fact they vary in their properties much more than do the haemoglobins of mammals. At one extreme are the pigments of *Ascaris lumbricoides* and *Strongylus* spp. These pigments show a greater absorption in the β–band than the α–band (Fig. 33) and they have an extremely high affinity for oxygen (Davenport, 1949*a*, 1949*b*) so that they show similarities to certain haemoglobins of plants (Keilin and Wang, 1945) rather than to the pigments found in animals. On the other hand the pigment from *Camallanus trispinosus* has an affinity for oxygen (Wharton, 1941) approaching that of some vertebrate pigments examined under similar circumstances.

Before discussing the properties of haemoglobins and their possible physiological functions in nematodes it should be emphasized that the affinity of haemoglobin for oxygen is very much affected by the conditions under which measurements are made. Factors such as temperature, pH and concentration may have marked effects on the oxygen dissociation curves.

Haemoglobins are frequently found in the tissues of the body wall of nematodes (see Table X). The pigment in *Ascaris lumbricoides* has been examined by Keilin (1925) and Davenport (1949*a*). In keeping with the very low pO_2 of the environment of this parasite, the T_L is extremely low. This body wall pigment becomes deoxygenated when the worm is maintained anaerobically; after two hours the intensity of the oxyhaemoglobin bands begins to decrease and after six hours the bands are very faint. Full intensity is restored when oxygen is admitted into the system (Davenport, 1949*a*). The deoxygenation velocity of this pigment is very much slower than in vertebrate pigments and this may limit its physiological usefulness. Nevertheless Davenport (1949*a*) found that the activity of these parasites ceased when the deoxygenation of the pigment in the tissues could be observed.

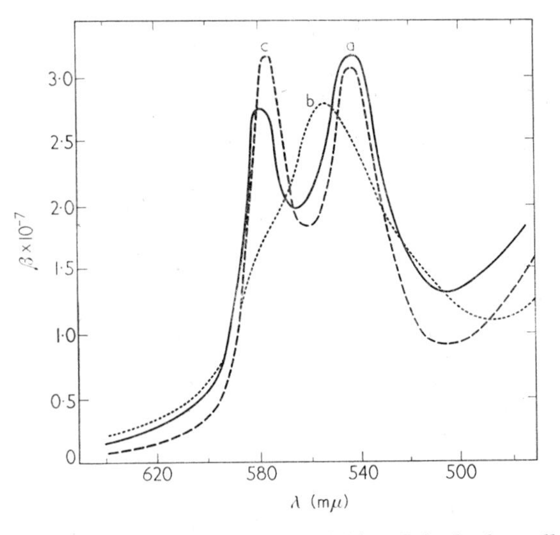

FIG. 33. Absorption spectra of: (a) oxyhaemoglobin of the body wall of *Ascaris lumbricoides;* (b) body wall haemoglobin; (c) human oxyhaemoglobin (after Davenport, 1945). The absorption coefficient,

$$\beta = \frac{1}{cd} \log_e \frac{I_0}{I},$$

where c is the concentration of haematin in g mol/cc, d is the depth in cm, I_0/I is the ratio of the intensities of the incident to transmitted light.

The deoxygenation velocity of oxyhaemoglobin of the body wall of *Ascaris* increased with a rise in pH (Davenport, 1949*a*).

The properties of the haemoglobin from the tissues and body fluid of *Nippostrongylus muris* have been examined by Davenport (1949*b*). The purified pigment at a concentration of 0.6×10^{-4}M (as haematin) at pH 9.2 and 18°C gave a T_U of about 0.1 mm of mercury. Rogers (1949*c*), working with this haemoglobin at a concentration of 1×10^{-4}M (as haematin) and at 17°C and pH 7.4, obtained a T_U slightly greater than this, i.e. there seems to be no pronounced Bohr effect. In the tissues of the intact parasites, where the concentration is about 2×10^{-3}M, and at 39°C the pigment became completely deoxygenated when the pO_2

in the medium close to the parasite fell to about 13 mm of mercury (Rogers, 1949*d*). Oxygen pressures of about this figure are not outside the limits found in the small intestine of the rat where this parasite normally lives (Rogers, 1949*a*).

The haemoglobins which occur in the tissues of other parasites of the gut also seem to be well adapted to function at low pressures of oxygen. Thus the pigments extracted from the tissues of *Nematodirus* spp. and *Haemonchus contortus* gave T_L values of about 0.12 mm of mercury at pH 7.4 and 17°C, and at a concentration of 1×10^{-4}M (Rogers, 1949*c*). In the intact parasites at 39°C the haemoglobins were deoxygenated when the pO_2 of the medium close to the parasites was reduced to about 9 mm of mercury (Rogers, 1949*d*). This pressure of oxygen is somewhat higher than has been recorded for the environment of these parasites (Rogers, 1949*a*).

Camallanus trispinosus which lives close to the mucosa in the intestine of the turtle contains haemoglobin. Wharton (1941) showed that oxyhaemoglobin in the tissues of the living parasite was deoxygenated under anaerobic conditions. At pH 6.8 the isolated pigment gave a T_L of about 20 mm of mercury. This figure is much higher than that obtained with haemoglobin from other nematodes. Nevertheless, it is still much lower than that of the host's haemoglobin and it is possible that these parasites "which live in close contact with the blood stream of the host" may take up oxygen, even from the venous blood of the host (Wharton, 1941).

It seems unlikely that the pigment in the body fluid of *Ascaris lumbricoides* can function as an oxygen carrier. Thus Davenport (1949*a*) showed that it was not deoxygenated in living parasites even when they had been incubated for 6 hours under anaerobic conditions. Moreover, the deoxygenation velocity was decreased by increased hydrogen ion concentration. In *Strongylus* spp. too, the properties of the pigment in the fluid are such that an oxygen-transporting function is unlikely (Davenport, 1949*b*).

The presence of haemoglobin in the body fluid of larvae of *Eustrongylides ignotus* has been noted by von Brand (1937). This pigment is present in concentrations sufficient to give the parasites a bright red colour. Under anaerobic conditions it is rapidly deoxygenated by the living parasites and probably assists in the transport of oxygen *in vivo* (von Brand, 1938*b*, 1942).

If a respiratory pigment is to have a significant effect as an oxygen carrier it must not only have suitable physical properties but it must be present in the tissues of the parasite in suitable concentrations. It seems that the amount of haemoglobin in *Nippostrongylus muris* is sufficient to supply its oxygen requirements when it is respiring at its maximum *in vitro* rate, assuming that the time for half-dissociation of the oxygen from the parasite's oxyhaemoglobin (t_{50}) is less than 9 seconds. (The t_{50} for sheep haemoglobin is given by Hartridge and Roughton (1923) as 0.0025 seconds at 37°C.) With oxyhaemoglobin from *Haemonchus contortus* and *Nematodirus* spp., a t_{50} of less than 0.25 seconds would be required (Rogers, 1949*d*). All these pigments are rapidly deoxygenated when reducing agents are added and it seems reasonable to suppose that the values for t_{50} are low.

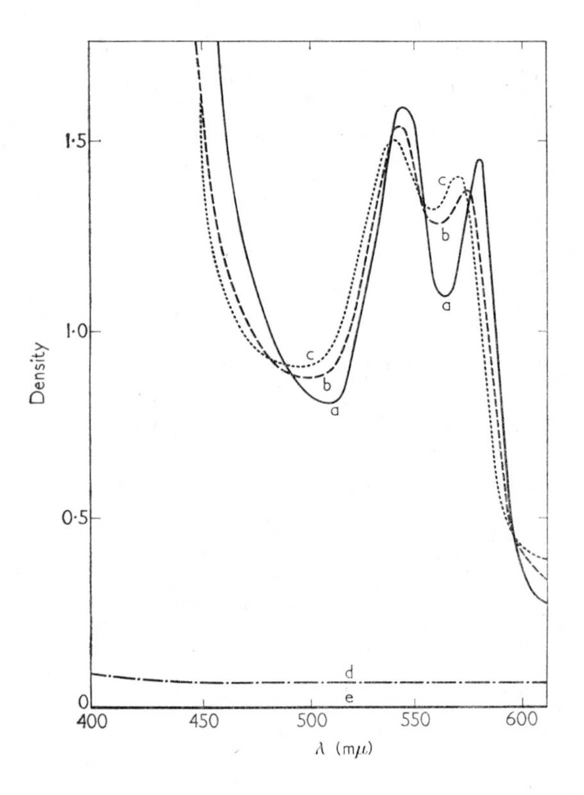

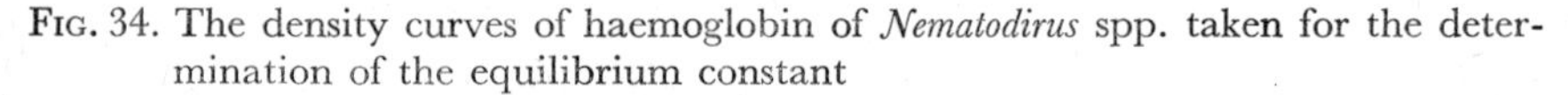

FIG. 34. The density curves of haemoglobin of *Nematodirus* spp. taken for the determination of the equilibrium constant

$$K = [HbCO] \times pO_2 \,/\, [HbO_2] \times pCO$$

at pH 7.4: (a) the curve of oxyhaemoglobin; (b) the curve of mixed oxyhaemoglobin and carboxyhaemoglobin formed in the presence of a mixture of carbon monoxide and oxygen of known composition; (c) the curve of carboxyhaemoglobin; (d) the curve obtained with water only in the cell; (e) the 100% transmission characteristic of the spectrophotometer which exactly followed the base line. All the haemoglobin solutions contained a small and constant amount of methaemoglobin and choleglobin (after Rogers, 1949*c*).

An attempt has been made to determine the proportion of aerobic respiration which is supported by oxygen transported by haemoglobin in these three species of nematodes (Rogers, 1949*d*). In these experiments the oxygen uptake of parasites in which the haemoglobin was poisoned with carbon monoxide was compared with that of parasites which were respiring normally at the same pO_2. The affinity of the pigments of these parasites for carbon monoxide is low (Fig. 34); the value of the equilibrium constant,

$$K = [HbCO] \times pO_2 \,/\, [HbO_2] \times pCO = 1$$ (Rogers, 1949*c*).

In some of these experiments, therefore, it was necessary to use a pCO / pO_2 ratio of 2. But even under these circumstances carbon monoxide did not decrease the oxygen uptake. Thus at a pO_2 of 3.8 mm of mercury the presence of carbon monoxide at a pressure of 15.2 mm of mercury did not greatly reduce the oxygen uptake. In view of the properties of the isolated pigments from these parasites which have loading tensions of about 0.1 mm of mercury these results may not seem surprising. But it was expected that the pigments would behave somewhat differently in the living parasites so that the effects at 3.8 mm of mercury would be apparent. Unfortunately the respiratory activity, even at this pO_2, is low and difficult to measure so that the possibility that haemoglobin in the parasites might be an effective carrier at lower tensions has not been examined.

The Significance of Aerobic Metabolism in Nematode Parasites

From the preceding discussion it is clear that the dependence of nematode parasites on aerobic metabolism varies from species to species. Probably all have the capacity to obtain useful energy from oxidative processes and, except in the larvae of *Trichinella spiralis*, there is little experimental evidence to suggest that the energy produced in this way is coupled to any specific physiological mechanisms. The observation that the muscular activity ceases at about the time when the supply of oxygen is exhausted, even when the glycogen reserves are still present, does not necessarily mean that muscular activity requires an oxidative metabolism. It may be that oxygen tensions above those occurring *in vivo* stimulate the worms to make active movements. After all, evidence from X-ray examinations and from direct observation (Archer and Peterson, 1930) shows that *Ascaris lumbricoides* in the gut is largely motionless and it seems reasonable to suppose that this applies to many parasites in other tissues and organs.

Oxidative metabolism in nematode parasites does not lead to the conservation of substrates to the extent found in most animals. Thus the larvae of *Eustrongylides ignotus* which, of the parasites so far examined, shows the most pronounced Pasteur reaction, are inefficient compared with free-living annelids in which glycogen consumption may be reduced to one sixth (von Brand, 1946, p. 182). However, there does not seem to be a correlation between the extent of the Pasteur reaction and the dependence of the parasite on oxygen for its survival. As pointed out earlier, however, the efficiency with which a parasite used its substrates for the production of energy should not necessarily be judged on the same standards as the host. If partially oxidized substrates from the parasite are available to the host for the resynthesis of glycogen, the loss of energy in the host–parasite complex would be small.

If oxidative mechanisms are not coupled to specific physiological processes, an essential requirement of oxygen *in vivo* may be due to (a) difficulties in excreting end-products of metabolism, (b) insufficient substrate for the provision of energy, (c) the possibility that, though the quantity of substrate may not be limiting, the rate at which energy could be obtained by anaerobic processes could be too low. There is insufficient information to decide on the relative importance of these three factors except in a few species. In *Litomosoides carinii* it seems that (c) is most important. This conclusion is supported by the finding that the reduction of the rate of respiration of these parasites by the administration of cyanine dyes to the host leads to their death (Welch *et al.*, 1947; Peters *et al.*, 1949). The results obtained with the larvae of *Eustrongylides ignotus* indicated that this parasite did not feed under anaerobic conditions (von Brand and Simpson, 1945). This, together with the increased use of substrate, probably led to the depletion of carbohydrate reserves and the death of the parasite under anaerobic conditions. But factor (a) also may be concerned in these parasites because acid production is greatly increased and partially oxidized end-products are retained in the tissues when oxygen is not available.

There is no information which indicates what deficiencies in anaerobic processes lead to the death of small parasites of the intestine *in vitro* when oxygen is not available (Davey, 1938*a*). The size of these parasites, the probability that the movements of their body fluids assist in oxygen transport, and their close association with the mucosa of the host suggest very strongly that oxidative processes are a normal feature of their metabolism *in vivo*. With the large parasites from the small intestine the position is not so clear. However, an appreciable aerobic metabolism seems unlikely.

The Oxygen Requirements of Parasitic Platyhelminthes and Acanthocephala

The Consumption of Oxygen

Like the nematodes, the adult cestodes, trematodes and Acanthocephala use oxygen when it is available (von Brand, 1952, p. 150; Ward, 1952; Mansour, 1959) though the rate of uptake for endogenous respiration varies greatly from a QO_2 of 0.03 for thick, fleshy *Paramphistomum cervi* (Lazarus, 1950) to 10.7 in the thread-like, slender females of *Schistosoma mansoni* (Bueding, 1950). All the larval stages examined so far also show aerobic respiration (Friedheim and Baer, 1933; Agosin *et al.*, 1957; Hunter and Vernberg, 1955*a*).

The transport of oxygen in the tissues of the parasites of this group seems, as in the nematodes, to be a limiting factor for respiratory rates. Thus the oxygen uptake is dependent upon the pO_2 in the following organisms: *Diphyllobothrium latum*, adults and plerocercoids (Friedheim and Baer, 1933); *Triaenophorus nodulosus* (Harnish, 1933); *Fasciola hepatica* (van Grembergen, 1949); *Schistosoma mansoni* (Bueding, 1949*a*); *Gynaecotyla adunca* (Hunter and Vernberg, 1955*a*, 1955*b*); and *Hymenolepis diminuta* (Read, 1956). The results with *Gynaecotyla adunca* differed from the others; though the oxygen uptake rose when the pO_2 was increased from 38 to 160 mm of mercury, it fell to a low value when the pO_2 was raised further to 760 mm. The degree to which a post-anaerobic increase in oxygen consumption is developed in these groups of parasites varies. Thus *Schistosoma mansoni* shows no oxygen debt (Bueding, 1950) whereas in *Paragonimus westermani* (Read and Yogore, 1955) and *Hymenolepis diminuta*, for instance, the oxygen uptake is considerably increased after one hour of anaerobiosis. Like most nematodes the Acanthocephala and parasitic platyhelminths show little Pasteur effect in the amount of substrate used or in the production of end-products. With *Macracanthorhynchus hirudinaceus* the consumption of glycogen was only increased by a proportion of about 1 : 1.3 when the worms were transferred from aerobic to anaerobic conditions (von Brand, 1940; Ward, 1952). In *Schistosoma mansoni* neither the rate of use of glycogen nor the rate of production of lactic acid was affected by shifting from aerobic to anaerobic conditions; i.e. the rate of glycolysis in this parasite was not affected by oxygen at about 160 mm of mercury (Bueding, 1950). Hopkins (1952), who worked with plerocercoids of *Schistocephalus solidus*, found that during the 48 hours in which the worms matured *in vitro* in a non-nutrient medium the amounts of glycogen consumed were slightly greater under anaerobic conditions than when oxygen was present. After this time, and also when the parasites were cultured in a medium containing glucose, the presence or absence of oxygen had no demonstrable effect (Hopkins, 1952). When *Hymenolepis diminuta* was incubated in a medium containing glucose the amount removed from the medium was about the same in the presence or absence of oxygen. However, lactic acid production was increased by as much as 30% under anaerobic conditions and the parasites stored less polysaccharide. Read (1956) regarded this as a Pasteur effect. No Pasteur effect was found in the scolices of *Echinococcus granulosus* from hydatid cysts (Agosin, 1957). Though the amounts of glycogen used by this parasite were not significantly different under aerobic and anaerobic conditions there were definite changes, quantitative and qualitative, in the nature of the end-products excreted into the medium. With adult *Fasciola hepatica* Mansour (1959) found that the presence of oxygen did not appreciably affect the use of carbohydrate or the nature of the organic acids which were excreted.

Most of these experiments were carried out under axenic conditions and there is little doubt about the significance of the results; aerobic metabolism in these organisms does not lead to the economy of substrate found in most free-living invertebrates (von Brand, 1946). However, this does not necessarily mean that these parasites are normally anaerobic. For some, oxygen promotes survival *in vitro* (Wilmoth, 1945; von Brand, 1952, p. 182) though for others it has little effect (Wilmoth and Levitas, 1945). Moreover, small amounts of oxygen are essential for the survival *in vivo* of the blood fluke *Schistosoma mansoni* (Bueding *et al.*, 1953). This view is based on results which were obtained from chemotherapeutic trials with a cyanine dye which inhibits about 80% of the oxidative metabolism of the parasite. When infected hamsters were dosed with the drug a mild but definite chemotherapeutic action was noted if the treatment was started before the parasites became mature and if the treatment was continued for about 5 weeks. The authors concluded that, in contrast to the nematode *Litomosoides carinii*, on which the dye had a pronounced effect, *Schistosoma mansoni* obtained most of its energy for reproduction and survival from anaerobic processes. The requirement for oxygen, however, though small, was a definite and essential one, and was greater just before the parasites reached maturity.

That a small organism like *Schistosoma mansoni* which lives in an environment relatively well provided with oxygen has such a small aerobic respiration seems surprising; and it might imply that the oxygen needed by large trematodes which live in places low in oxygen would be even less. Indeed the experiments which have been carried out to examine the survival of adult trematodes *in vitro* suggest that *Schistosoma mansoni* has a greater need for oxygen than most other species (Wilmoth and Levitas, 1945; von Brand, 1952, p. 182).

Some adult cestodes and plerocercoids are damaged by oxygen in media exposed to air (Smyth, 1954) and oxygen has been used as a chemotherapeutic agent against *Hymenolepis nana* and *Taenia saginata* (Mishchenko, 1956*a*). Specific toxic actions of oxygen which lead to the premature oxidation of phenolic substances concerned in the formation of egg-shells of cestodes have been noted by Smyth (1950). Nevertheless, most cases of the successful cultivation of cestodes *in vitro* have been carried out under "semi-anaerobic" conditions in which small amounts of oxygen have been available to the parasites (for references, see Smyth, 1955). It is uncertain, however, whether this oxygen is necessary and Hopkins (1952), from his studies on *Schistocephalus solidus*, concluded that these parasites are well adapted to live in the absence of oxygen and that they normally respire anaerobically in the small intestine of the host.

Read (1956), however, suggested that a limited aerobic respiration may be essential in adult cestodes. His view was partly based on the observation that the size of the worms is often approximately inversely proportional to the number of the parasites in a host. This "crowding effect" is related to the area/weight ratio of the parasites and indicates that some factor, required in roughly uniform amounts per unit weight, is taken up by the worms through the body surface and is available only in limited amounts in the environment. As the "crowding effect" is found even when food is available to the parasite from the ingesta of the host, Read (1951) suggested that oxygen might be the limiting factor.

Oxygen Transport in the Tissues of Parasitic Platyhelminthes

The flattened shape of most adult trematodes and cestodes gives a greater surface area per unit weight than in the thread-like nematodes. The arrangement and solid nature of the internal tissues, however, does not suggest an adaptation for oxygen transport. Moreover, haemoglobin is rarely found in these parasites; it has not been reported so far in any cestode and in only four trematodes, *Allassostoma magnum*, *Telorchis robustus*, *Fasciola hepatica*, and *Dicrocoelium lanceatum* (Wharton, 1941; Stephenson, 1947; van Grembergen, 1949). And most adult forms are too thick to allow oxygen to penetrate to the central tissues by diffusion alone.

Read (1956), in discussing the oxygen requirements of cestodes, pointed out that partially oxidized end-products of metabolism formed in central tissues would diffuse to the outer tissues where they might be oxidized. The villus-like projections which cover the surface of some species of cestodes (Read, 1955, p. 27) would come into close contact with the mucosa of the host so that considerable amounts of oxygen might be available for aerobic respiration. This increased supply of energy might be correlated with the peripheral distribution of nerves and muscles in cestodes (Read, 1952).

Summary

The oxygen requirements of helminths vary greatly. For some oxygen is essential; but it has not been shown conclusively that any species can continue to live normally under physiological conditions without oxygen.

It is not known whether an essential requirement of oxygen in helminths is related to (a) difficulty in excreting partly oxidized end-products of metabolism, (b) insufficient substrates for provision of energy, (c) limitations in the rate at which energy can be provided through anaerobic routes, or (d) the production of basic materials for synthetic processes which cannot be readily provided by anaerobic reactions.

Compared with most free-living invertebrates which have been studied so far, many helminths are well adapted for living at low tensions of oxygen. The absence of an appreciable Pasteur effect in many of these parasites shows that efficiency in using energy reserves has little selective advantage or that oxygen is not commonly available to the parasites *in vivo*.

Although the ratio of the surface area to volume is small in nematodes, other features of the anatomy of these animals are such that oxygen transport to central tissues is likely to be more effective than in platyhelminths of comparable size. Haemoglobins of suitable loading tension in the body wall and body fluid of nematodes would aid oxygen transport, especially if the affinity of the pigments for oxygen decreased with rises in hydrogen ion concentration.

References

Agosin, M. (1957) *Exp. Parasit.* **6**, 586.

——, von Brand, T., Rivera, G. F. and McMahon, P. (1957) *Exp. Parasit.* **6**, 37.

Archer, V. W. and Peterson, C. H. (1930) *J. Amer. med. Ass.* **95**, 37.

Berkhina, R. A. (1955) *Med. Parazit.* **24**, 300 (seen as *Helminth. Abstr.* **24**, 319).

Berl, S. and Bueding, E. (1951) *J. biol. Chem.* **191**, 401.

Bird, A. F. (1958) *Parasitology*, **48**, 32.

Bird, A. F. and Deutsch, K. (1957) *Parasitology*, **47**, 319.

Bishop, D. W. (1950) *In* "Comparative Animal Physiology". (C. L. Prosser, ed.), W. B. Saunders, Philadelphia.

Bueding, E. (1949*a*) *Physiol. Rev.* **29**, 195.

—— (1949*b*) *J. exp. Med.* **89**, 107.

—— (1950) *J. gen. Physiol.* **33**, 475.

—— (1953) *J. biol. Chem.* **202**, 505.

—— and Most, H. (1953) *Ann. Rev. Microbiol.* **7**, 295.

—— and Oliver-Gonzalez, J. (1950) *Brit. J. Pharmacol.* **5**, 62.
——, Peters, L., Koletsky, S. and Moore, D. V. (1953)*Brit. J. Pharmacol.* **8**, 15.
—— and Yale, H. W. (1951) *J. biol. Chem.* **193**, 411.
Carter, G. S. (1931) *Biol. Rev.* **6**, 1.
Chin, C. and Bueding, E. (1954) *Biochim. biophys. Acta*, **13**, 331.
Clifton, C. E. (1947) *Leeuwenhoek ned. Tijdschr.* **12**, 186.
Davenport, H. E. (1945) *Nature, Lond.* **155**, 516.
—— (1949*a*) *Proc. roy. Soc.* **B136**, 255.
—— (1949*b*) *Proc. roy. Soc.* **B136**, 271.
Davey, D. G. (1938*a*) *J. exp. Biol.* **15**, 217.
—— (1938*b*) *Parasitology*, **30**, 378.
Dixon, K. C. (1937) *Biol. Rev.* **12**, 43.
Epps, W., Weiner, M. and Bueding, E. (1950) *J. infect. Dis.* **87**, 149.
Fenn, W. O. (1927) *J. gen. Physiol.* **10**, 767.
Friedheim, E. A. H. and Baer, J. G. (1933) *Biochem. Z.* **265**, 329.
Gerard, R. W. (1931) *Biol. Bull., Woods Hole*, **60**, 245.
Glocklin, V. C. and Fairbairn, D. (1952) *J. cell. comp. Physiol.* **39**, 341.
Goddard, D. R. and Meeuse, B. J. D. (1950) *Ann. Rev. Pl. Physiol.* **1**, 207.
Harnish, O. (1933) *Z. vergl. Physiol.* **19**, 310.
Harris, J. E. and Crofton, H. D. (1957) *J. exp. Biol.* **34**, 116.
Hartridge, M. D. and Roughton, F. J. W. (1923) *Proc. roy. Soc.* **A104**, 395.
Hill, A. V. (1929) *Proc. roy. Soc.* **B104**, 39.
Hobson, A. D. (1948) *Parasitology*, **38**, 183.
Hopkins, C. A. (1952) *Exp. Parasit.* **1**, 196.
Hsü, H. F. (1938) *Bull. Fan Inst. Biol., Peking, Zool. Ser.* **8**, 347.
Hunter, W. S. and Vernberg, W. B. (1955*a*) *Exp. Parasit.* **4**, 54.
—— (1955*b*) *Exp. Parasit.* **4**, 427.
Hyman, L. H. (1951) "The Invertebrates" Vol. III. McGraw-Hill Book Co., New York.
Janicki, M. J. (1939) *Zool. Polon.* **3**, 189.
Keilin, D. (1925) *Proc. roy. Soc.* **B98**, 312.
—— and Wang, Y. L. (1945) *Nature, Lond.* **155**, 227.
Krogh, A. (1919) *J. Physiol.* **52**, 391.
Krüger, F. (1936) *Zool. Jb. Abt. 3*, **57**, 1.
—— (1937) *Z. vergl. Physiol.* **24**, 687.
—— (1940) *Z. wiss. Zool.* **152**, 547.
Laser, H. (1944) *Biochem. J.* **38**, 333.
Lazarus, M. (1950) *Aust. J. sci. Res.* **B3**, 245.
Makidono, J. (1956) *Amer. J. trop. Med. Hyg.* **5**, 699.
Mansour, T. E. (1959) *Biochim. biophys. Acta*, **34**, 456.
Mendes, M. V. (1949) *Ann. Acad. bras. Sci.* **21**, 19.
Mishchenko, O. S. (1956*a*) *Soviet Med., Moscow*, **20**, 71 (seen as *Helminth. Abstr.* **25**, 204).
—— (1956*b*) *Med. Parazit.* **25**, 54 (seen as *Helminth. Abstr.* **25**, 20).
Nisman, B. (1954) *Bact. Rev.* **18**, 16.
Peters, L., Bueding, E., Valk, A., Higashi, A. and Welch, A. D. (1949) *J. Pharmacol.* **95**, 212.
Prestage, J. J. (1960) *J. Parasit.* **46**, 69.
Prosser, C. L. (1950) *In* "Comparative Animal Physiology". (C. L. Prosser, ed.), W. B. Saunders, Philadelphia.
Read, C. P. (1950) *Rice Inst. Pamphl.* **37**, 1.

—— (1951) *J. Parasit.* **37**, 174.
—— (1952) *J. Parasit.* **38**, Suppl. 24.
—— (1955) *In* "Some Physiological Aspects and Consequences of Parasitism". (W. H. Cole, ed.), Rutgers University Press, New Brunswick.
—— (1956) *Exp. Parasit.* **5**, 325.
—— and Yogore, M. (1955) *J. Parasit.* **41**, Suppl. 28.
Ribeiro, L. P. and Villela, G. G. (1956) *Rev. bras. Biol.* **16**, 145.
Rogers, W. P. (1948) *Parasitology*, **39**, 105.
—— (1949*a*) *Aust. J. sci. Res.* **B2**, 157.
—— (1949*b*) *Aust. J. sci. Res.* **B2**, 166.
—— (1949*c*) *Aust. J. sci. Res.* **B2**, 287.
—— (1949*d*) *Aust. J. sci. Res.* **B2**, 399.
Ross, O. A. and Bueding, E. (1950) *Proc. Soc. exp. Biol. Med.* **73**, 179.
Ruud, J. T. (1954) *Nature, Lond.* **173**, 848.
Scott, J. K. (1949) "Respiration in Bulky Plant Tissues". (Doctoral thesis, University of Cambridge); quoted by Goddard and Meeuse (1950).
Slater, W. K. (1925) *Biochem. J.* **19**, 604.
Smyth, J. D. (1950) *J. Parasit.* **36**, 371.
—— (1954) *Quart. J. micr. Sci.* **95**, 139.
—— (1955) *Rev. ibér. Parasit.*, Tom. extraord. 65.
Stannard, J. N., McCoy, O. R. and Latchford, W. B. (1938) *Amer. J. Hyg.* **27**, 666.
Stephenson, W. (1947) *Parasitology*, **27**, 81.
Toryu, Y. (1935) *Sci. Rep. Tôhoku Univ.* **10**, 361.
—— (1936) *Sci. Rep. Tôhoku Univ.* **10**, 687.
van Grembergen, G. (1949) *Enzymologia*, **13**, 241.
—— (1954) *Nature, Lond.* **174**, 35.
van Niel, C. B. (1949) *Amer. Scient.* **37**, 371.
Villela, G. G. and Ribeiro, L. P. (1955) *Ann. Acad. bras. Sci.* **27**, 87.
von Brand, T. (1934) *Z. vergl. Physiol.* **21**, 220.
—— (1937) *J. Parasit.* **23**, 225.
—— (1938*a*) *Biodynamica*, **2**, 1.
—— (1938*b*) *J. Parasit.* **24**, 445.
—— (1940) *J. Parasit.* **26**, 301.
—— (1942) *Biol. Bull., Woods Hole*, **82**, 1.
—— (1946) "Anaerobiosis in Invertebrates". Biodynamica, Normandy, Missouri.
—— (1947) *Biol. Bull., Woods Hole*, **92**, 162.
—— (1952) "Chemical Physiology of Endoparasitic Animals". Academic Press, New York.
—— and Simpson, W. F. (1945) *Proc. Soc. exp. Biol. Med.* **60**, 368.
—— (1947) *J. Parasit.* **33**, 71.
——, Weinstein, P. P., Mehlman, B. and Weinbach, E. C. (1952) *Exp. Parasit.* **1**, 245.
Vora, D. D. (1955) *Indian J. med. Sci.* **9**, 573.
Ward, H. L. (1952) *J. Parasit.* **38**, 493.
Weinland, E. (1901) *Z. Biol.* **42**, 55.
Welch, A. D., Peters, L., Bueding, E., Valk, A. and Higashi, A. (1947) *Science*, **105**, 486.
Wharton, G. W. (1941) *J. Parasit.* **27**, 81.
Wilmoth, J. H. (1945) *Physiol. Zool.* **18**, 60.
—— and Levitas, N. (1945) *J. Parasit.* **31**, Suppl. 22.
Zimmerman, J. F. and Berry, L. J. (1949) *Biochim. biophys. Acta*, **3**, 198.

CHAPTER 8

The Nutrition of Parasites

THE factors needed in the medium for the nutrition of metazoan parasites are clearly of basic importance for the survival of these organisms. But just how far nutritional factors are concerned in determining the parasitic habit of an organism, or its specificity as a parasite, is unknown.

Even among micro-organisms the position is not clear except for the viruses. These organisms require the actual machinery on and in the cell of the host for their metabolism and reproduction; their dependence on parasitism as a mode of life may thus be attributed to their nutritional dependence on the host cell. "Nutritional dependence" in this sense, however, is more than the requirement of certain substances in the medium; it involves a certain organization of the medium as well.

The properties that confer infectiousness on many species of bacteria and so enable them to live a parasitic mode of life are largely unknown though sufficient information is available to indicate that different species differ widely in this respect. The ability of bacteria to multiply *in vivo* can rarely be attributed to any known nutritional or other environmental requirement (Dubos, 1948). There are some parasitic bacteria which have not yet been grown in media of known composition; others, like the tubercle bacillus, can be grown in simple synthetic media. Others again, like *Haemophilus influenzae*, which need haem and cozymase as growth factors, must normally live as parasites to get the nutrients they require.

In some respects the parasitic protozoa are similar to the infectious bacteria. They may be intra- or extracellular; many cannot yet be cultivated *in vitro;* others require specific nutrients such as *p*-aminobenzoic acid or haematin (Hawking, 1955; McKee, 1951, p. 25) which are freely available when they live as parasites. Some intracellular parasitic protozoa may be similar to viruses, if, as seems likely, the structural organization of their environment, as well as the sort of molecules it contains, is important.

The evidence that it is the nutritional requirements of parasitic micro-organisms that determine their mode of life can be applied to only a few species. And for many species there is evidence to the contrary. There is even less evidence that the specificity of a parasite can be based on its nutritional requirements, except perhaps in some parasitic protozoa. Indeed, specificity in the ability of micro-organisms to multiply *in vivo* may be more closely related to the interaction of the offensive and defensive mechanisms in the host and parasite.

Our understanding of the nutrition of metazoan parasites and its significance in relation to parasitism is even less than it is for unicellular parasites. Something is known about the basic nutrients required by some Cestoda for obtaining energy; and complex culture media which will support some nematode parasites through the whole life cycle have been skilfully devised. We also have some knowledge of the tissues and the fluids of the host which are ingested by the parasitic nematodes. This knowledge, however, does not go far in helping us to understand the biochemistry of their nutrition, the part it plays in parasitism, and its relation to specificity. In this chapter information will be sought indirectly by briefly examining the processes of digestion, the feeding habits and diet *in vivo* and the culture *in vitro* of some metazoan parasites.

Nutrition of Parasitic Nematodes

Digestion and Diet

The anatomy of the alimentary canal of nematode parasites has been described in detail by Chitwood and Chitwood (1940, pp. 100–121) and only those features which may relate especially to their mode of life need be mentioned here. The œsophagus (more properly called the pharynx) is a triradiate, syncytial muscular organ lined with cuticle; it usually contains one dorsal and two ventrolateral glands. It is concerned chiefly with regulating the movement of food into the intestine. No precise generalizations can be made about the function of the glands which discharge into the lumen of the œsophagus anteriorly and posteriorly. There is some evidence that the secretion may have an anti-coagulant action in blood-sucking worms, or may provide enzymes for the partial digestion of host's tissue before or after ingestion in tissue feeders (Hoeppli and Feng, 1931, 1933; Thorson, 1955).

The intestine is usually a straight tube formed by a single-layered cellular epithelium which may be provided with cilia (Browne and Chowdhury, 1959). The cells differ somewhat in shape and in the nature of their inclusions in different parts of the intestine but there is no clear evidence of a demarcation in function.

The intestine of the Mermithoidea often shows unusual features. In most mermithids, and especially in those which have a long period as a free-living adult, the intestine grows rapidly during the parasitic larval period until it fills most of the free spaces in the body of the worm. The cells of the intestine become loaded with reserve food granules, which, according to Chitwood and Jacobs (1938), are largely protein. Finally, in some species the cells of the intestine may become so packed with food granules that the cavity is obliterated and even the cell walls disappear. The adult free-living worm does not feed, but lives at the expense of its internal food reserves.

All nematodes seem to have a small sphincter muscle at the junction of the intestine with the posterior gut or rectum. This muscle serves to control the intestino-rectal valve. In many nematodes there are glands of unknown function which open into the rectum. The rectum in nematodes apparently has no digestive or absorptive function; it probably regulates the rate of escape of materials from the intestine.

The isolated cuticle of *Ascaris lumbricoides* is permeable to water and some inorganic ions (Hobson, 1948). It is doubtful, however, if this is an important route by which nematodes obtain nutrients; even phosphate ions and glucose do not enter through the hypodermis (Mueller, 1928; Rogers and Lazarus, 1949; Cavier and Savel, 1952*a*). On the other hand, there is a large body of evidence, both histological (Hirsch and Bretschneider, 1937; Janicki, 1939; Carpenter, 1952) and physiological, which suggests that absorption and extracellular digestion occur in the intestine. Much of this evidence is open to criticism; but there seems little doubt that it is correct in general terms. The breakdown of ingested cells in the intestine of a number of different species has been demonstrated by histological means (see, for example, Hsü, 1938; Hsü and Li, 1940), and the presence of haematin in the intestine of blood-sucking parasites (Hsü, 1938; Rogers, 1940*a*) suggests the digestion of haemoglobin. Protease, peptidase, carbohydrase and lipase have been found in the whole intestines of *Ascaris lumbricoides* and *Strongylus edentatus* (Rogers, 1940*b*, 1941*a*, 1941*b*; Carpenter, 1952; Savel, 1955). It has not yet been shown that these enzymes have an extracellular digestive function. But in the absence of evidence indicating intracellular digestive processes in the cells of the intestines of parasites which, like *Strongylus*, are known to ingest solid masses of the host's gut (Carpenter, 1952), it seems reasonable to postulate active digestive and absorptive systems in the intestine.

The feeding habits and the diets of nematode parasites of animals have been reviewed by Ackert and Whitlock (1940). More recently, several papers have appeared in which radioactive tracers have been used in attempts to follow the feeding habits of parasites of the alimentary canal (Rogers and Lazarus, 1949; Esserman and Sambell, 1951). It appears from this work that most small nematodes, like *Nippostrongylus muris*, feed on the blood and tissue of the host, whereas larger parasites, like *Ascaridia galli*, ingest material from the lumen of the gut of the host (Figs. 35, 36). Garoian (1957), who used Thiry fistulae in dogs, found that *Ancylostoma caninum* derived its nutriment from the intestinal mucosa, but *Toxocara canis* required the addition of intestinal contents to survive.

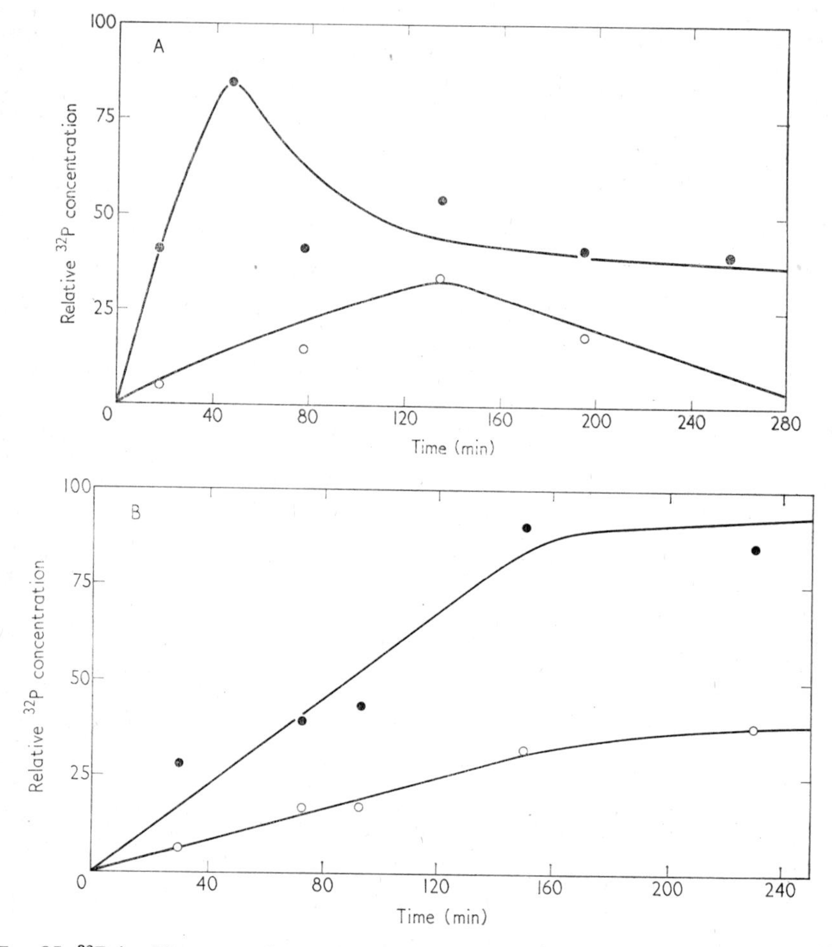

FIG. 35. ^{32}P in *Nippostrongylus muris* (O) and in the tissues of the small intestine of the rat (●) after dosing the infected host with disodium hydrogen phosphate containing ^{32}P *per os*, A, and intramuscularly, B (after Rogers and Lazarus, 1949).

There seems to be little precise information on the feeding habits of plant parasitic nematodes (Christie, 1959, p. 7). These animals may feed on cell walls or contents, cell exudate or sap. The harder tissues of the host are pierced by the buccal stylets as in *Heterodera* or by chemical

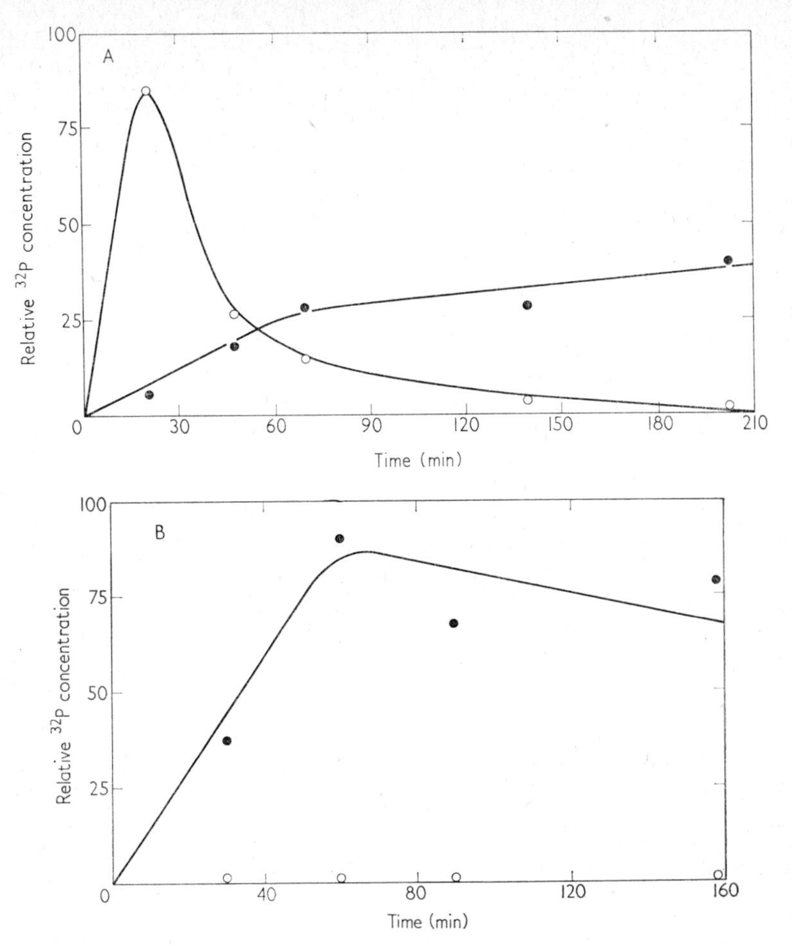

FIG. 36. ^{32}P in *Ascaridia galli* (O) and in the tissues of the small intestine of the chicken (●) after dosing the infected host with disodium hydrogen phosphate containing ^{32}P *per os*, A, and intramuscularly, B (after Rogers and Lazarus, 1949).

action of the œsophageal secretions as in *Ditylenchus* (Dropkin, 1955). Some plant parasitic nematodes (*Ditylenchus dipsaci, D. destructor*, and *D. myceliophagus*) produce cellulases and chitinases which presumably help them to invade the tissue of the host and provide carbohydrate in a form which can be assimilated (Tracey, 1958).

In only a few species of nematode parasites has it been possible to assess even roughly the amount of the tissue of the host which has been ingested. Wells (1931) and Nishi (1933) have shown that the amount of blood removed from the host by a single specimen of *Ancylostoma caninum* may range from 0.36 to 0.84 ml per day. Although a small part of this is spilt from the mouth of the parasite, it is still a formidable amount to be ingested by an organism which weighs less than 10 mg; indeed it suggests that the parasite needs a large amount of blood to obtain essential nutrients. Though Hsü (1938) found evidence that some blood corpuscles are digested, the rapid flow of host's blood through the intestine of the parasite would be too fast to allow digestion to proceed very far, as indeed Wells reported. If the absorptive mechanisms of *Ancylostoma* are similar to those in other animals the parasite would have to obtain its supply of amino acids, for instance, largely from the blood plasma. Large amounts of blood might not be needed for this purpose, but for other essential nutrients in low concentrations in the plasma it might be different. It has been suggested, however (Wells, 1931), that the large amount of blood taken in by some hookworms reflects a requirement for oxygen rather than for nutrients. The presence of large numbers of mitochondria in the cells of the intestinal wall (Browne and Chowdhury, 1959) supports this view.

The amount of tissue taken by *Strongylus edentatus* and *Strongylus vulgaris*, which feed on the mucosa of the large intestine of the horse, has been examined by Rogers (1940*c*). The results, which give the minimum amounts taken in by these species during the period in which they live as parasites of the large intestine, range from 3.9 to 21.2 g for *Strongylus edentatus* and 0.7 to 3.4 g for *Strongylus vulgaris*. Or, in other words, *Strongylus edentatus* consumes at least 52 to 282, and *Strongylus vulgaris* at least 62 to 244 times its own weight of tissue during its adult life.

Most investigations of diet and feeding habits of nematodes have been carried out with adult parasites. There is no reason to believe, however, that larval parasites are much different, though larvae which feed on the gut contents of the host are more rare than adults with this habit. For instance, the larval stages of *Ascaris lumbricoides* and *Oxyuris equi* feed on host tissue whereas the adults feed on intestinal contents (Wetzel, 1931).

The digestive cavity of nematode parasites can be closed off from the rest of the medium. Processes of digestion and absorption can thus be carried out under conditions which differ from those in the bulk of the medium in which the parasite lives. This may be of some physiological importance to these parasites. For instance, a nematode parasite which lives in the highly acid medium of the stomach of a vertebrate animal and feeds on cells of the host's mucosa can carry out its own processes of digestion and absorption under optimal conditions independent of the pH of the stomach contents of the host. Parasites in which absorption takes place over the outer surface of the body cannot do this, and probably for this reason are rarely found as parasites of the stomach. The form of the alimentary canal in nematodes also has advantages over the blind-ending gut of the Trematoda because it allows, if necessary, the rapid passage of materials along the intestine. It is this, for instance, which would make it possible for nematodes to extract oxygen, or nutrients in low concentration, from relatively large volumes of the host's blood.

The Effect of the Host's Diet on the Parasite

The diet of the host can affect the parasite in a number of ways. An essential nutrient for both the parasite and the host must be supplied in the diet of the host or synthesized by micro-organisms in the gut of the host. A deficiency of the nutrient would be reflected in the parasite and the host according to their relative requirements. Deficiency diseases in the host are known and are recognizable; in the parasite a reduction in the size of the individuals and the number in the infection would be expected. But deficiencies in the diet of the host may lead to increased size and number of parasites. Thus the host has quantitative and qualitative requirements for substances which affect the parasite only indirectly by affecting the capacity of the host to resist infection, or to resist the growth of established parasites. Components in the diet of the host may also have direct and indirect pharmacological actions on the parasite.

For these reasons the interpretation of results of experiments on the effect of the host's diet on parasitism is difficult. Nevertheless, a great deal of work has been carried out in this field because of its practical importance (see, for instance, reviews by Hunter, 1953; Chandler, 1953; Gaafar and Ackert, 1953). The effect of nutrition of the hosts on parasitic nematodes of plants has not been studied extensively though some information on specific elements has been obtained. Thus Oteifa (1953) showed that when increased amounts of potassium were available to the plant host, *Meloidogyne incognita* developed and reproduced more rapidly. Information on this subject is included in reviews by Chitwood and Oteifa (1952) and Dropkin (1955).

The quality and quantity of vitamins, proteins, carbohydrates and minerals in the diet of the host have effects on nematode parasites. Generally, however, these effects are indirect and result from the altered resistance of the host. Thus deficiencies in vitamin A, vitamin D, the vitamin B complex and its individual members, riboflavin, pyridoxine, pteroylglutamic acid and vitamin B_{12} have caused increases in the size and number of parasites in infections with *Ascaridia galli* and sometimes with other parasites (for examples, see Ackert and Spindler, 1929; Ackert *et al.*, 1931; Ackert and Nolf, 1931; Clapham, 1934; Watt, 1944; Brody, 1954). Protein and mineral deficiencies have similar effects (Donaldson and Otto, 1946; Riedel and Ackert, 1951; Clapham, 1934). In many of these experiments the host animals have shown marked signs of deficiency disease whereas the parasite profited. These results may be interpreted in several ways: (a) the parasites may have fed in regions of the host where the local concentrations of the substances which were deficient in the diet were relatively high; (b) the parasites' requirements were less than the host's; (c) the lowered concentration of the nutrients in the tissues of the host may have been countered by an increased food intake by the parasites—a course which may not have been open to the host; (d) the capacity of the host to produce substances which inhibited the growth of the parasites may have been lowered. The lowered resistance of the host alone, or in combination with (a), (b) or (c) could have given these results. With parasites such as *Ascaridia galli*, which feed on the contents of the gut of the host, (a) and (c) could not have operated. It seems possible, then, that *Ascaridia galli* has less need of vitamins A, D, and some of the B vitamins than its host.

Some results have been obtained in which the dietary deficiency of the host has had no effect, or an adverse effect, on the parasites. Thus a deficiency of vitamin B_{12} and pteroylglutamic acid had no effect on *Nippostrongylus muris* in the rat (Maldonado and Asenjo, 1953) though Threlkeld *et al.* (1956) found fewer *Haemonchus contortus* in sheep deficient in cobalt. Zaiman (1940) found fewer *Trichinella spiralis* in rats fed on a diet which was devoid of vitamin E; and Gaafar and Ackert (1953) showed that low-phosphorus or low-calcium diets decrease the size and number of *Ascaridia galli* in chickens.

The Cultivation of Nematode Parasites in vitro

Attempts have been made to cultivate nematode parasites in their free-living stages, as parasitic larvae and as adults (reviewed by von Brand, 1952, pp. 207–210). Though this work has been remarkably successful with some species, the complex media which have been necessary make it difficult to draw any specific conclusions about the nutrition of nematodes and only a few points can profitably be discussed here. The progress of this work, however, makes it clear that this approach to the study of parasitism will shortly become one of the most important avenues for gaining information about nutrition and other aspects of the physiology of these animals.

Some of the most interesting experiments on the cultivation of larval parasitic nematodes have been carried out by von Brand and Simpson (1942, 1944, 1945) who worked with *Eustrongylides ignotus* from cysts in the fish *Fundulus heteroclitus*. In the media containing "Bacto-Proteose Peptone" and 0.5% glucose the larvae were maintained for periods up to 2½ years under axenic conditions at 20°C. Glucose could be replaced by xylose without greatly reducing the survival of the parasites, but mannose, fructose and maltose were not effective.

During the period of cultivation the worms appeared healthy but they did not grow appreciably, and only one of more than a thousand moulted. In fact the larvae behaved very much as if they were still in the intermediate host. It seems, therefore, that the medium used by von Brand and Simpson provided the essential pattern of components needed for the maintenance of the larvae *in vivo*. As might be expected, however, this medium did not provide the components necessary to induce the larvae to moult. *In vivo* this takes place in the gut on the final host *Nycticorax*, and so might require a different sort of medium. Von Brand and Simpson (1944) showed that changes in temperature and pH were not sufficient to cause moulting in the "Bacto-Proteose Peptone" medium.

Neoaplectana glaseri and *Neoaplectana chresima*, usually found as parasites of coleopterous larvae in soil, have been cultured in sterile media throughout their entire life cycles (Glaser, 1940; Glaser, McCoy and Girth, 1942). The most successful medium consisted of sterile rabbit kidney on glucose-agar slopes. Using *Neoaplectana glaseri*, Stoll (1953) took this work a stage further and devised a liquid medium containing glucose, acid veal- or beef-heart infusion broth, and raw liver extract. The raw liver extract, prepared without heating and sterilized by filtration, was essential. It could not be replaced by commercial liver extracts, yeast extract, casein hydrolysate, casein factor of Price (1948), protogen, vitamin B_{12}, Simms ultrafiltrate, horse or ox serum, ascitic fluid or milk. Though *Neoaplectana glaseri* requires heat-labile nutrients which occur in mammalian liver and which would not occur commonly in the environments of free-living animals, there is no indication that the culture media used by Glaser or Stoll were similar to the natural environment of the parasite in its host in any specific way. It seems reasonable to assume, therefore, that the pattern of nutrients required by *Neoaplectana glaseri* has little relation to its specificity.

Weinstein and Jones (1956) have succeeded in culturing *Nippostrongylus muris* through its life cycle in media in which bacterial growth was prevented by antibiotics. The most successful medium for the cultivation of the parasitic stages contained chick embryo extract, sodium caseinate, liver extract and rat serum. The liver extract could not be replaced by yeast extract and rat serum could not be replaced by horse serum. In these experiments the parasites underwent the third and fourth moults and developed into sexually mature males and females. Thus the medium provided all the factors for the development of the parasites which *in vivo* takes place in the blood, the lungs, and in the small intestine. Silverman (1959) has cultured *Haemonchus contortus* using a similar medium.

The feat of culturing *Neoaplectana glaseri*, *Neoaplectana chresima*, *Nippostrongylus muris* and *Haemonchus contortus* through their life cycles has not yet been achieved with other species of parasitic nematodes. Weller (1943) and Pitts and Ball (1955) have made some progress in cultivating larvae of *Trichinella spiralis* and *Ascaris lumbricoides* in sterile media but growth was not pronounced. The culture of filarial worms has been more successful (Hawking, 1954; Taylor, 1960). Thus adult *Litomosoides carinii* lived in a medium containing rat serum for 23 days and produced microfilariae for 18 days.

A number of attempts have been made to cultivate nematodes in non-sterile media (see, for example, Hoeppli, Feng and Chu, 1938; Ackert, Todd and Tanner, 1938; Davey, 1938; Fenwick, 1939). As might be expected, however, non-sterile media have not shown much promise for the cultivation of parasitic stages though McCoy (1929, 1930) and Lapage (1933) were able to grow all the free-living larval stages of several parasites in such media. These organisms were cultured from the egg to the infective stage on single strains of bacteria. With sterile media or media containing antibiotics Glaser and Stoll (1938), Lawrence (1948), Weinstein (1953) and Weinstein and Jones (1957*a*) obtained similar results (see Chapter 4).

Progress in the culture of plant parasites has not advanced as far as it has with the animal parasites. Most notable, so far, is the work of Mountain (1955) and Tiner (1960) who maintained *Pratylenchus minyus* and *Pratylenchus penetrans* for several months in root tissue cultures.

Studies on the cultivation of free-living nematodes (see, for example, Dougherty and Keith, 1953; Dougherty and Hansen, 1956; Nicholas and McEntegart, 1957) have made considerable progress and it seems possible that these organisms may be grown in media of known chemical composition before long. Information gained from this work will aid studies with parasites. For instance, a full understanding of the rather unusual nutritional requirements of *Caenorhabditis briggsae* may have some significance in understanding the parasitic habits of nematodes generally.

It appears that work on the cultivation of nematode parasites *in vitro* is at a most interesting stage, both in the development of techniques and in the results which are being obtained. The technical problems of handling these organisms under axenic conditions seem to have been largely overcome. And there is no doubt that sterility is important even for the cultivation of parasites that live in the gut of the host. Fortunately many antibiotics have no toxic effects on nematodes so they can be used in conjunction with the more usual methods of maintaining sterility, though not, of course, replacing them.

The results which have been obtained so far suggest that nematode parasites (and, for that matter, free-living ones as well) may have some unusual nutritional requirements. There is little to suggest, however, that these requirements may be greatly concerned with specificity, though they may have some general significance in relation to the parasitic mode of life. At present, however, it would be unwise to be dogmatic. It seems possible, for instance, that a medium, that could support, say, a parasite of the intestine of man as well as, say, a parasite of the liver of the mouse might be devised. But surely it is also probable that a little modification of the medium would make it unsuitable for one parasite without greatly affecting the other and *vice versa* (see Chapter 1).

Food Reserves and Metabolism in Relation to Nutrition

Glycogen is common in the tissues of nematodes where it serves as an energy reserve and as a store of carbohydrate for the synthesis of N-acetylglucosamine for the chitin of egg-shells. Von Brand (1950) has suggested that the amount of glycogen stored is associated with two features of the physiology of parasites. In parasites which do not have direct access to the hosts' carbohydrate reserves, or in which metabolism is predominantly anaerobic, large amounts of glycogen are stored. This occurs, for instance, in *Ascaris lumbricoides*, *Parascaris equorum*, *Ascaridia galli* and *Strongylus vulgaris* (Table XI). On the other hand, tissue glycogen is generally low in parasites which have direct access to the hosts' carbohydrate reserves because they suck blood or live in tissues high in glycogen, or in parasites which have a predominantly aerobic metabolism. Examples here are *Trichinella spiralis, Ancylostoma caninum*, *Litomosoides carinii* and *Dirofilaria immitis* (Table XI).

In both types of parasites glycogen is formed from carbohydrate which the parasite ingests (von Brand, 1950). This may take place rapidly and from low concentrations in the medium. Thus *Litomosoides carinii* doubled its glycogen reserve in 3 hours in a medium containing 0.02M glucose (Bueding, 1949). Glycogen can also be lost rapidly, even *in vivo*. In chickens which have been fasted for 24 hours the glycogen in *Ascaridia galli* fell from 4.6% to 1.3% (Reid, 1944).

A number of investigations of the intermediary metabolism of nematodes has shown that glucose is oxidized aerobically or anaerobically by routes most of which are similar to those in vertebrates (see, for example, Rogers and Lazarus, 1949; Bueding, 1949; Massey and Rogers, 1950; Bueding and Yale, 1951; Rathbone and Rees, 1954; Entner, 1957; Entner and Gonzalez, 1959). These activities result in the formation of adenosine triphosphate which seems to have the same sort of functions in the intermediary metabolism of parasites as in other animals.

TABLE XI

The Relationship between Glycogen in Nematode Parasites and the Food and Oxygen in their Environments

Glycogen is given as the percentage of the wet weight

Species	Glycogen	Food	Oxygen	References
Ascaris lumbricoides (females)	5.3	gut contents	low	von Brand (1937)
Parascaris equorum (females)	3.1–3.8	gut contents	low	Toryu (1933)
Ascaridia galli	3.6–4.7	gut contents	low	Reid (1945*a*, 1945*b*)
Strongylus vulgaris	3.5	gut mucosa	low	Toryu (1933)
Trichinella spiralis (larvae)	2.4	tissue fluid (?)	moderate	von Brand *et al.* (1952)
Ancylostoma caninum	1.6	blood	moderate (?)	von Brand and Otto (1938)
Litomosoides carinii	0.73–0.81	pleural exudate (?)	high	Bueding (1949)
Dirofilaria immitis	1.9	blood	high	von Brand (1950)

These findings show that the basic mechanisms by which most nematode parasites obtain energy for synthetic processes and muscular activity are similar to those in free-living animals. Evidently the parasite cannot take advantage of the machinery of the host to obtain a directly usable source of energy. The nutritional requirements of the nematode parasite must therefore include substances for the general supply of energy. In species in which glycogen is a major reserve substance or in which glucose is metabolized preferentially, the most important energy-providing substance would presumably be glucose (von Brand, 1950). There is evidence, however, that routes for the conversion of amino acids to carbohydrate are present in nematodes. Though it is clear that fat may be converted to carbohydrate in free-living stages (see Chapter 4) no definite evidence of this has been obtained for parasitic stages. Nor indeed has the use of fat as a substrate for providing energy been shown to occur except in the infective larvae of *Trichinella spiralis* (von Brand *et al.*, 1952). From the evidence on feeding habits, culture and intermediary metabolism, it seems that glucose is the quantitatively important nutrient which serves as a source of energy.

How far glucose can be replaced by other monosaccharides in the diet of the parasitic nematodes has not been widely studied. But it is known, for instance, that glucose, fructose, sorbose, and maltose are equally well absorbed by *Ascaris lumbricoides* and converted into glycogen *in vitro*; maltose, lactose, and galactose were used less efficiently (Cavier and Savel, 1952*a*). Von Brand and Simpson (1944) showed that the larvae of *Eustrongylides ignotus* could be maintained longest *in vitro* when glucose, xylose, and perhaps inulin were in the medium; mannose, fructose, and maltose were less effective. Bueding (1949), who worked with *Litomosoides carinii*, found that glucose, fructose, and mannose were equally effective in maintaining motility and oxygen uptake, whereas galactose, ribose, and a number of organic acids were ineffective.

It appears that no critical experiments have been made on the capacity of nematode parasites to use dietary amino acids or fats for the synthesis of carbohydrate reserves in amounts large enough to be important in the economy of the parasite. Nor, indeed, is it known if any amino acids or fats are essential components in the diet. The necessity for sodium caseinate, in addition to the protein in the embryo extract, serum and liver concentrate, for the cultivation *in vitro* of *Nippostrongylus muris* (Weinstein and Jones, 1956) suggests that the parasites require amino acids, either free or in peptides.

The uptake of amino acids by *Trichinella spiralis* has been shown to take place *in vitro* and may also occur *in vivo*. Thus Stoner and Hankes (1955, 1958) and Hankes and Stoner (1956, 1958) found that ^{14}C from *dl*-alanine-2-^{14}C, glycine-2-^{14}C, *dl*-tyrosine-2-^{14}C and *dl*-tryptophane-2-^{14}C was incorporated in the protein of the larvae exposed to the amino acids *in vitro* and *in vivo*. The proportion of ^{14}C found in protein was generally greater *in vivo*. So far there are no indications in this work which show whether the ^{14}C was taken up as part of an essential nutrient. Moreover, the larvae were at the infective stage in the host's muscle so the results were probably the outcome of a metabolism which was concerned mainly with the maintenance of the parasite rather than with its growth and development.

Cavier and Savel (1954), who studied the effect of amino acids in the culture medium of *Ascaris lumbricoides* under axenic conditions, claimed that four amino acids, glycine, alanine, glutamic acid and tyrosine, were sufficient to cause an increased production of protein in the perienteric fluid. These results imply that the amino acids were absorbed from the medium but, again, they do not show whether any amino acid was essential.

Studies on the nutrition of nematode parasites do not yet tell us much about their requirements for vitamins. The finding that a mixture of B vitamins and vitamin C had some value in the medium for the culture of *Nippostrongylus muris* was made by Weinstein and Jones (1956) who have also (1957*b*) begun to measure the influence of single vitamins. Other evidence for the absorption of vitamins from the medium (see, for instance, Cavier and Savel, 1952*b*) is slender. There is, however, abundant evidence from the analytical work and from studies on metabolism that many vitamins are present in the tissues of nematodes and that most of the B vitamins have, in these animals, the same sort of functions as they have in non-parasitic forms (Bueding and Most, 1953). Chance and Dirnhuber (1949), Yamao (1951) and Nyberg (1952) found that thiamine, nicotinic acid, riboflavin, pyridoxine, pantothenic acid and cyanocobalamine occurred in the tissue of *Ascaris lumbricoides* and *Nippostrongylus muris* in amounts that were usually of the same order as in the hosts. Ascorbic acid, it has been claimed, occurs in the tissue of *Ascaris lumbricoides, Parascaris equorum* and *Toxocara canis* (Giroud and Rakato-Ratsimananga, 1936; Smyth *et al.*, 1945; Rogers, 1945). Though some of the methods which were used for the identification of ascorbic acid are open to criticism there is little doubt that this vitamin occurs in some nematodes.

There is a large amount of evidence (see, for instance, Bueding and Most, 1953; von Brand, 1952; Fairbairn, 1957; Goldberg, 1958) which shows that reactions involving the conventional vitamin B–containing coenzymes take part in the metabolism of parasitic nematodes as in the tissues of other animals. Though these coenzymes have seldom been isolated and identified from the tissues of parasites it seems reasonable to accept the presence of such coenzymes as the phosphopyridine nucleotides, diphosphothiamine, pyridoxal and pyridoxamine phosphate and coenzyme A.

Analytical and metabolic studies show or imply the presence in parasitic nematodes of substances which are not commonly synthesized by other animals. Whether these parasites have greater or smaller synthetic powers is unknown. Even our information on vitamins does little to establish their possible nutritional role in parasites.

The Nutrition of Other Metazoan Parasites

As with the nematodes, there is as yet little direct information about the nutrition of the Trematoda, Cestoda or Acanthocephala. For some of these groups, however, there is information which borders, and has implications on this subject. It will be briefly summarized here. Details of earlier papers are given in monographs and reviews (Dawes, 1946, pp. 530–531; Smyth, 1947, 1955; Hyman, 1951, pp. 45, 309, 411, 412; Wardle and McLeod, 1952, pp. 105–108; von Brand, 1952, pp. 204–211; Bueding and Most, 1953). Parasitic arthropods have been studied extensively (House, 1958) but they are largely ectoparasites and will not be discussed here.

Digestion and Absorption

The gut of trematodes ranges from a simple sac to a bilobed structure which usually ends blindly and which has lateral anastomizing branches. Extracellular digestion and absorption of nutrients take place in the gut of most species. Some flukes such as strigeids seem to secrete digestive enzymes externally and ingest material which is already partially digested (Szidart, 1929). In *Fasciola hepatica* the epithelial cells of the gut pass through glandular and absorptive cycles during which marked changes in the form of the cells take place (Gresson and Threadgold, 1959). The food usually consists of blood and tissue of the host, though some forms like *Diplodiscus* are said to ingest material from the gut contents of the host (Hsü and Li, 1940; Stephenson, 1947). Except in those species in which the posterior ends of the gut open to the exterior or into an excretory bladder, undigested material must be ejected from the mouth or else remain in the gut during the lifetime of the fluke. The movement of food into the gut is probably governed by the oral and pharyngeal suckers which are usually well developed except in the blood flukes. In addition, the columnar epithelium lining the gut is surrounded by a layer of circular and longitudinal muscles.

Mansour (1959) has shown that the absorption of glucose *in vitro* is not affected by ligaturing the oral opening of adult *Fasciola hepatica*. It is not known, however, if other nutrients are absorbed via the body surface. In the sporocyst, of course, this is probably the only route by which nutrients are taken up. Unfortunately little is known about the physiology of sporocysts or rediae.

The Cestoda and Acanthocephala which lack an alimentary canal must obtain all nutrients through the surface of the body. In the adult cestodes this is covered by a cuticle, similar, it seems, in structure and origin to that of the Trematoda, which rests directly on the mesenchyme. The body surface of the Acanthocephala is quite different. There is a thin cuticle overlaying a syncytial fibrous epidermis of unusual structure.

There is no evidence to show that solid food or colloidal particles can be ingested through the body surface of these parasites and it seems reasonable to suppose that most nutrients are absorbed from solution in the medium. Chandler (1943), to explain his findings that *Hymeno-*

lepis diminuta was independent of the dietary intake of protein of the host, suggested that the parasite absorbed nitrogenous substances from the intestinal mucosa. Some experimental support for this comes from the work of Chandler *et al.* (1950) who showed that labelled thiamine which was given to the host by parenteral injection reached a concentration in the parasite similar to that in the adjacent tissues of the host. Read (1951) has also emphasized the importance of close contact between the tapeworm and the intestinal mucosa. He has shown (1955) that in some species of cestodes this is facilitated by the presence of fine projections on the body surface. Following a similar line of thought, Van Cleave (1952) suggested that the body spines of the Acanthocephala may have an important function in the nutrition of these parasites because they maintain close contact between the parasite and the intestinal mucosa of the host.

In parasites that have an alimentary canal the physical and chemical properties of the medium may influence the mechanical processes concerned with the ingestion of food, a matter which needs no consideration in the Cestoda or Acanthocephala. In these animals where the absorptive surface is not enclosed in any way the animal itself has little control over the physico-chemical properties of the medium in which the absorption of nutrients must occur. Secretions from the surface of the parasite, aimed at changing the composition of the medium, might be diluted too rapidly to be effective. For these reasons it might be expected that the places in the host where cestodes and Acanthocephala could grow might be more limited than for many other parasites. In fact, these animals are not found in the stomach of vertebrates and, with few exceptions, the adults are found only in the intestine. The stomach might be unsuitable because the absorption or adsorption of nutrients might not function efficiently at high hydrogen ion concentrations. There seems no reason, however, why the adult parasites should not obtain nutrients in a suitable form, as larval stages evidently do, at some sites outside the alimentary canal.

The mechanisms by which some substances are taken up by cestodes have been examined by Read *et al.* (1960), Simmons *et al.* (1960), and Phifer (1960*a*, 1960*b*, 1960*c*). Urea, which has an important osmotic function in tissues of cestodes from elasmobranchs and may form 3.7% of the dry weight, enters the parasites by simple diffusion. Valine and leucine are taken up by more specific routes and their absorption is coupled with metabolic processes. The uptake of glucose by *Hymenolepis diminuta* is a highly specific process which takes place against a concentration gradient and probably requires the expenditure of energy which can be obtained from the metabolism of glucose or galactose.

The unusual capacity of the adult *Diphyllobothrium latum* to absorb vitamin B_{12} from the media *in vitro* or from the intestinal contents of the host *in vivo* (von Bonsdorf, 1956; Brante and Ernberg, 1957; Nyberg, 1958) seems to be characteristic of this species. At present the interest in this phenomenon arises largely in relation to the anaemia developed by the host rather than in relation to the physiology of the parasite. It is known, however, that the vitamin forms within the worm a non-dialysable complex which can be precipitated with ammonium sulphate. Treatment of the complex with alcohol, proteases, or drying and heating frees the vitamin (Nyberg and Gräsbeck, 1957). The vitamin remains in the tissues of the worm for at least 2 months after the host has been dosed (Brante and Ernberg, 1958).

Cultivation in vitro

Attempts to culture parasitic platyhelminths have often been more successful than with nematodes. This has been due in part to the use of larval stages, metacercariae or plerocercoids, which have considerable food reserves and which reach an advanced stage of development in the intermediate host so that development of adult characters takes place rapidly, sometimes even without organic nutrients in a sterile medium. For example, the plerocercoid larvae of *Ligula intestinalis* and *Schistocephalus solidus*, which occur in the body cavity of a fish, have large food reserves and are more fully developed than most larval tapeworms so that sexual maturity is reached in a few days in the final host. This can also be achieved *in vitro* in a medium lacking organic nutrients if proper attention is paid to physical and physico-chemical conditions such as temperature, oxygen tension, pH, and osmotic pressure (Joyeux and Baer, 1942; Smyth, 1955).

Among earlier work on the cultivation of cestodes the most successful seems to be that of Stunkard (1932) who kept *Crepidobothrium lönnbergii* alive for 32 days *in vitro*. During this time the parasite trebled its length and the terminal part of the strobila formed proglottids which, however, were sterile. The salt-glucose medium was fortified with a veal digest; the addition of extracts of the tissue of the host (*Necturus*) did not improve growth. Fresh serum from the host was toxic.

The cultivation of the sparganum of *Spirometra mansonoides* to the infective plerocercoid has been carried out by Mueller (1959). The procercoids from copepods grew to a length of about 2 cm in 60 days under axenic conditions in a medium containing calf serum and chick embryo extract. The plerocercoids so formed gave normal adult worms in cats.

The problems of cultivating the cestodes which lack food reserves and which do not reach a high degree of development in the intermediate host have been discussed by Smyth (1958). Some success has been obtained with *Diphyllobothrium dentriticum* which is a cestode of this sort. Smyth found that fragments cut from the posterior quarter of the plerocercoid of this species could be maintained under axenic conditions in duck embryo extract in Tyrode solution. Differentiation occurred, and by the sixth day recognizable proglottids containing parts of the reproductive system were formed. Though an advanced stage of differentiation was reached, little cytoplasmic growth occurred, so that each fragment gave rise to proglottids 1/5th to 1/10th the normal size. On the seventh or eighth day, after an advanced state of spermatogenesis had been reached, the proglottids suddenly autolysed. Smyth attributed this to shortage of nutrients necessary for cytoplasmic growth. Increased concentrations of embryo extract did not meet this need and, in fact, proved inhibitory.

Smyth's work in this field has brought the study of the nutrition of cestodes to a most interesting point where many of the technical difficulties have been overcome. And he has pointed the way in which biochemical information about the nutrition of these parasites may shortly be obtained (Smyth, 1959).

Work with trematodes has followed much the same line as that carried out with cestodes; species with well-developed larval stages which mature rapidly, largely at the expense of endogenous food reserves, have given good results. The larger flukes which develop more slowly have proved difficult.

After excysting metacercariae in pepsin-hydrochloric acid, Hunter and Chait (1952) successfully cultured *Gynaecotyla adunca* in dilute seawater; *Posthodiplostomum minimum* required yeast extract and chicken blood plasma in Tyrode solution (Ferguson, 1940). *Diplostomum flexicaudum* proved more difficult. Following the observation that cercariae of this parasite would develop to metacercariae in the eyes of vertebrates, Ferguson (1943*a*, 1943*b*) found that the addition of the lens of the eye of several species of vertebrates to "frog Ringer" allowed this to occur *in vitro*.

Adult *Haplometra cylindracea*, small flukes from the lungs of frogs, have been kept alive in Ringer's and Hédon-Fleig solutions at 20°C for about 60 to 70 days. The addition of glucose to the medium increased the deposition of glycogen in the flukes but did not increase the time of survival. In a glucose-broth medium the time of survival was 88 days (Dawes and Muller, 1957).

Results that have a more obvious bearing on the physiology of nutrition have been obtained with adult schistosomes. *Schistosomatium douthitti*, which normally lives in the veins of small rodents, will live for long periods when surgically implanted into the anterior chamber of the eyes of rats (Goodchild, 1958). This medium was not sufficient, however, to maintain normal growth of young flukes. Nor was it sufficient to maintain the sex organs, which atrophied in female worms after 25 days and in male worms after 50 days. Goodchild tentatively suggested that the low protein and low glucose content of the fluid in the anterior chamber of the eye caused this.

Ross and Bueding (1950) and Bueding and Most (1953) examined the culture *in vitro* of *Schistosoma mansoni*; even synthetic media were used. This parasite, which uses glucose rapidly, survived as well in an ultrafiltrate of the horse serum as in the whole serum. Impure protogen increased the time of survival but thioctic acid, α- and β-lipoic acids did not. The addition of amino acids to a basic synthetic medium did not greatly affect survival except when the proportions and types of amino acids were similar to those in globin (Timms and Bueding, 1959; Table XII). This, together with the presence of a protease which

TABLE XII

The Effect of Amino Acids on the Survival of Schistosoma mansoni in vitro *(after Timms and Bueding, 1959)*

The time of survival is given in days ± S.E. Survival times in (2), (3), (4) and (5) were significantly longer than in (1). There was no significant difference between (2) and (4), and (3) and (5).

	Medium	Survival time
(1)	No amino acids	2.1 ± 0.17
(2)	Mixed amino acids	3.4 ± 0.22
(3)	Globin amino acids	6.3 ± 0.24
(4)	Globin	4.2 ± 0.22
(5)	Globin plus mixed amino acids	6.4 ± 0.24

showed considerable specificity towards haemoglobin (Timms and Bueding, 1959), suggests that globin may be an important but perhaps not essential nutrient for these parasites. Other workers have kept adult *Schistosoma mansoni* alive for long periods in media of which whole blood serum was the basic component (Newsome and Robertson, 1954; Mao and Lee, 1957). The addition of glucose up to 0.1% increased the activity of the worms and allowed them to maintain normal reserves of glycogen. In addition to serum, Senft and Weller (1956) used amniotic fluid and embryo extract in their medium; the addition of red cells of mice increased the movements of the worms. In terms of survival of the adult parasite, undiluted blood serum containing 0.1% glucose seems the best medium so far devised (Robertson, 1956).

The maintenance *in vitro* of adult *Fasciola hepatica* has proved more difficult than the maintenance of most smaller flukes (Stephenson, 1947; Dawes, 1954; Rohrbacher, 1957). It has been kept alive under axenic conditions in a medium containing liver extract for 30 days. Glucose, fructose and glycerol seemed more effective in the medium than galactose, maltose, ribose or sorbitol.

The cultivation of trematodes as stages in the life cycles preceding cercariae has seldom been attempted though Ingersoll (1956) was able to maintain axenic rediae of *Cyclocoelum microstomum* in a medium containing glucose, rabbit serum and chick embryo extract for 14 days. No growth occurred and red cells in the medium were not digested by the rediae.

Gettier (1942) and Van Cleave and Ross (1944) studied the survival of *Neoechinorhynchus emydis* in saline media. Survival in 0.5% sodium chloride plus 0.02% calcium chloride was not increased by adding potassium chloride or magnesium chloride; a solution of 0.85% sodium chloride seemed to be isotonic.

The Effect of Nutrition of the Host on Parasitic Platyhelminthes

The effect of the nutrition of the final host on the number and size of the parasites has been examined extensively, though chiefly with cestodes (von Brand, 1952, pp. 204–206; Wardle and McLeod, 1952, pp. 106–107).

With some species of trematodes and cestodes deficiencies in the diet of the host do not prevent the parasites obtaining all the nutrients they need. For example, *Cryptocotyle lingua* will develop fully in gulls on vitamin-deficient diets (Rothschild, 1939); *Hymenolepis diminuta* is independent of the proteins and amino acids in the host's diet (Chandler, 1943) and more schistosomes develop in rats on a vitamin A-deficient diet than in rats on a full diet. However, there are a number of reports that host dietary deficiencies have adverse effects on cestodes and trematodes (von Brand, 1952, p. 226). The adverse effect may be small, or the parasite may fail to develop. Thus *Schistosoma mansoni* will grow normally in scorbutic guinea-pigs but the shells of the eggs of the parasites are abnormal; *Echinostoma revolutum* often failed to develop at all in pigeons kept on a diet which was deficient in vitamins A and D. The absence in the diet of the "vitamin G complex" (riboflavin) may affect the development of cestodes. Thus Addis and Chandler (1944, 1946) found that in the absence of the complex from the diet of rats it became difficult to establish infections with the cysticercoids of *Hymenolepis diminuta*, and even when they were established the growth of the parasites was poor.

The amount and quality of carbohydrate in the host's diet has pronounced effects on growth and egg production of many adult cestodes. A number of workers have shown that reducing the host's intake of carbohydrate leads to a reduction in glycogen stored in the parasite. Read and Rothman in particular have approached the study of the nutrition of cestodes in this way (Read and Rothman, 1957*a*, 1957*b*, 1957*c*; Read, 1957; Read *et al.*, 1958). This and a large volume of earlier work make it clear that carbohydrate is an essential component of the environment of a number of species. Studies *in vitro* and *in vivo* show that only a limited range of carbohydrates can be used by the parasites (Table XIII). Features of this sort may be basic in the relationship between some adult cestodes and their hosts (Read, 1959).

Metabolism and Composition of Parasites in relation to their Nutrition

The capacity of trematodes, cestodes and Acanthocephala to use carbohydrates has been assessed by (a) measuring the production of acids during fermentation (see, for example, Laurie, 1957; Read, 1957); (b) estimating the rate at which glycogen is used in the presence and absence of carbohydrate in the medium (Wardle, 1937; Read and Rothman, 1958*a*) and (*c*) by measuring the disappearance of carbohydrate from the medium (Read and Rothman, 1958*b*).

The finding that glycogen is frequently the major reserve substance in parasitic platyhelminths (Axmann, 1947; von Brand, 1952; Vernberg and Hunter, 1956) also indicates that glucose is an important substrate for the production of energy. Moreover glucose is rapidly metabolized in these parasites via both conventional and unusual pathways (see, for example, Bueding, 1950; Read, 1956; Chapter 6). Hopkins (1952), who studied the culture of *Schistocephalus solidus* in sterile medium, obtained results which implied that nutrients were absorbed only when glucose was added above a certain threshold in the medium.

In discussing their own and previous work, Read and Rothman (1958*b*) pointed out that of nine species of adult cestodes which have been examined, eight could use monosaccharides only, and of these, glucose and galactose were the only ones freely used. *Cittotaenia* sp. was the only one which used disaccharides (maltose and sucrose) in addition to the two monosaccharides. *Moniliformis dubius* (Acanthocephala) ferments glucose, fructose, galactose, mannose and maltose to acidic end-products (Laurie, 1957; Table XIII).

The amino acid or protein requirements of the parasitic platyhelminths have not been studied extensively. Though some proteins in these animals have an unusual composition (see, for example, Kent, 1957) the amino acids of the tissue show the presence of the common "essential" and "non-essential" amino acids of their host's tissues (von Brand, 1952, p. 40; Aldrich, Chandler and Daugherty, 1954; Good-

TABLE XIII

Carbohydrates Metabolized by Cestodes and Acanthocephala in vitro
(*after Read, 1959*)

Species	Carbohydrate							References
	Glucose	Galactose	Mannose	Fructose	Xylose	Maltose	Sucrose	
Cestodes								
Hymenolepis diminuta	++++	++	+?	—	+?	—	—	Read (1956); Laurie (1957)
Hymenolepis nana	++++	+++	—	—	—	—	—	Read and Rothman (1958*b*)
Hymenolepis citelli	++++	++	—	—	—	—	—	Read and Rothman (1958*b*)
Oochoristica symmetrica	++++	+++	+?	—	—	—	—	Laurie (1957)
Mesocestoides latus	++++	++	—	—	—	—	—	Read and Rothman (1958*b*)
Moniezia expansa	++++	—	?	—	?	—	?	Wardle (1937)
Cittotaenia sp.	++	+	—	—	—	+++	+++	Read and Rothman (1958*b*)
Calliobothrium verticillatum	++++	++	—	—	—	—	—	Read (1957)
Lacistorhynchus tenuis	++++	+++	—	—	—	—	—	Read (1957)
Acanthocephala								
Moniliformis dubius	+++	++	+++	++++	—	++++	?	Laurie (1957)

child and Wells, 1957; Campbell, 1960). It is not known if any of these amino acids are essential nutrients for parasites though some of them are absorbed and metabolized *in vitro* (Daugherty, 1952, 1957; Daugherty and Foster, 1958) and certain amino acids, given in the correct proportions, promote the survival of *Schistosoma mansoni* in synthetic media (Bueding and Most, 1953; Timms and Bueding, 1959).

There is evidence both from the analysis of tissues of the parasitic platyhelminths and from the studies on their metabolism that the B vitamins have the same sort of function as in other animals. There is, however, no direct biochemical evidence as to whether they can synthesize these vitamins or not.

Effects of the Host's Hormones on Parasites

There seems little doubt that the sex of the host often influences the development and metabolism of nematode and platyhelminth parasites (Todd and Hollingsworth, 1952; Aldrich *et al.*, 1954; Daugherty, 1956). It is not known, however, if these effects take place via the nutrition of the parasite.

REFERENCES

Ackert, J. E. and Spindler, L. A. (1929) *Amer. J. Hyg.* **9**, 292.
——, McIlvaine, M. F. and Crawford, N. Z. (1931) *Amer. J. Hyg.* **13**, 320.
—— and Nolf, L. O. (1931) *Amer. J. Hyg.* **13**, 337.
——, Todd, A. C. and Tanner, W. A. (1938) *Trans. Amer. micr. Soc.* **57**, 292.
—— and Whitlock, J. H. (1940) *In* "Introduction to Nematology". (J. R. Christie, ed.), M. B. Chitwood, Babylon, New York.
Addis, C. J. and Chandler, A. C. (1944) *J. Parasit.* **30**, 229.
—— (1946) *J. Parasit.* **32**, 581.
Aldrich, D. V., Chandler, A. C. and Daugherty, J. W. (1954) *Exp. Parasit.* **3**, 173.
Axmann, M. C. (1947) *J. Morph.* **80**, 321.
Brante, G. and Ernberg, T. (1957) *Scand. J. clin. lab. Invest.* **9**, 313.
—— (1958) *Acta med. scand.* **160**, 91.
Brody, G. (1954) *Exp. Parasit.* **3**, 240.
Browne, H. G. and Chowdhury, A. B. (1959) *J. Parasit.* **45**, 241.
Bueding, E. (1949) *J. exp. Med.* **89**, 107.
—— (1950) *J. gen. Physiol.* **33**, 475.
—— and Most, H. (1953) *Ann. Rev. Microbiol.* **7**, 295.
—— and Yale, H. W. (1951) *J. biol. Chem.* **193**, 411.
Campbell, J. W. (1960) *Exp. Parasit.* **9**, 1.
Carpenter, M. F. P. (1952) "The Digestive Enzymes of *Ascaris lumbricoides* var. *suis*: their Properties and Distribution in the Alimentary Canal". Abstract of Dissertation, University of Michigan, Publ. No. 3729, University Microfilms, Ann Arbor, Michigan.
Cavier, R. and Savel, J. (1952*a*) *C. R. Acad. Sci., Paris,* **234**, 2562.
—— (1952*b*) *C. R. Acad. Sci., Paris,* **234**, 1403.
—— (1954) *C. R. Acad. Sci., Paris,* **238**, 2035.
Chance, M. R. A. and Dirnhuber, P. (1949) *Parasitology,* **39**, 300.
Chandler, A. C. (1943) *Amer. J. Hyg.* **37**, 121.

—— (1953) *J. Egypt. med. Ass.* **36**, 533.
——, Read, C. P. and Nicholas, H. O. (1950) *J. Parasit.* **36**, 523.
Chitwood, B. G. and Jacobs, L. (1938) *J. Wash. Acad. Sci.* **28**, 12.
—— and Chitwood, M. B. (1940) *In* "Introduction to Nematology". (B. G. Chitwood and M. B. Chitwood, eds.), M. B. Chitwood, Babylon, New York.
—— and Oteifa, B. A. (1952) *Ann. Rev. Microbiol.* **6**, 151.
Christie, J. R. (1959) "Plant Parasitic Nematodes, their Bionomics and Control". Agricultural Experiment Stations, University of Florida, Gainesville, Florida.
Clapham, P. A. (1934) *J. Helminth.* **11**, 9.
Daugherty, J. W. (1952) *Exp. Parasit.* **1**, 331.
—— (1956) *J. Parasit.* **42**, 17.
—— (1957) *Exp. Parasit.* **6**, 60.
—— and Foster, W. B. (1958) *Exp. Parasit.* **7**, 99.
Davey, D. G. (1938) *Parasitology*, **30**, 278.
Dawes, B. (1946) "The Trematoda". Cambridge University Press, Cambridge.
—— (1954) *Nature, Lond.* **174**, 654.
—— and Muller, R. (1957) *Nature, Lond.* **180**, 1217.
Donaldson, A. W. and Otto, G. F. (1946) *Amer. J. Hyg.* **44**, 384.
Dougherty, E. C. and Keith, D. F. (1953) *J. Parasit.* **39**, 381.
—— and Hansen, E. L. (1956) *Proc. Soc. exp. Biol. Med.* **93**, 223.
Dropkin, V. H. (1955) *Exp. Parasit.* **4**, 282.
Dubos, R. J. (1948) *Bact. Rev.* **12**, 273.
Entner, N. (1957) *Arch. Biochem. Biophys.* **71**, 52.
—— and Gonzalez, C. (1959) *Exp. Parasit.* **8**, 471.
Esserman, H. B. and Sambell, P. M. (1951) *Aust. J. sci. Res.* **B4**, 575.
Fairbairn, D. (1957) *Exp. Parasit.* **6**, 491.
Fenwick, D. W. (1939) *J. Helminth.* **17**, 211.
Ferguson, M. S. (1940) *J. Parasit.* **26**, 359.
—— (1943*a*) *J. Parasit.* **29**, 319.
—— (1943*b*) *J. Parasit.* **29**, 136.
Gaafar, S. M. and Ackert, J. E. (1953) *Exp. Parasit.* **2**, 185.
Garoian, G. (1957) *Diss. Abstr.* **17**, 443.
Gettier, A. (1942) *Proc. helm. Soc. Wash.* **9**, 75.
Giroud, A. and Rakato-Ratsimananga, A. (1936) *Bull. Soc. Chim. biol., Paris,* **18**, 375.
Glaser, R. W. (1940) *Proc. Soc. exp. Biol. Med.* **43**, 512.
——, McCoy, E. E. and Girth, H. B. (1942) *J. Parasit.* **28**, 123.
—— and Stoll, N. R. (1938) *Parasitology*, **30**, 324.
Goldberg, E. (1958) *J. Parasit.* **44**, 363.
Goodchild, C. G. (1958) *Exp. Parasit.* **7**, 152.
—— and Wells, O. C. (1957) *Exp. Parasit.* **6**, 575.
Gresson, R. A. R. and Threadgold, L. T. (1959) *J. biophys. biochem. Cytol.* **6**, 157.
Hankes, L. V. and Stoner, R. D. (1956) *Proc. Soc. exp. Biol. Med.* **91**, 443.
—— (1958) *Exp. Parasit.* **7**, 92.
Hawking, F. (1954) *Ann. trop. Med. Parasit.* **48**, 382.
—— (1955) *In* "Mechanisms of Microbial Pathogenicity". 5th Symp. of Soc. gen. Microbiol. (J. W. Howie and A. J. O'Hea, eds.), Cambridge University Press, Cambridge.
Hirsch, G. C. and Bretschneider, L. H. (1937) *Cytologia, Tokyo, Fugii Jub. Vol.* 424.
Hobson, A. D. (1948) *Parasitology*, **38**, 183.
Hoeppli, R. and Feng, L. C. (1931) *Chin. med. J.* **17**, 589.
—— (1933) *Arch. Schiffs.-u Tropenhyg.* **37**, 176.

——, Feng, L. C. and Chu, H. J. (1938) *Chin. med. J.* **2**, Suppl. 343.
Hopkins, C. A. (1952). *Exp. Parasit.* **1**, 196.
House, H. L. (1958) *Exp. Parasit.* **7**, 555.
Hsü, H. F. (1938) *Bull. Fan Inst. Biol., Peking, Zool. Ser.* **8**, 121.
—— and Li, S. Y. (1940) *Chin. med. J.* **57**, 559.
Hunter, G. C. (1953) *Nutr. Abstr. Rev.* **23**, 705.
Hunter, W. S. and Chait, D. C. (1952) *J. Parasit.* **38**, 87.
Hyman, L. H. (1951) "The Invertebrates", Vols. II and III. McGraw-Hill Book Co., New York.
Ingersoll, E. M. (1956) *Exp. Parasit.* **5**, 231.
Janicki, M. J. (1939) *Zool. Polon.* **3**, 189.
Joyeux, C. and Baer, J. G. (1942) *Bull. Mus. Hist. nat. Marseille*, **2**, 1.
Kent, H. N. (1957) *Exp. Parasit.* **6**, 486.
Lapage, G. (1933) *Nature, Lond.* **131**, 583.
Laurie, J. S. (1957) *Exp. Parasit.* **6**, 245.
Lawrence, J. J. (1948) *Aust. J. exp. Biol. med. Sci.* **26**, 1.
Maldonado, J. F. and Asenjo, C. F. (1953) *Exp. Parasit.* **2**, 374.
Mansour, T. E. (1959) *Biochim. biophys. Acta*, **34**, 456.
Mao, S. P. and Lee, K. L. (1957) *Med. Parazit.* **26**, 166 (seen as *Helminth. Abstr.* **26**, 78).
Massey, V. and Rogers, W. P. (1950). *Aust. J. sci. Res.* **B3**, 251.
McCoy, O. R. (1929) *Amer. J. Hyg.* **10**, 140.
—— (1930) *Amer. J. Hyg.* **11**, 413.
McKee, R. W. (1951) *In* "Biochemistry and Physiology of Protozoa". (A. Lwoff, ed.), Academic Press, New York.
Mountain, W. B. (1955) *Proc. helm. Soc. Wash.* **22**, 49.
Mueller, J. F. (1928) *Z. Zellforsch.* **8**, 361.
—— (1959) *J. Parasit.* **45**, 561.
Newsome, J. and Robertson, D. L. H. (1954) *Amer. J. trop. Med. Parasit.* **48**, 194.
Nicholas, W. L. and McEntegart, M. G. (1957) *J. Helminth.* **31**, 135.
Nishi, M. (1933) *J. med. Ass. Formosa*, **32**, 677.
Nyberg, W. (1952) *Acta med. scand.* **144**, Suppl. 271. 1.
—— (1958) *Exp. Parasit.* **7**, 178.
—— and Gräsbeck, R. (1957) *Scand. J. clin. lab. Invest.* **9**, 383.
Oteifa, B. A. (1953) *Phytopathology*, **43**, 171.
Phifer, K. (1960*a*) *J. Parasit.* **46**, 51.
—— (1960*b*) *J. Parasit.* **46**, 137.
—— (1960*c*) *J. Parasit.* **46**, 145.
Pitts, T. D. and Ball, G. H. (1955) *J. Parasit.* **41**, Suppl. 47.
Price, W. H. (1948) *J. gen. Phys.* **31**, 233.
Rathbone, L. and Rees, K. R. (1954) *Biochim. biophys. Acta*, **15**, 126.
Read, C. P. (1951) *J. Parasit.* **37**, 174.
—— (1955) *In* "Some Physiological Aspects and Consequences of Parasitism". (W. H. Cole, ed.), Rutgers University Press, New Brunswick.
—— (1956) *Exp. Parasit.* **5**, 325.
—— (1957) *Exp. Parasit.* **6**, 288.
—— (1959) *Exp. Parasit.* **8**, 365.
—— and Rothman, A. H. (1957*a*) *Exp. Parasit.* **6**, 1.
—— (1957*b*) *Exp. Parasit.* **6**, 280.
—— (1957*c*) *Exp. Parasit.* **6**, 294.
—— (1958*a*) *Exp. Parasit.* **7**, 191.
—— (1958*b*) *Exp. Parasit.* **7**, 217.

——, Schiller, E. L. and Phifer, K. (1958) *Exp. Parasit.* **7**, 198.
——, Simmons, J. E. and Rothman, A. H. (1960) *J. Parasit.* **46**, 33.
Reid, W. M. (1944) *J. Parasit.* **30**, Suppl. 12.
—— (1945*a*) *J. Parasit.* **31**, 406.
—— (1945*b*) *Amer. J. Hyg.* **41**, 150.
Riedel, B. B. and Ackert, J. E. (1951) *Poult. Sci.* **30**, 497.
Robertson, D. L. H. (1956) *J. Helminth.* **29**, 193.
Rogers, W. P. (1940*a*) *J. Helminth.* **18**, 53.
—— (1940*b*) *J. Helminth.* **18**, 143.
—— (1940*c*) *J. Helminth.* **18**, 103.
—— (1941*a*) *J. Helminth.* **19**, 35.
—— (1941*b*) *J. Helminth.* **19**, 47.
—— (1945) *Parasitology*, **36**, 211.
—— and Lazarus, M. (1949) *Parasitology*, **39**, 245.
Rohrbacher, G. H. (1957) *J. Parasit.* **43**, 9.
Ross, O. A. and Bueding, E. (1950) *Proc. Soc. exp. Biol. Med.* **73**, 179.
Rothschild, M. (1939) *Novit. zool.* **41**, 178.
Savel, J. (1955) *Rev. Pathol. comp.* **55**, 213.
Senft, A. W. and Weller, T. H. (1956) *Proc. Soc. exp. Biol. Med.* **93**, 16.
Silverman, P. H. (1959) *Nature, Lond.* **183**, 197.
Simmons, J. E., Read, C. P. and Rothman, A. H. (1960) *J. Parasit.* **46**, 43.
Smyth, J. D. (1947) *Biol. Rev.* **22**, 214.
—— (1955) *Rev. ibér. Parasit.*, Tom. extraord., 65.
—— (1958) *Nature, Lond.* **181**, 1119.
—— (1959) *Ann. N. Y. Acad. Sci.* **77**, 102.
——, Bingley, W. J. and Hill, G. R. (1945) *Parasitology*, **21**, 214.
Stephenson, W. (1947) *Parasitology*, **38**, 116.
Stoll, N. R. (1953) *J. Parasit.* **39**, 422.
Stoner, R. D. and Hankes, L. V. (1955) *Exp. Parasit.* **4**, 435.
—— (1958) *Exp. Parasit.* **7**, 145.
Stunkard, H. W. (1932) *J. Parasit.* **19**, 163.
Szidart, L. (1929) *Z. Parasitenk.* **1**, 612.
Taylor, A. E. R. (1960) *Exp. Parasit.* **9**, 113.
Thorson, R. E. (1955) *J. Parasit.* **41**, Suppl. 41.
Threlkeld, L. N. L., Price, N. O. and Linkous, W. H. (1956) *Amer. J. vet. Res.* **17**, 246.
Timms, A. R. and Bueding, E. (1959) *Brit. J. Pharmacol.* **14**, 68.
Tiner, J. D. (1960) *Exp. Parasit.* **9**, 121.
Todd, A. C. and Hollingsworth, K. D. (1952) *Exp. Parasit.* **1**, 303.
Toryu, Y. (1933) *Sci. Rep. Tôhoku Univ.* **8**, 65.
Tracey, M. V. (1958) *Nematologica*, **3**, 179.
Van Cleave, H. J. (1952) *Exp. Parasit.* **1**, 305.
—— and Ross, E. (1944) *J. Parasit.* **30**, 369.
Vernberg, W. B. and Hunter, W. S. (1956) *Exp. Parasit.* **5**, 441.
von Bonsdorff, B. (1956) *Exp. Parasit.* **5**, 207.
von Brand, T. (1937) *J. Parasit.* **23**, 68.
—— (1950) *J. Parasit.* **36**, 178.
—— (1952) "Chemical Physiology of Endoparasitic Animals". Academic Press, New York.
—— and Otto, G. F. (1938) *Amer. J. Hyg.* **27**, 683.
—— and Simpson, W. F. (1942) *Proc. Soc. exp. Biol. Med.* **49**, 245.
—— (1944) *J. Parasit.* **30**, 121.

—— (1945) *Proc. Soc. exp. Biol. Med.* **60**, 368.
——, Weinstein, P. P., Mehlman, B. and Weinbach, E. C. (1952) *Exp. Parasit.* **1**, 245.
Wardle, R. A. (1937) *Canad. J. Res.* **D15**, 117.
—— and McLeod, J. A. (1952) "The Zoology of Tapeworms". University of Minnesota Press, Minneapolis.
Watt, J. Y. C. (1944) *Amer. J. Hyg.* **39**, 145.
Weinstein, P. P. (1953) *Amer. J. Hyg.* **58**, 352.
—— and Jones, M. F. (1956) *J. Parasit.* **42**, 215.
—— (1957*a*) *J. Parasit.* **43**, Suppl. 45.
—— (1957*b*) *Amer. J. trop. Med. Hyg.* **6**, 480.
Weller, T. H. (1943) *Amer. J. Path.* **19**, 503.
Wells, H. S. (1931) *J. Parasit.* **17**, 167.
Wetzel, R. (1931) *J. Parasit.* **17**, 93.
Yamao, Y. (1951) *Igaku to Seibutsugaku* (*Med. and Biol.*) **20**, 134 (seen as *Chem. Abstr.* **46**, 9734).
Zaiman, H. (1940) *J. Parasit.* **26**, Suppl. 44.

PART IV

The Development and Maintenance of Parasitism

General Introduction

IF the harmonious evolution of a parasite and its host is to proceed, a balance must be reached between the harmful actions of the parasite on the host and the capacity of the host to resist the parasite or its harmful actions. A highly pathogenic parasite may cause, directly or indirectly, the death of the host and this could lead to the elimination of the host species and the parasite. On the other hand the host might develop a complete resistance to the parasite.

The balance between the host and the parasite would be influenced by many factors, though some would be more important for some species than for others. In parasites which multiply within the host at least part of the balancing mechanism must function by affecting this multiplication. However, metazoan parasites, though they increase in size, rarely multiply within the host and the size of an infection is largely limited by the number of infective agents picked up by the host. The evolution of the metazoan parasite and its host might involve a balanced condition in which the disadvantages experienced by the host in becoming infected might be balanced by advantages gained during exposure to infection.

The chief factors which would influence the chances that infective agents should reach the host would be the numbers of infective agents produced during the life cycle of the parasite, their capacity to survive outside the host, and their behaviour in relation to that host. In this part of the book some of these factors are discussed, especially in relation to the maintenance and evolution of parasitism.

CHAPTER 9

The Propagation of Parasites

ONE stage or other of most metazoan parasites must leave the host, either to be free living or to be transferred to another host for a period, before the life cycle can be completed. Thus the continued multiplication of a metazoan parasite within the one host is rare. When it does occur, as in *Probstmayria vivipara*, there is often some doubt if the organism is a true parasite. The size of an infection with metazoan parasites is thus limited unless new infective agents become available. Under these circumstances the host is protected, to some degree, against overwhelming numbers of parasites. The parasites might benefit too, because their antigenic structure might vary more than in an infection built up from a few individuals.

This type of life cycle requires large numbers of infective agents because the hazards of transfer from host to host are considerable, even when there is an intermediate host. Commonly, but not always, the parasite produces more offspring than its free-living relative. This may be achieved by the greater production of eggs and sperm, by parthenogenesis, hermaphroditism of various types, and by asexual reproduction. Other adaptations, such as the development of a bursa in strongylid nematodes, which increases the efficiency of fertilization, are also found.

In view of the importance of reproduction in the life cycle of parasites it is surprising that so little work has been conducted on the physiology of the process. Thus little or nothing is known of the mechanisms which inhibit or accelerate the development of asexual or sexual reproduction during the life cycle. And though information on the biochemistry of embryonation is available (see Chapter 4) little is known of the biochemistry of fertilization and the synthesis of components of the egg. A connected account of the physiology of reproduction of parasites is not possible at the present time and only a few isolated facts and inferences are discussed here.

The Eggs and Sperm of Nematode Parasites

Much of the early work on the cytology of germ cells was carried out with *Parascaris equorum* and as a result this aspect of oögenesis and spermatogenesis in the Nematoda is well understood. The early work was summarized by Walton (1924); later reviews are by Chitwood and Chitwood (1940, p. 139) and Walton (1940, p. 205). In some nematodes the germ cells are formed throughout the length of the gonad, but as a rule, proliferation takes place at the blind proximal end, usually from a single large terminal cell. The germinal zone of the gonad is followed by the growth zone, usually much elongated in parasitic forms, where the gametogonia enlarge and differentiate. The oögonia or, in the male, the spermatogonia are on a germinal chord or a central cytoplasmic strand called the rachis. As they move distally oöcytes or spermatocytes are freed as single cells at the beginning of the duct.

The oögonia and oöcytes enlarge as they pass down the reproductive organ (Chitwood and Chitwood, 1940, p. 139). In *Ascaris lumbricoides*, and probably in other species of parasitic nematodes also, this is due to the accumulation of lipid, carbohydrate, and protein (Fairbairn, 1957). The basic materials for the synthesis of these substances must be supplied in the fluid medium surrounding the cells or from the rachis (Prestage, 1960) because follicle cells are absent. Presumably the materials pass through the wall of the gonad from the perienteric fluid. The form in which the basic materials are supplied to the oöcytes is unknown. Certainly conditions in the ovaries of *Ascaris lumbricoides*, unlike those in other tissues, seem to be directed towards the synthesis of amino acids (Pollak and Fairbairn, 1955*a*, 1955*b*). No detailed studies on the actual synthesis of proteins or other large molecules in the ovaries or testes have been carried out though it is known that the oöcytes contain granules which are composed largely of three similar proteins which are high in proline (Ebel and Colas, 1954; Fauré-Fremiet, Ebel and Colas, 1954). It is thought that later in development these proteins take part in the synthesis of one of the coverings of the egg (Yanagisawa, 1955).

The spermatozoa of nematodes are generally lobate and make slow amoeboid movements. In some species, e.g. *Passalurus ambiguus*, the sperm bear a superficial resemblance to the flagellate type and it has been suggested that the sperm of the free-living *Trilobus longus* are truly flagellate (Chitwood, 1931; Walton, 1940, p. 206). The cone-shaped spermatozoa of *Parascaris equorum* have in their posterior, more pointed region a large "refringent body" which is regarded as the homologue of the acrosome of flagellate sperm (Bowen, 1925). Similar structures probably exist in the sperm of other species.

The origin, structure and function of the acrosome in nematodes have been examined by a number of workers (Fauré-Fremiet, 1913; Fauré-Fremiet and Filhol, 1937; Panijel, 1950). In *Parascaris equorum* it consists of a Gram-staining protein, "ascaridine". An electrophoretically homogeneous sample contained no lipid or reducing sugar; it was high in aspartic acid and tryptophane, and contained purine (0.2% purine nitrogen) and phosphorus (0.02%). On fertilization the entire sperm entered the egg. As it moved towards the centre of the egg the acrosome became faint and ribonucleic acid appeared in the cytoplasm ahead of it. The deoxyribonucleic acid contributed by the sperm would be about 2.5×10^{-6} μg whereas the fertilized egg contained 290×10^{-6} μg. Even allowing for the two pronuclei and polar bodies this was a large excess and it seems that some deoxyribonucleic acid was present in the cytoplasm (Nigon and Bovet, 1955).

The Formation of the Egg-shell

The structure and composition of the coverings (the "egg-shell") of eggs of nematodes have been examined extensively. The results are confused, however, because it is difficult to identify the origin of different layers and because unsatisfactory chemical tests have sometimes been used for examining the composition. Little work on the synthesis of components of the shell has been carried out. Early work has been reviewed by Wottge (1937) and Jacobs (1940, p. 177); Fairbairn (1957) has reviewed work on *Ascaris*.

To avoid confusion several of the alternative names which have been used for each layer will be given. The different layers will be discussed in order of their formation, i.e. the layers of the primary egg envelope will be described in order from the outermost inwards because each layer is formed *under* the previous one. Finally the tertiary envelope, which is secreted by the uterus and forms the coat *over* the primary egg envelope, will be discussed.

The Primary Egg Envelope

As the egg passes down the oviduct following fertilization, three or possibly four layers are formed by the activity of the egg itself. Sometimes layers may be missing or fused with one another. Moreover individual layers may be laminated so it is difficult to compare different species. The primary egg envelope consists of an inner membrane of lipid, about which there is little dispute, and a complex outer "shell proper" (Chitwood, 1938), "homogeneous membrane" (Wottge, 1937) or "membrana lucida" (Zawadowsky, 1928; Zawadowsky, Vorobieva and Petrova, 1929) which is composed of two or three layers of different composition and optical properties.

The outer layer of the primary egg envelope

The oöcyte is covered by a membrane which in some species, e.g. *Syphacia obvelata*, is thick and is said to have a micropyle through which the sperm passes. Many workers doubt this. After the sperm has entered the egg, in many species the membrane becomes thickened and lifted from the surface to form a "fertilization membrane" (Wottge, 1937; Yanagisawa, 1955). This layer may be formed or thickened by secretions from granules which are extruded from the egg after fertilization, e.g. in the Oxyuroidea (Monné and Hönig, 1955*a*). It is the outer layer of the primary egg envelope; other layers secreted by the egg form underneath it. It has been called "fertilization membrane", exterior layer or membrane, and cortical layer. In some species (see Table XIV) it can be distinguished clearly as a separate layer, in others it is said to be merely the outermost and thickest of a number of lamellae which are interposed in the underlying layer; or it may be greatly reduced and completely fused with the underlying layer.

The optical properties and structure may vary in different species. It may be formed of rodlets or lamellae and it is usually birefringent with respect to the axes of the egg. Electron micrographs of sections of the egg-shell of *Ascaris lumbricoides* (Rogers, 1956) show a denser layer about 0.4 μ thick at the outer edge of the primary egg envelope. Rogers did not regard this as a separate layer because it had a "typical chitin structure". On the other hand there is evidence that a layer of protein is present in this part of the shell. It seems that the fertilization membrane is a protein which undergoes changes following fertilization. In some species it becomes brown and resistant to the action of sulphuric acid, hydrochloric acid, sodium sulphide, sodium thioglycollate and a variety of proteases (Chitwood, 1938; Ammon and Debusmann-Morgenroth, 1953; Kreuzer, 1953; Monné and Hönig, 1954, 1955*a*). However it is generally soluble in sodium hypochlorite and in 10% sodium hydroxide. On the basis of these results and on staining reactions Monné and Hönig (1954, 1955*a*) regarded this protein as quinone-tanned, with and without cystine cross-links in different species. It is doubtful if information obtained in this way is sufficient or specific enough to identify the protein. Acid hydrolysates of this material from *Ascaris lumbricoides* contained the following amino acids: leucine, valine, methionine, alanine, α-aminobutyric acid, lysine, histidine, proline, aspartic acid and arginine (Kreuzer, 1953), a composition which suggests a non-keratinous scleroprotein.

It seems reasonable to accept this outer protein layer of the primary egg envelope as occurring commonly in parasitic nematodes, but it would seem unwise to designate the protein specifically at present (Table XIV). The thickness of the protein layer varies greatly in different

TABLE XIV

The Occurrence and Possible Composition of the Outer Layer of the Primary Egg Envelope of Nematodes

Organism	Occurrence	Composition	References
Ascaris sp. *Parascaris* sp. *Ascaridia* spp. *Paraspidodera* sp. *Toxocara* spp. *Heterakis* sp.	present (as the thickened outermost layer of lamellae extending into the underlying layer?)	protein (lipoprotein? quinone-tanned protein without cystine cross-links?)	Monné and Hönig (1955*a*); Kreuzer (1953) Wottge (1937)
Trichuris spp. *Capillaria* sp.	present (consists of several lamellae?)	protein (quinone-tanned, cystine cross-linked?)	Monné and Hönig (1954)
Dioctophyme sp.	present	probably protein (formalin-fixed material)	Chitwood (1938)
Heterodera sp. *Ditylenchus* sp.	absent or fused with underlying layer?	—	Chitwood (1938)
Passalurus sp. *Oxyuris* sp. *Syphacia* sp. *Aspicularis* sp. *Enterobius* sp.	present (fused with underlying layer in *Enterobius*?)	protein (quinone-tanned?)	Monné and Hönig (1955*a*) Jacobs and Jones (1939)
Cruzia sp.	absent		Crites (1958)
Strongyloidea (15 genera)	present? (fused with underlying layer?)	protein (quinone-tanned)	Monné and Hönig (1955*a*)

species. In the Strongyloidea it is very thin except in *Nematodirus*, *Nematodirella* and *Syngamus*; it is thicker in the Ascaroidea, Oxyuroidea and in *Trichuris* and *Capillaria*. Monné and Hönig (1955*a*) therefore suggested that infective eggs, which might have to withstand unfavourable climatic conditions, would have a thick layer of this protein, especially if the underlying layer was not thickened. In species in which only a short part of the life cycle was spent as the egg this layer of protein would be thin. Just what protective function it serves is unknown.

In *Ascaris lumbricoides* the layer is permeable to vital stains and water (Wottge, 1937), so its function may be to give mechanical strength to the shell and protect more brittle but less permeable layers below.

In some operculate eggs such as those of *Passulurus ambiguus*, *Syphacia obvelata* (Fig. 37), *Capillaria* sp. and *Trichuris* spp. this outer layer of the primary egg envelope is interrupted or incomplete (Monné and Hönig, 1954, 1955*a*). For *Enterobius vermicularis*, however, it is the underlying layer which is missing at the hatching area (Jacobs and Jones, 1939). Operculae, when definite structures are present, may be of chitin as in *Capillaria* sp. and *Trichuris* spp. (Monné and Hönig, 1954) or perhaps "mucoid" as in *Dioctophyme renale* (Chitwood, 1938).

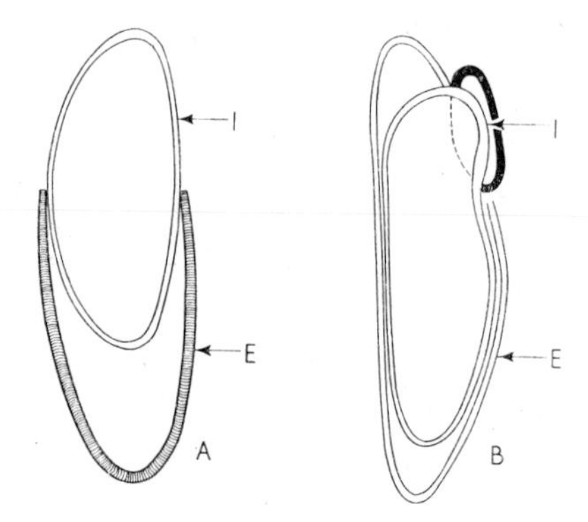

FIG. 37. The egg-shells of *Passalurus ambiguus* (A) and *Syphacia obvelata* (B) showing the separation of layers when crushed; E, outer layer of the primary egg envelope (protein); I, the hard shell layer of the primary egg envelope (largely chitin) thickened under the operculum (after Monné and Hönig, 1955*a*).

The "hard shell" layer of the primary egg envelope

The layer which lies immediately under the "fertilization membrane" has been called the hard shell, shell proper, chitinous layer, refractive layer, birefringent layer, homogeneous membrane and interior coat. It is perhaps best designated as that layer which lies immediately under the outermost layer of the primary egg envelope and which usually contains the chitin of the egg-shell. In *Parascaris equorum, Ascaris lumbricoides, Cruzia americana* and presumably in other species also, it is secreted by the cytoplasm of the egg soon after the fertilization membrane is formed (Wottge, 1937; Rogers, 1956; Crites, 1958). Generally it is a transparent layer which contains chitin (Table XV). This substance has been identified on the basis of solubility (it is soluble in sodium hypochlorite and in hot concentrated sulphuric acid, and insoluble in hot alkali), the chitosan colour reaction (Campbell, 1929) and by the identification of glucosamine or

TABLE XV

The Occurrence and Possible Composition of the Hard Shell in the Primary Egg Envelope of Nematodes

Organism	Occurrence	Composition	References
Ascaris sp. *Parascaris* sp. *Ascaridia* spp. *Paraspidodera* sp. *Toxocara* spp. *Heterakis* sp.	present as a thick transparent layer (made up of lamellae?)	chiefly chitin (some protein also present, nature of association with chitin unknown)	Chitwood (1938) Monné and Hönig (1955*a*) Schulze (1924)
Trichuris spp. *Capillaria* sp.	present (made up of submicroscopic lamellae?)	protein? (quinone-tanned cystine cross-linked?)	Monné and Hönig (1954)
Dioctophyme sp.	present	chitin (plus protein?)	Chitwood (1938)
Heterodera sp. *Ditylenchus* sp.	present present	chitin (plus protein?) presumably chitin	Chitwood (1938)
Passalurus sp. *Oxyuris* sp. *Aspicularis* sp. *Enterobius* sp. *Cruzia* sp.	present (thickened under the operculum in *Enterobius*) present	chitin and protein	Monné and Hönig (1955*a*) Jacobs and Jones (1939) Crites (1958)
Strongyloidea (15 genera)	present	protein but may contain small amounts of chitin	Monné and Hönig (1955*a*)

n-acetylglucosamine in the acid hydrolysates of material from *Ascaris lumbricoides* and *Parascaris equorum* (Fauré-Fremiet, 1913; Kreuzer, 1953). Fauré-Fremiet (1912, 1913) showed that about half the glycogen in the egg was used for the synthesis of glucosamine at the time of the formation of the chitin, but the actual route of the synthesis has not been examined.

Though many workers have regarded the hard shell as transparent and largely homogeneous (Schmidt, 1936; Wottge, 1937), Monné and Hönig (1955*a*) found that this layer in the egg-shells of *Ascaris* sp.,

Parascaris sp. and *Toxocara* spp. consisted of several lamellae. Studies on the birefringence and the disintegration of the egg-shells in concentrated sulphuric acid gave these authors the view that the hard shell consisted of layers of chitin separated by thin layers of protein. Electron micrographs of material fixed in osmium tetroxide or Carnoy's solution and sectioned in methylmethacrylate did not show this type of structure (Rogers, 1956). Instead the microfibres of chitin, which were branched and 75 to 400 Å in diameter, were found to form a loose, irregular reticulum, 3 to 4 μ thick.

There are indications that the proportion of chitin in the hard shell of nematodes varies greatly. Thus in the Ascaroidea and, to a less extent, the Oxyuroidea, the hard shell is largely chitin with small amounts of protein. At the other extreme are *Trichuris* spp. and *Capillaria* sp. where the chitin seems to be confined to the plugs, and the Strongyloidea, in which the hard shell may be entirely protein (Monné and Hönig, 1955*a*). It is the view of Monné and Hönig (1955*a*) that the protein in this part of the shell is quinone-tanned like that in the outer layer of the primary envelope.

"Yanagisawa's layer" in the primary egg envelope

A layer between the chitinous hard shell and the inner lipoid layer of the primary egg envelope is said to be present in egg-shells of *Ascaris lumbricoides* and *Enterobius vermicularis* (Zawadowsky and Schalimov, 1929; Yanagisawa, 1955). Yanagisawa and Ishii (1954) found that this hard layer was formed from granules which stained with acid dyes and which appeared in the cytoplasm early in the development of oögonia of *Ascaris*. Jacobs and Jones (1939) could not find this layer in the eggs of *Enterobius vermicularis* and thought that Zawadowsky and Schalimov (1929) had identified the interface between the inner lipoid layer and the chitinous layer as a separate structure. Electron micrographs of sections of egg-shells of *Ascaris lumbricoides* (Rogers, 1956) gave no indication that this layer was present.

The granules in the oöcyte which Yanagisawa (1955) regarded as precursors of the third membrane in the egg-shells of *Ascaris lumbricoides* are probably similar to the hyaline spheres in the eggs of *Parascaris equorum*. The spheres are composed of three closely related proteins in which proline forms more than 20% of the total amino acids (Fauré-Fremiet, 1913; Fauré-Fremiet, Ebel and Colas, 1953, 1954; Ebel and Colas, 1954).

The inner layer of the primary egg envelope

This layer is present as a membrane primarily composed of lipids in the egg-shells of most of the parasitic nematodes that have been examined. It has been called the lipoid layer, vitelline membrane, or fibrous membrane. It is formed soon after the chitinous hard shell is laid down. According to Fauré-Fremiet (1913) this layer is formed in *Parascaris equorum* from birefringent granules which move from the centre of the oöcyte to the surface of the cytoplasm where they are discharged to form the inner layer of the egg-shell. The thickness and structure of this layer varies in different nematodes; in the Strongyloidea it is thin and isotropic. When the egg is the infective stage and may be exposed to unfavourable climatic conditions the lipid is oriented and increases in thickness from that in *Trichuris* to *Oxyuris* and some Ascaroidea. In *Ascaris lumbricoides* the layer increases to 2 μ in thickness as the egg passes down the uterus (Monné and Hönig, 1955*a*; Yanagisawa, 1955).

The predominant material in this layer has, in the egg-shells of different species, been called lipid, wax-like, sterol, cholesterol and myricyl palmitate (see, for example, Wottge, 1937; Chitwood, 1938; Timm, 1950; Crites, 1958). However, only the material from *Ascaris lumbricoides* has been isolated and the structure examined. Flury (1912) first obtained this material as a waxy alcohol from saponified gonads and called it ascaryl alcohol. Later workers established the empirical formula, $C_{33}H_{68}O_4$ (Schulz and Becker, 1933) and the structural details (Polonsky, Fouquey, Ferreol and Lederer, 1955; Fouquey, Polonsky and Lederer, 1957). Ascaryl alcohol, prepared from material from whole *Parascaris equorum* which had been saponified, contained three glycosides: the glycoside of hydroxyhentriacontane and a 3,6-deoxyaldohexose, the glycoside of 2,6-dihydroxyhentriacontane and a 3,6-deoxyaldohexose, and the glycoside of 2,6-dihydroxyhentriacontane with two molecules of the 3,6-deoxyaldohexose. The refringent granules in the eggs of *Parascaris equorum*, which give rise to the inner layer of the primary egg envelope, seem to be composed largely of diacetate and dipropionate esters of one of the ascarosides. The layer itself, isolated from the eggs of *Ascaris lumbricoides*, is 75% unesterified ascarosides, 25% protein, with traces of sterols (Fairbairn and Passey, 1955; Fairbairn, 1957). There is evidence that protein is present in this layer in other species of nematodes (Monné and Hönig, 1955*a*).

It is clear that this layer of the primary envelope is the main permeability barrier of the egg-shell. Even when other layers of the shell have been removed by the action of sodium hypochlorite or by other methods the egg is still protected from a number of solutions which normally attack tissue (Ransom and Foster, 1920; Chitwood, 1938; Jacobs and Jones, 1939; Fairbairn and Passey, 1955). The layer melts at 70°C; treatment at this temperature makes the egg-shells of *Ascaris lumbricoides* much more permeable (Chitwood, 1938).

The Egg Envelope Secreted by the Uterus

Secretions from the ovary itself take no direct part in the formation of the egg-shells of nematodes. There is thus no chorion or secondary egg envelope. In some nematodes, however, there is a tertiary egg envelope, outside the primary egg envelope, which is secreted by cells in the wall of the uterus. This layer has been called albuminous membrane, proteinaceous membrane, protein coat, secondary or tertiary envelope, mammilated coat and cortical layer. It is present on the eggs of a number of species, especially in the Ascaroidea where it may be the thickest layer of the egg-shell. It is absent from most of the Oxyuroidea and Strongyloidea (see Table XVI). Generally this layer is found

TABLE XVI

The Occurrence and Nature of an Outer Covering, Secreted by the Uterus, on the "Egg-shells" of some Nematodes

Organism	Occurrence	Composition	References
Ascaris sp.	present	protein and carbohydrate ("mucoid")	Monné and Hönig (1955*a*) Chitwood (1938)
Parascaris sp.	present	"mucoid" + lipid (?)	Wottge (1937)
Ascaridia spp.	probably present	"mucoid"	Monné and Hönig (1955*a*)
Toxocara spp.	probably present	"mucoid"	Monné and Hönig (1955*a*)
Dioctophyme sp.	present	doubtful: probably protein	Chitwood (1938)
Passalurus sp.	absent or not obvious	—	Monné and Hönig (1955*a*)
Oxyuris sp.	absent or not obvious	—	Monné and Hönig (1955*a*)
Syphacia sp.	absent or not obvious	—	Monné and Hönig (1955*a*)
Enterobius sp.	present	protein	Jacobs and Jones (1939)
Cruzia sp.	present	mucoprotein, some lipid	Crites (1958)
Heterodera sp.	present	"mucoid"	Chitwood (1938)
Ditylenchus sp.	absent or not obvious	—	Chitwood (1938)
Strongyloidea (15 genera)	absent or not obvious	—	Monné and Hönig (1955*a*)
Trichuris spp.	absent or not obvious	—	Monné and Hönig (1954)
Capillaria sp.	absent or not obvious	—	Monné and Hönig (1954)

as a covering on individual eggs as in *Ascaris lumbricoides, Dioctophyme renale* (Chitwood, 1938) and *Enterobius vermicularis* (Jacobs and Jones, 1939) or as a gelatinous mass in which the eggs are embedded as in *Heterodera marioni* (Chitwood 1938). The gelatinous mass in which eggs of *Meloidogyne* spp. are embedded is secreted by the rectal glands and not by the uterus (Maggenti and Allen, 1960). Sections of the egg-shells of *Ascaris lumbricoides* examined with the electron microscope showed the layer as a dense reticulated material containing granules. The fibrils of the reticulum had a diameter of about 150 Å and branched irregularly from the granules (Rogers, 1956).

In most species material in this layer of the shell gives staining reactions for protein and carbohydrate and has therefore been regarded as a conjugated protein. Though some of the histochemical studies have been extensive (Monné and Hönig, 1955*a*) it seems unwise to describe the material as "mucoid" until more precise details of its composition are known. Wottge (1937) obtained a histological staining reaction for lipid with this layer on the eggs of *Parascaris equorum* but other workers have not confirmed this with other species. There is no doubt that proteins are present because a variety of proteolytic enzymes attack this layer. Acid hydrolysates of material from *Ascaris lumbricoides* contained leucine, valine, alanine, aspartic acid, lysine, arginine, proline, histidine, glutamic acid, and serine (Kreuzer, 1953).

In some species this outer covering of the egg-shell changes considerably during the passage of the eggs down the gut of the host. For instance the uterine secretion on the eggs of *Ascaris lumbricoides* is at first colourless and transparent, and is attacked by dilute acids and alkalis or proteases. However, the covering on eggs collected from faeces is brown and is not attacked by these substances (Monné and Hönig, 1955*a*). It is not known what substances in the gut of the host bring about this change.

The synthesis of the outer coverings of the egg-shell has not been studied. On the basis of staining reactions Monné and Hönig (1955*a*) considered that in *Ascaris lumbricoides* it consisted of "protein and a mucopolysaccharide provided with sulphuric acid residues". Staining with periodic acid Schiff reagent indicated the presence of the same polysaccharide in the cells of the uterine wall.

The Function of the Egg-shell in Nematode Parasites

One or more layers of the egg-shell may be thickened in different species (Fig. 38). This is seen to the greatest extent in parasites of the alimentary canal, like *Ascaris lumbricoides*, in which the egg is the infective stage. The thickened lipoid layer is impermeable to most substances except gases and lipoid solvents. Monné and Hönig (1955*a*) gave special emphasis to the importance of this layer as a protection against desiccation and they suggested that it would be absent from the egg-shells of marine nematodes. It is absent from the egg-shells of *Strongyloides ratti* which are produced parthenogenetically by parasitic females (Chitwood and Graham, 1940). These eggs develop normally though the shells are more permeable to dyes than in most species. It is not known if they are more sensitive to desiccation than other eggs.

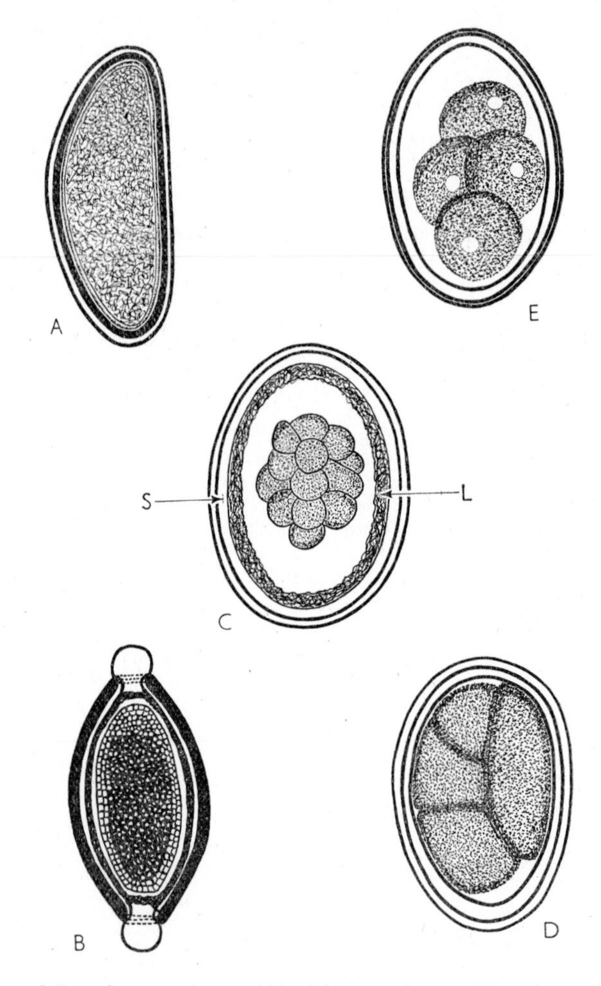

FIG. 38. Eggs of *Passalurus ambiguus* (A), *Trichuris leporis* (B), *Toxascaris leonina* (C), *Trichinella spiralis* (D), and *Strongylus equinus* (E). The layer of lipid (L) is thick and chitin is present in the middle layer of the shell (S) in eggs like A, B and C. Eggs like D and E, which hatch soon after they are laid, have a thin shell and both the outer layers may be protein (A, B, C and D, after Christenson, 1940; E, after Yorke and Maplestone, 1926).

According to most workers (see, for instance, Jacobs and Jones, 1939) the chitin of the egg-shell gives structural strength and protects the more delicate lipoid layer from mechanical stress. The remaining layers of the primary egg envelope and the tertiary envelope also strengthen the egg-shell physically. But in addition they provide protection against the action of a variety of chemicals and the tertiary layer is said to retain water, so giving the embryo further protection against desiccation (Jaskoski, 1952; Jacobs and Jones, 1939).

The egg-shells of nematode parasites which are formed largely from the secretions of the egg itself and which lack a chorion secreted by the ovary, differ considerably from the egg-shells of most other parasites and from those of the Arthropoda and Mollusca. In the Insecta, for instance, the chorion forms the hard chitinous layer, and in the Mollusca, the firm, thick layer may be either the chorion or the tertiary membrane.

Changes in the Egg during the Formation of the Shell

The maturation of the egg proceeds while the egg-shell is being formed. According to Gothié (1942) this process will not take place in *Parascaris equorum* if oxygen is present, but other workers have not reported this requirement and Painter (1915) considered that oxygen was essential for the final processes of maturation. Under normal circumstances the first polar body is enclosed between the inner lipoid membrane and the chitinous layer of the shell. The second polar body is discharged into the space between the egg and the inner membrane (Fauré-Fremiet, 1913; Wottge, 1937; Walton, 1940, p. 209; Yanagisawa, 1955). Because the egg itself contributes so much towards the formation of the shell—36% of the solids originally present in the oöcyte are transformed into the primary egg envelope which has a low water content (Passey and Fairbairn, 1957)—there is a pronounced change in the size of the egg and the distribution of water during maturation. Thus in *Parascaris equorum* the oöcyte has a volume of 113 mm^3 and the zygote 33.5 mm^3 and the space between the zygote and the shell becomes filled with fluid as a result of "deutoplasmolysis" (Lams, 1952).

Except in species in which parthenogenetic development is a feature of the life cycle, normal egg-shell formation does not occur without fertilization though it may proceed to some degree in different species (Christenson, 1940). In *Ascaris lumbricoides* the shell of the unfertilized egg corresponds to the thin membrane which covers the oöcyte when it enters the upper part of the seminal vesicle. During the passage down the oviduct this membrane may become thicker but the other layers of the primary egg envelope are not formed. This gives a primary egg envelope of about 0.5 μ in thickness in unfertilized eggs—about one tenth of the thickness of the corresponding structure in fertilized eggs. The tertiary coat secreted by the walls of the uterus is usually found on unfertilized and fertilized eggs.

In species in which parthenogenetic development is a normal feature of the life cycle the inner lipoid membrane is probably absent.

The Production of Eggs and Sperm in Parasitic Platyhelminthes and Acanthocephala

The formation of eggs and sperm in the parasitic platyhelminths has been reviewed by Dawes (1946, pp. 494–498), Wardle and McLeod (1952, p. 46) and Smyth and Clegg (1959). Except for the digenetic families Didymozoonidae and Schistosomatidae and the taenioid genus *Dioecocestus* these parasites are hermaphrodites. The structure of the reproductive organs, the processes of fertilization and the formation of the egg-shell is basically the same throughout the whole group. Cells from the vitellaria, which vary in numbers characteristically for different forms, e.g. about 30 for *Fasciola hepatica* (Stephenson, 1947) or 1 in cyclophyllidean cestodes (Ogren, 1956), join each oöcyte in the oötype. The vitellaria are loaded with granules, some of which are discharged and run together to form a thin shell enclosing sperm, the oöcyte and vitelline cell or cells. This thin shell is usually formed close to the wall of the oöcyte which gives the egg a characteristic shape in many species. In the uterus the remaining granules from the vitelline cells are freed and build up the egg-shell from the inside. The role of Mehlis' gland in the formation of the egg-shell is uncertain. It has been suggested that the secretion of this gland may (a) affect the hardening of the egg-shell, (b) cause the release of the granules from the vitelline cells, (c) form the thin membrane which surrounds the oöcyte and its associated cells, or (d) simply act as a lubricant.

The chief covering of the egg of the parasitic platyhelminths is thus a chorion or secondary egg membrane. Its form varies considerably. In both cestodes and trematodes it may be operculate or non-operculate; it is thick in most pseudophylidean tapeworms and in the trematodes it is thin, in the family Cyclocoelidae for instance. A primary or vitelline membrane may be present and embryonic envelopes of considerable complexity are often found. In some cestodes, e.g. the Cyclophyllidea, part of the uterus or even the whole proglottid may act as a "tertiary egg membrane" and protect the eggs until they reach the intermediate host.

In spite of the variety in the form of the covering of the eggs of parasitic platyhelminths it is clear that the origin of these structures is generally different from that in the Nematoda. In this respect the egg-shells of the parasitic platyhelminths are often more like those in the Insecta (Wardle and McLeod, 1952, pp. 47, 51). They lack chitin, however, and seem to be chiefly composed of quinone-tanned protein. This material occurs as a structural protein in a wide variety of invertebrates, and sometimes in vertebrates (Brown, 1950, 1955); in particular it is found throughout the Arthropoda, where, in combination with a waterproofing layer of wax, it forms the basis of the hard impermeable cuticle (Pryor, 1940; Richards, 1951). The mechanism by which protein may be hardened by "tanning" with phenolic materials to form sclerotin (Pryor, 1940) has been examined both by histochemical and analytical procedures but there is little agreement on the processes which occur in the insect cuticle (Richards, 1951; Dennell, 1958).

The evidence for the occurrence of quinone-tanned proteins in the vitelline cells and newly-formed egg-shells of trematodes comes largely from histochemical tests which indicate the presence of phenolic material, protein and phenolase. Analytical procedures have been confined largely to substances from the vitelline glands of *Fasciola hepatica* (Clegg, 1958). From these no free phenolic material could be extracted but protein which gave positive histochemical tests for phenolic substances was obtained. The acid hydrolysate contained 13 amino acids of which tyrosine, phenylalanine and histidine formed a large proportion; there was some evidence that 3:4-dihydroxyphenylalanine was also present. It is possible that a tyrosine-rich protein might become tanned if a suitable phenolase was present to oxidize the tyrosine residues (Blower, 1950; Brown, 1952; Smyth, 1954). Smyth and Clegg (1959) have tentatively suggested that such a system may be responsible for the production of the tanned protein in the egg-shells of *Fasciola hepatica*.

As indicated by histochemical tests "quinone-tanned" protein occurs widely in the egg-shells of trematodes and pseudophyllidean cestodes. The colour reactions of the phenolic substances in the vitelline cells of different species vary considerably, however, so Smyth and Clegg (1959) suggested that the chemistry of the substances may also vary. In some trematodes phenolase cannot be demonstrated histochemically; for these, non-enzymatic processes are suggested.

The egg-shells of the Acanthocephala have not been examined in detail. It appears that they are formed largely as a result of the activity of the egg itself and consist of three or four layers. Monné and Hönig (1955*b*) observed the effects of solvents and histochemical reagents on the egg-shells of two species of *Polymorphus*. They found four layers which in order from the inside were (a) the innermost membrane chiefly of chitin but with some keratin-like protein, (b) the "shell" similar to (a) but with much less chitin, (c) the fibrillar coat of keratin-like protein without chitin, and (d) the outermost coat of non-keratinous protein. Von Brand (1940) found chitin to be present in the innermost membrane of *Macracanthorhynchus hirudinaceus*. There has been no suggestion that quinone-tanned protein is present, nor has a layer of lipid been reported. In spite of this, however, the egg-shells of the Acanthocephala are clearly more like those of the Nematoda than those of the parasitic platyhelminths.

THE SEX RATIOS

The ratio of the sexes in some parasites is affected by differential mortality which occurs in some environments. Sometimes a less common phenomenon in which the sex of the developing individual is influenced by the environment has been observed. Thus development into males or females in some mermithid nematodes is determined by the size of the infection. Christie (1929) found that when one to three parasites were present in grasshoppers, all were females; when four to twenty-three were present the sexes were mixed, and above twenty-three, all the parasites were males. Selective mortality, as an explanation for these results, was ruled out by feeding the hosts with a known number of eggs. Similar results have been obtained with the plant parasitic nematode *Heterodera rostochiensis*. Here again more larvae develop into males as the intensity of the infection is increased (Ellenby, 1954).

The mechanism by which the density of a population of parasites may influence the sex of developing individuals has not been examined.

PARTHENOGENETIC AND ASEXUAL REPRODUCTION

Reproduction in parasitic nematodes is usually bisexual. Hermaphrodites are not uncommon among free-living forms but are rare among parasites. Parthenogenesis has been proved for parasites such as *Meloidogyne* sp. (Tyler, 1933) and *Strongyloides* spp. Males of *Meloidogyne* are common, however, and parthenogenesis is not a necessary feature of the life cycle. With *Strongyloides* the parasitic phase of the life cycle is necessarily parthenogenetic and reports of parasitic males (Kreis, 1932; Faust, 1933) have rarely been made. The interest that life cycles of this sort have provoked has not been due to their importance in parasitism. In fact, it is clear that bisexual reproduction suffices to produce enough infective agents to ensure the infection of the next host; as in many other features, the reproductive system of parasitic nematodes is unspecialized.

Studies of the parthenogenetic development in *Strongyloides* are important because they may throw light on the relative importance of genetical and environmental factors in determining a type of life cycle.

These nematodes lack parasitic males (see, however, Kreis, 1932; Faust, 1933); eggs produced parthenogenetically by parasitic females may give rise to filariform, infective larvae or to rhabditiform, free-living males and females which in turn give eggs which give rise to filariform infective larvae. The life cycle may thus be homogonic (direct) or heterogonic (indirect). Environmental factors such as the pH of the culture medium, the food, temperature, and the oxygen tension, it has been said, influence the type of development (see, for example, Beach, 1936; Premvati, 1957). On the other hand, the evidence, obtained largely from Graham's work in which rats infected with single larvae were used to study differences in the homogonic and heterogonic strains (Graham, 1938*a*, 1938*b*, 1939*a*, 1939*b*, 1940), suggested that the type of the life cycle was determined by genetic factors in the eggs of parasitic females (Hyman, 1951, p. 309). Chang and Graham (1957) showed that the chromosomes of the homogenetic phase of the life cycle of *Strongyloides papillosus* differed from those in the heterogenetic phase of the life cycle. It seems possible then that the genetic constitution is of immediate importance in determining the type of life cycle but the environment of the developing larvae may influence the proportion in which the two strains survive.

In the Acanthocephala, as in the parasitic nematodes, very large numbers of eggs are produced by sexual reproduction. Thus *Macracanthorhynchus hirudinaceus* may produce 260,000 eggs per day for 10 months (Kates, 1944). In the parasitic platyhelminths egg production by sexual processes is also large but it is often reinforced by other forms of reproduction. The reproductive mechanism of the larval digenetic trematodes has been interpreted in many ways (Dawes, 1946, pp. 501–503; Cort, 1944). It was widely held that multiplication in sporocysts and rediae was parthenogenetic in nature. Many workers now accept the view that these processes are more correctly described as polyembryony—the simple multiplication of germ balls or propagatory cells (Cort, 1944; Hyman, 1951, p. 265). In the Cestoda one egg usually gives rise to one adult and asexual reproduction is rare, but the multiplication of sex organs along the strobila increases egg production very considerably.

Nutrition and Reproduction

The energy requirements, and perhaps the requirements for special nutrients, must be increased during the periods when eggs and sperm are produced by nematode parasites. This has not been shown directly but there is circumstantial evidence. Thus a single female of *Ascaris lumbricoides* may produce about 0.49 g of eggs per day (Fairbairn, 1957), i.e. the female worm produces each day an amount of eggs which may be 5% of its body weight. This is greater than the amount of tissue synthesized per day during the growth of the worm which is probably less than 0.2 g. With *Haemonchus contortus* the situation is probably similar. This parasite in calves produces about 6,000 eggs per day per female worm (Kelley, 1955); according to Martin and Ross (1934) the egg output requires 2.85 μg of phosphorus per day which is probably greater than the daily need for growth. It may be generally true that the demand on the host for nutrients increases during the reproductive phase of metazoan parasites.

So far, the culture of nematode parasites *in vitro* has not revealed any special needs for the production of eggs or sperm. Thus *Neoaplectana glaseri* has been cultured throughout its life cycle and continuously for many generations in axenic liquid culture (Stoll, 1953). And eggs and sperm have been freely formed in cultures of *Nippostrongylus muris* though fertilization did not take place (Weinstein and Jones, 1957). Evidently the medium provided sufficient materials for the synthesis of eggs and sperm but either the numbers of worms were too small to give adequate opportunity for fertilization (Weinstein and Jones, 1956) or else the physical properties of the medium were unsuitable. It seems that the same limitations may apply to the culture of *Haemonchus contortus* and *Ostertagia* sp. *in vitro* (Silverman, 1959).

Knowledge of special quantitative and qualitative nutritional needs for reproduction in parasitic platyhelminths is no further advanced than with parasitic nematodes. Failure to produce eggs or sperm, or the dissolution of the testis, often occurs in parasitic platyhelminths cultured *in vitro* under the best conditions at present available (Smyth, 1958; Robertson, 1956). Species in which the reproductive system is formed in the larval stages will produce normal eggs under the right physical conditions *in vitro* (Smyth, 1955, 1959) but here the nutritional needs are met entirely from food reserves and not from the environment.

Summary

Knowledge of the physiology of reproduction of metazoan parasites is scanty. Much of what is known lies on the fringe of this subject and deals with the composition and origin of the coverings of the egg. In nematode parasites the primary egg envelope contains an inner layer of lipid and an outer layer of chitin and protein. There is no secondary egg envelope but a coat of protein secreted by the uterus is present as an outer covering in many species. The parasitic platyhelminths have an egg covering composed of quinone-tanned proteins, which is secreted by the vitellaria.

There is evidence to suggest that the nutritional needs of parasites are increased during the periods when eggs are produced.

REFERENCES

Ammon, R. and Debusmann-Morgenroth, M. (1953) *Med. Mschr., Stuttgart,* **7**, 705.
Beach, T. D. (1936) *Amer. J. Hyg.* **23**, 243.
Blower, G. (1950) *Nature, Lond.* **165**, 569.
Bowen, R. H. (1925) *Anat. Rec.* **31**, 201.
Brown, C. H. (1950) *Quart. J. micr. Sci.* **91**, 331.
—— (1952) *Quart. J. micr. Sci.* **93**, 487.
—— (1955) *Quart. J. micr. Sci.* **96**, 483.
Campbell, P. L. (1929) *Ann. ent. Soc. Amer.* **22**, 401.
Chang, P. C. H. and Graham, G. L. (1957) *J. Parasit.* **43**, Suppl. 13.
Chitwood, B. G. (1931) *J. Wash. Acad. Sci.* **21**, 41.
—— (1938) *Proc. helm. Soc. Wash.* **5**, 68.
—— and Chitwood, M. B. (1940) *In* "Introduction to Nematology". (B. G. and M. B. Chitwood, eds.), M. B. Chitwood, Babylon, New York.
—— and Graham, G. L. (1940) *J. Parasit.* **26**, 183.
Christenson, R. O. (1940) *In* "Introduction to Nematology". (B. G. and M. B. Chitwood, eds.), M. B. Chitwood, Babylon, New York.
Christie, J. R. (1929) *J. exp. Zool.* **53**, 59.
Clegg, J. A. (1958) Unpublished work quoted by Smyth and Clegg (1959).
Cort, W. W. (1944) *Quart. Rev. Biol.* **19**, 275.
Crites, J. L. (1958) *Ohio J. Sci.* **58**, 343.
Dawes, B. (1946) "The Trematoda". Cambridge University Press, Cambridge.
Dennell, R. (1958) *Biol. Rev.* **33**, 178.
Ebel, J. P. and Colas, J. (1954) *C. R. Soc. Biol., Paris,* **148**, 1580.
Ellenby, C. (1954) *Nature, Lond.* **174**, 1016
Fairbairn, D. (1957) *Exp. Parasit.* **6**, 491.
—— and Passey, B. I. (1955) *Canad. J. Biochem. Physiol.* **33**, 130.
Fauré-Fremiet, E. (1912) *Bull. Soc. Zool. Fr.* **37**, 233.
—— (1913) *Arch. Anat. micr.* **15**, 435.
——, Ebel, J. P. and Colas, J. (1953) *C. R. Soc. Biol., Paris,* **237**, 629.
—— (1954) *Exp. Cell. Res.* **7**, 153.
—— and Filhol, J. (1937) *J. Chim. phys.* **34**, 444.
Faust, E. C. (1933) *Amer. J. Hyg.* **18**, 114.
Flury, F. (1912) *Arch. exp. Path. Pharmak.* **67**, 275.
Fouquey, C., Polonsky, J. and Lederer, E. (1957) *Bull. Soc. Chim. biol., Paris,* **39**, 101.
Gothié, S. (1942) *C. R. Soc. Biol., Paris,* **136**, 487.
Graham, G. L. (1938*a*) *Amer. J. Hyg.* **27**, 221.
—— (1938*b*) *J. Parasit.* **24**, 233.
—— (1939*a*) *Amer. J. Hyg.* **30**, 15.
—— (1939*b*) *J. Parasit.* **25**, 365.
—— (1940) *J. Parasit.* **26**, 207.
Hyman, L. H. (1951) "The Invertebrates" Vol. II. McGraw-Hill Book Co., New York.
Jacobs, L. (1940) *In* "Introduction to Nematology". (B. G. and M. B. Chitwood, eds.), M. B. Chitwood, Babylon, New York.
—— and Jones, M. F. (1939) *Proc. helm. Soc. Wash.* **6**, 57.
Jaskoski, B. J. (1952) *Exp. Parasit.* **1**, 291.
Kates, K. C. (1944) *Amer. J. vet. Res.* **5**, 166.
Kelley, G. W. (1955) *J. Parasit.* **41**, 218.
Kreis, H. A. (1932) *Amer. J. Hyg.* **16**, 450.
Kreuzer, L. (1953) *Z. vergl. Physiol.* **35**, 13.
Lams, H. (1952) *Acta anat.* **14**, 141.

Maggenti, A. R. and Allen, M. W. (1960) *Proc. helm. Soc. Wash.* **27**, 4.
Martin, C. J. and Ross, I. C. (1934) *J. Helminth.* **12**, 137.
Monné, L. and Hönig, G. (1954) *Ark. Zool.* **6**, 559.
—— (1955*a*) *Ark. Zool.* **7**, 261.
—— (1955*b*) *Ark. Zool.* **7**, 257.
Nigon, V. and Bovet, P. (1955) *C. R. Soc. Biol., Paris*, **149**, 129.
Ogren, R. E. (1956) *J. Parasit.* **42**, 414.
Painter, T. S. (1915) *J. exp. Zool.* **19**, 355.
Panijel, J. (1950) *Biochim. biophys. Acta*, **6**, 79.
Passey, R. F. and Fairbairn, D. (1957) *Canad. J. Biochem. Physiol.* **35**, 511.
Pollak, J. K. and Fairbairn, D. (1955*a*) *Canad. J. Biochem. Physiol.* **33**, 297.
—— (1955*b*) *Canad. J. Biochem. Physiol.* **33**, 307.
Polonsky, J., Fouquey, C., Ferreol, G. and Lederer, E. (1955) *C. R. Soc. Biol., Paris*, **240**, 2265.
Premvati, (1957) *Canad. J. Zool.* **36**, 185.
Prestage, J. J. (1960) *J. Parasit.* **46**, 69.
Pryor, M. G. M. (1940) *Proc. roy. Soc.* **B128**, 378.
Ransom, H. B. and Foster, W. D. (1920) *Bull. U. S. Dep. Agric.* No. 817.
Richards, A. Glenn (1951) "The Integument of Arthropods". University of Minnesota Press, Minneapolis.
Robertson, D. L. H. (1956) *J. Helminth.* **29**, 193.
Rogers, R. A. (1956) *J. Parasit.* **42**, 97.
Schmidt, W. I. (1936) *Z. Zellforsch.* **25**, 181.
Schulz, F. N. and Becker, M. (1933) *Biochem. Z.* **265**, 253.
Schulze, P. (1924) *Z. Morph. Ökol. Tiere*, **2**, 643.
Silverman, P. H. (1959) *Nature, Lond.* **183**, 197.
Smyth, J. D. (1954) *Quart. J. micr. Sci.* **95**, 139.
—— (1955) *Rev. ibér. Parasit.*, Tom extraord. 65.
—— (1958) *Nature, Lond.* **181**, 1119.
—— (1959) *Ann. N. Y. Acad. Sci.* **77**, 102.
—— and Clegg, J. A. (1959) *Exp. Parasit.* **8**, 286.
Stephenson, W. (1947) *Parasitology*, **38**, 128.
Stoll, N. R. (1953) *J. Parasit.* **39**, 422.
Timm, R. W. (1950) *Science*, **112**, 167.
Tyler, J. (1933) *Hilgardia*, **7**, 373.
von Brand, T. (1940) *J. Parasit.* **26**, 301.
Walton, A. C. (1924) *Z. Zell-u. Gewebelehre*, **1**, 167.
—— (1940) *In* "Introduction to Nematology". (B. G. and M. B. Chitwood, eds.), M. B. Chitwood, Babylon, New York.
Wardle, R. A. and McLeod, J. A. (1952) "The Zoology of Tapeworms". University of Minnesota Press, Minneapolis.
Weinstein, P. P. and Jones, M. F. (1956) *J. Parasit.* **42**, 215.
—— (1957) *Amer. J. trop. Med. Hyg.* **6**, 480.
Wottge, K. (1937) *Protoplasma*, **29**, 31.
Yanagisawa, T. (1955) *Jap. J. med. Sci. Biol.* **8**, 379.
—— and Ishii, K. (1954) *Jap. J. med. Sci. Biol.* **7**, 215.
Yorke, W. and Maplestone, P. A. (1926) "The Nematode Parasites of Vertebrates". J. and A. Churchill, London.
Zawadowsky, M. M. (1928) *Trans. Lab. exp. Biol. Zoopark, Moscow*, **4**, 201.
—— and Schalimov, L. G. (1929) *Z. Parasitenk.* **2**, 12.
——, Vorobieva, E. I. and Petrova, M. I. (1929) *Trans. Lab. exp. Biol. Zoopark, Moscow*, **5**, 251.

CHAPTER 10

The Specificity of Parasites

THE specificity of parasites, host specificity, host–parasite specificity—these terms are often used in referring to the range of organisms which will serve as hosts. Some authors, however, use these terms in a somewhat different sense. Thus Becker (1933) regarded host specificity as "the peculiar adaptation of one species (the parasite, in the broad sense) to the *milieu* within or on another species or more or less limited groups of species (host or hosts)". By specificity of a parasite he meant "its quality of distinctiveness from all others". It is chiefly in relation to the range of hosts that I will use the term here. Thus a specific parasite (sometimes called species-specific or monoxenous) can live on or in one species of host only, e.g. *Wuchereria bancrofti*, the adults of which are found only in man; a moderately specific, or oligoxenous parasite, has a small host range, e.g. the adult *Echinococcus granulosus* which occurs only in the dog and three or four related animals; a parasite of low specificity (polyxenous, see Sandground, 1929) has a wide range of hosts e.g. *Fasciola hepatica*, of which the adult can live in the dog, rabbit, horse, cow, elephant and kangaroo.

The specificity of different parasites varies greatly (see, for instance, Culbertson, 1941, pp. 14–22; Baer, 1952, pp. 155–172; Caullery, 1952, pp. 171–191). As more work is carried out it is often found that the host range of a parasite is wider than was generally thought. Initially the taxonomist examines the host range. Information so obtained, purely the statistics of parasites and their hosts, not only gives a measure of the specificity of different species but also indicates the nature of the mechanisms which determine specificity. Thus in some groups one species of parasite or closely related species of parasites occur only in closely related species of hosts, e.g. cestode parasites of birds (Baer, 1957). Phylogenetic specificity like this suggests that the morphological and physiological characters of the parasite and host are of major importance in determining specificity. The needs of these parasites or their capacity to resist the damaging actions of their hosts are such that they can live only in the closely related groups of animals which share the necessary specialized physiological and morphological characters needed in a host. The high degree of adaptation or specialization in such parasites suggests that they have long been parasites and that they have evolved with their hosts (Baylis, 1938; Baer, 1952, p. 168).

In many groups of metazoan endoparasites the host range does not seem to be determined by phylogenetic considerations. Rather it is the behaviour and habitats of the parasites and the hosts which govern specificity (Baylis, 1938; Baer, 1952, pp. 155–172; Theodor, 1957; Hopkins, 1957). In ethological and ecological specificity the range of hosts is wide and this is said to indicate a more recent association between the parasite and the host. The fact that specificity is so frequently determined more by the mere chance of the parasite's making contact with the potential host than by physiological relationships between potential hosts suggests that the requirements of the parasites from the hosts may not be exacting. But this would be expected in any organism which had "recently" assumed a parasitic mode of life. What is perhaps more surprising is that a variety of hosts, whose common characteristics were those of habit and habitat, should also share the lack of mechanisms to repel a particular parasite.

The specificity of parasites which have an indirect life cycle often varies during the life cycle. Thus the early stages of the Digenea are, with one exception, parasites of molluscs, and even within this range of hosts specificity is high. On the other hand, the genera of the adults are fairly evenly distributed among most groups of vertebrates (Baer, 1934) and usually have a low specificity (Baylis, 1938). In the cestodes it is the adults which show high specificity; larval stages are more catholic in their "choice" of hosts. This presumably is an outcome of the evolutionary history of the parasites (see Chapter 11) and supports the view that high specificity indicates a long history of parasitism.

To the ecologist, who is concerned with the distribution and abundance of parasites, specificity might be measured in terms of the species of hosts found infected in the field. To the physiologist, who is studying the properties of the parasite and the host which govern specificity, all species which can act as hosts under experimental conditions are of interest. But, from the standpoint of specificity, what constitutes a "host"? A species which serves as host should be capable of becoming infected, and of maintaining the parasite so that infective agents may be produced, according to the type of life cycle, and the next host infected in turn. Some hosts will be more suited to the parasite than others. This will be reflected in the rate of growth of the parasite, its fecundity and longevity.

Parasites show specificity in the sites which they occupy in or on the host. Some, such as the larval stages of *Echinococcus granulosus*, can develop in many different tissues and organs. Generally, however, the range of sites in which a given species of parasite can develop normally is limited and the mechanisms which determine this often seem to be more exacting than those which determine the range of hosts. Thus the adult *Trichinella spiralis* can develop in a variety of warm-blooded hosts but only in the small intestine; similarly the infective larvae live only in the musculature, but in many sorts of hosts.

Explanations for specificity must be sought over the whole range of factors which concern the relationship of the parasite to the host throughout its life cycle. And the relative importance of these different factors in the host–parasite relationship in determining specificity will differ in different parasites and in different hosts. It is impossible therefore to discuss fully the whole field of the specificity of metazoan parasites in this chapter. Instead a brief outline of those factors and processes which may be important in influencing the range of hosts and the sites at which parasites live on or in their hosts will be given, and an attempt will be made to place them within a framework which encompasses the host–parasite relationship generally.

Factors which influence the specificity of parasites have been grouped and named in various ways (see, for instance, Sandground, 1929; Chandler, 1932; Schneider, 1951; Dubois and Chabaud, 1957). Here the view is taken that the "susceptible" organism can provide the parasite with an environment containing all the components needed for its growth and reproduction; in the "insusceptible" organism the environment lacks some essential features (Read, 1958). "Resistance" is distinguished from "insusceptibility" in that the former is due to the presence, on or in an organism, of physical or chemical factors which are unfavourable to the parasite. In "naturally resistant" organisms these unfavourable factors are part of the organism's normal heritage and are independent of its previous contact with parasites. "Acquired resistance" is regarded as the outcome of an organism's previous contact with parasites or related materials.

It will be convenient to discuss the factors which affect specificity in turn as they may operate during the life cycle of a parasite. Some factors will be more important than others in the sense that they may be more exacting for more species of parasites. But in the sense that failure at any point in the life cycle of the parasite will have its effect on specificity, all are equally important.

Specificity in the First Stage of the Association of the Parasite with the Host

In this stage of the life cycle the infective agent must make contact with the host and infect it. If the life cycle is direct and has free-living stages the factors that influence the range of hosts are those which affect the development and survival of the infective stage, and the behaviour of the infective stage and the host. If more than one host is involved in the life cycle the importance of behaviour in determining the range of hosts would be generally increased. Parasites with a direct life cycle are generally more specific than those with an indirect life cycle (Baylis, 1924). According to Baylis (1924, 1938) this is probably because the larvae of parasites with a direct life cycle are younger and less resistant when they enter the definitive host and therefore they are less tolerant of hosts to which they are imperfectly adjusted. A similar explanation was offered for the observation that nematode parasites with an indirect life cycle show a higher specificity for the intermediate host than they do for the definitive host. The processes which cause the infective stage to resume development so that the host becomes infected may also affect specificity. How far the capacity of the infective stage to resist toxic and damaging actions of the host is involved at this stage is uncertain. In some species of parasites where the infective agent is enclosed in protective coverings such as egg-shells or cyst-walls these actions of the host may not influence specificity until the protective coverings are lost.

The Development and Behaviour of Infective Stages

Under natural circumstances the possible hosts which are available to a parasite will be determined partly by the conditions necessary for the development and survival of free-living infective stages. This may limit the host range in a broad way only. Thus free-living stages which require an aquatic environment will usually be restricted to hosts living in the same medium. This may be the sole factor which determines the host range for some parasites, e.g. many larval gordiids. Clearly the geographical range of the hosts of a particular species of parasite must lie within the region where the climate is suitable for the development of the free-living stages. Thus the free-living larvae of the nematodes *Oesophagostomum columbianum* and *Stephanurus dentatus* require warm, moist conditions for development and survival and so are rarely found outside temperate regions (Sarles, 1943; Spindler, 1934). The influence of certain factors in the environment, especially temperature and moisture, on the development of free-living stages of nematode parasites and their distribution has been discussed by Gordon (1948, 1949) and Hyman (1951, pp. 408–418).

There is little doubt that the habits and habitats of free-living and infective stages of parasites and their potential hosts are generally of major importance in determining specificity (Baylis, 1938). One of the simplest examples of this has come from studies on the ectoparasitic larval stages of the Unionidae. The infective forms of these molluscs lie on the sea floor; when they are appropriately disturbed they become active and fix themselves to nearby objects. The speed and level at which fishes swim influence the range of species which are available as hosts (Baer, 1952, p. 156).

Mechanisms by which several species of miracidia locate their hosts have been studied (for example see Faust, 1924; Miller and McCoy, 1930; Nerhaus, 1953) and our present knowledge of this problem has been succinctly reviewed by Wright (1959). In species such as *Cryptocotyle jejuna* which hatch only when they have been ingested by the molluscan host, it is the habits of the host and the physical features of the environment which bring about the contact between host and parasite (Rothschild and Clay, 1953). But most Digenea have free-swimming miracidia, and it is the pattern of behaviour of these larvae which leads to contact with the host. A physical stimulus, which for some species of *Schistosoma* is a positive phototropism, brings miracidia to the surface layers of water where the snail host is most numerous. Here the miracidia move at random until they come within the orbit of chemical attraction of the snail. Under the influence of this chemical stimulus it seems that movements are still irregular but the larvae remain close to the snail until penetration is attempted. Then a stimulus from the proper host leads to metamorphosis and penetration.

The feeding habits of the host in relation to behaviour of the infective stage of the parasite seem to be a common feature which influences the range of hosts under natural conditions. Animals occupying the same niche, largely independent of their phylogenetic relationship, frequently have the same species of parasites, or closely-related species (Baylis, 1938; Elton, 1947). Fish-eating animals, mammals or birds, are definitive hosts for nematodes like *Porrocaecum* and *Contracaecum* which have larval stages in fish; *Trichinella spiralis* has a wide natural host range which seems to be determined by the sole requirement that the warm-blooded host should eat infected flesh of a recently-killed carnivore or omnivore. *Fasciola hepatica* and many species of trichostrongyles are found in a wide range of herbivores, and even in some omnivores, but not in carnivores, evidently because the infective stages either encyst or crawl on to herbage.

Factors which affect feeding habits indirectly may influence the range of hosts of a parasite. Thus the structure of feathers on ducks prevents the infection of *Simulium venustrum* with the microfilariae of *Ornithofilaria fallisensis* because this species of *Simulium* lacks the specially modified claws on its tarsi needed for the penetration of a duck's feathers. Under experimental conditions it can be infected without difficulty; under natural conditions it rarely acquires or transmits the parasite (Anderson, 1956).

The possibility that differences in the behaviour of sympatric host species may affect the range of hosts of cestodes under natural conditions has been discussed by Read (1958). Read and Millemann (1953) and Millemann (1955) found *Oochoristica deserti* in trapped specimens of *Dipodomys merriami merriami* but not in *Dipodomys panamintinus mohavensis*. In the laboratory both species could be infected. These results would be explained if the behaviour of *Dipodomys panamintinus mohavensis* and the intermediate host prevented contact under natural conditions or if the natural diet of the rodent contained substances which were directly or indirectly deleterious to the parasite. Evidence that the natural diet of the grey squirrel, *Sciurus carolenensis*, prevents its infection with *Hymenolepis nana* in the field was also given by Read (1958). The influence of the feeding habits of possible hosts on the growth and reproduction of adult cestodes may be mediated via the quantity and quality of carbohydrate available to the parasite (Read, 1959; see Chapter 8).

It is natural that ecological factors should initially determine the ranges of hosts of parasites. Superimposed upon this, other isolating mechanisms might be expected to affect specificity and give rise to speciation as parasites evolved with their hosts. Thus in long-established parasites specificity becomes phylogenetic rather than ecological (see Chapter 11). But even in groups of parasites in which specificity is primarily phylogenetic, the role of behaviour, though clearly only one factor in a series which constitutes the mechanism of specificity, can still be seen. Thus the segments of *Taenia saginata* and *Taenia solium* in the faeces of man have a behaviour suited to the feeding habits of their respective intermediate hosts. The segments of *Taenia saginata* are active and move onto herbage where they are most likely to be eaten by cattle. On the other hand, the segments of *Taenia solium* are flaccid and remain in the faecal mass where they are more likely to be eaten by a pig (Mönnig, 1941).

The Process of Infection

The view that the infective stage is a "resting" stage which requires factors from the host in order to resume development has been expressed earlier (see Chapter 5, Fig. 15). These factors may influence specificity. The examples given below are drawn largely from parasites which infect the host via the alimentary canal but it is reasonable to suppose that the processes which involve infection by other routes would also influence specificity. As yet, however, little is known of these processes.

(i) The specificity of developmental stimuli

For a variety of nematode parasites which infect the host via the alimentary canal, the stimulus for the hatching of eggs or exsheathment of larvae which precedes the resumption of development depends upon the concentration of undissociated carbonic acid plus dissolved gaseous carbon dioxide, the oxidation-reduction potential, the hydrogen ion concentration and the temperature (see Chapter 5; Rogers, 1958, 1960, 1961; Rogers and Sommerville, 1960; Fairbairn, 1960). The pattern in which these components are required in the environment differs for different species and serves, in varying degrees of efficiency, (a) to differentiate the alimentary canal of vertebrates from other sorts of environments, (b) to differentiate different parts of the alimentary canal, and (c) to distinguish different sorts of hosts (Rogers, 1960). Most of the information on which this is based has been discussed in Chapter 5; here this information is used to discuss the specificity of a few species taken as examples.

Experiments with the infective eggs of *Ascaris lumbricoides* (pig strain) showed that at 37°C they hatched at low oxidation-reduction potentials when the concentration of undissociated carbonic acid plus dissolved gaseous carbon dioxide was about 1 to 2×10^{-3}M at pH 6.0 and 0.25 to 0.5×10^{-3}M at pH 7.3. Conditions like this would occur rarely outside the intestine of animals, but whether they would limit the range of hosts is not known. The eggs of *Toxocara mystax* were rather similar to those of *Ascaris lumbricoides* in their requirements; the hatching of eggs of *Ascaridia galli*, however, seemed to be inhibited at somewhat lower concentrations of the undissociated carbonic acid than those of the other two species. It appears, therefore, that the initial requirement for infection with the eggs of these species ensures that the early stages of development of the parasitic stages should take place in the small intestine; but, as our knowledge stands at present, little limitation on the range of hosts would be expected (Rogers, 1960, 1961).

The exsheathment of infective larvae of *Trichostrongylus colubriformis* requires a relatively high concentration of undissociated carbonic acid plus dissolved gaseous carbon dioxide, about 5×10^{-3}M, and, for a biological system, a very low pH -1.5 to 2.5. Conditions like these are rarely found except in the stomachs of vertebrates. Thus the specificity of the initial requirements for infection with this species is such as would determine the site in the host where the first developmental changes would occur but it would have little effect on limiting the range of hosts. And this is what has been found; the exsheathment of *Trichostrongylus colubriformis* occurs in the stomachs of many mammals, and the adults, living in the small intestine, are found in many species (Rogers, 1960).

Trichostrongylus axei and *Haemonchus contortus*, the adults of which normally live in the abomasum of a ruminant, have infective larvae which normally exsheath in the rumen of the host. The information available on the nature of the stimuli necessary for this process allows speculation on the importance of infective processes in determining specificity. The exsheathment of both species took place at temperatures above 30°C, was aided by low oxidation-reduction potentials, and, in contrast to other species so far examined, was not inhibited by high concentrations of undissociated carbonic acid. They differed in one respect, however; whereas relatively high concentrations of undissociated carbonic acid plus dissolved gaseous carbon dioxide (2 to 6 $\times$ 10^{-3}M at pH 7.3) were essential for the exsheathment of larvae of *Haemonchus contortus*, 0.5 $\times$ 10^{-3}M was sufficient to stimulate the process in *Trichostrongylus axei*. As the rumen is the only place where an environment of low oxidation-reduction potential and high concentration of undissociated carbonic acid plus dissolved gaseous carbon dioxide at hydrogen ion concentrations near neutrality is normally found, the initial requirements for the process of infection with *Haemonchus contortus* might be expected to limit the range of hosts for this species. In fact this parasite is rarely found except in the abomasum of ruminants. With *Trichostrongylus axei*, on the other hand, a short exposure at low concentrations of undissociated carbonic acid plus dissolved gaseous carbon dioxide at pH values near neutrality and even extending into the acid range is often sufficient to start exsheathment. Clearly the rumen is not the only organ which could provide the stimulus. In accordance with this, *Trichostrongylus axei* is found in the stomachs of a wide range of hosts and sometimes even in the small intestine as well.

(ii) Substances needed for developmental mechanisms in infective stages

It has been suggested without experimental evidence that the host might be required to provide substances which take part in processes such as the hatching of infective eggs or moulting of infective larvae of some species of parasites. In contrast to the stimuli needed to initiate development of infective stages of some species (Fig. 15, I) these substances might take a direct part in some aspect of a developmental process by replacing some substance which the infective stage cannot produce itself (Fig. 15, II).

It has been suggested that substances related to the hatching factor excreted by the roots of plants which act as hosts of *Heterodera rostochiensis* might act in a way like this (Rogers, 1960). Ellenby and Gilbert (1957) have shown that the hatching factor, eclepic acid (Calam *et al.*, 1949; Marrian *et al.*, 1949), has cardiotonic properties and is similar to the cardiac glycosides. They have also suggested that it may act on the embryo of this parasite by affecting the active transport of ions (Ellenby and Gilbert, 1958). Whatever the precise physiological action of the hatching factor, it is clear that it is essential for the further development of the parasite. Only a small range of hosts, largely species of *Solanum*, is known (Franklin, 1951; Ellenby, 1945, 1954); and the species that have been examined all produce the hatching factor (Ellenby, 1945). Presumably the production of the hatching factor by the host is necessary for infection, but other factors would also be required. Thus *Digitalis purpurea* produces the hatching factor (Ellenby, 1958) but it is not listed as a host. Clearly plants which do not produce the hatching factor could not become affected under natural circumstances.

Though the eggs of other species of *Heterodera* may be stimulated to hatch by the root excretions of their hosts, specificity is not generally as high as in *Heterodera rostochiensis*. Moreover, the action of the hatching factors is less exacting and even hosts which do not produce the appropriate hatching factor may become infected (Winslow, 1953). As far as our present knowledge goes, the mechanism by which infection is initiated in *Heterodera* is unique among parasitic nematodes. The degree of adaptation required for such a mechanism is probably very high so it may not be common. But the discovery of the process in *Heterodera rostochiensis* was aided because the action of the host on the eggs to induce infection occurs at a distance from the host. It would be easy to overlook similar processes where infection takes place via the alimentary canal, for instance. Even if it is found that this process of infection is specialized and restricted to a few species the possibility that substances related to eclepic acid have a general function in the physiology of nematodes should be considered.

Except for the action of hatching factors the process of infection in plant parasitic nematodes, as far as is known, has little specificity. *Meloidogyne*, for instance, is attracted or repelled by substances which diffuse from particular regions of the host (Wieser, 1956) but the attractive substances, some reducing agents and amino acids (Bird, 1959) are unlikely to give specificity to the process. The actual process of penetration of the host by *Heterodera* also seems to be unspecific. A hydrophobic surface is required. To this the larvae attach themselves by the sucking action of their lips and then, by movements of their stylets, the walls of cells in the host are pierced. These actions are stimulated by the physical conditions (Dickinson, 1959). Cellulases and enzymes attacking pectic substances (Tracey, 1958) which aid in penetrating the tissues of the host may be secreted by the infective larvae of some plant parasites. These again are unlikely to give specificity to the processes of infection.

(iii) The direct action of the host on infective stages

The stimuli discussed under (i) clearly have an *indirect* action in initiating infection; they induce infective stages, eggs or sheathed larvae of nematodes, to produce themselves the substances which bring about hatching or exsheathment. In (ii) it is suggested that the host supplied substances which are necessary parts of the developmental mechanism lost in the infective agent. Here (iii) the concern is with substances which act directly on the infective stage and so allow development to proceed (Fig. 15, III).

The simplest examples of this process of infection come from the parasitic platyhelminths. Thus it appears that the initial action of the host in the process of infection with metacercariae of *Clonorchis sinensis* is simply the successive attacks by gastric and intestinal proteases on the walls of the cysts (Faust and Khaw, 1925, 1927). It seems that peptic digestion alone serves to free the larvae of *Gynaecotyla adunca* from the cysts (Hunter and Chait, 1952).

Conditions which lead to the excystment of larval tapeworms have been examined extensively, especially by Read (1955, pp. 27–43, 1958) and by Rothman (1959). The process of infection here is started primarily by the host's digestive enzymes and substances which augment their action, so it is probable that the host has a direct action on the larvae. It is possible, however, that a part of the action could be indirect (see Chapter 5). Much of the information on the excystment of larval tapeworms and its relation to specificity has been discussed by Rothman (1959). As shown in Table XVII, which has been taken from Rothman's work, the requirements for the excystment are not exacting and would not be expected to limit the ranges of hosts except in a broad way.

In general, where a simple direct action of the host is sufficient to start the development of an infective stage as a parasite, the specificity of the process is likely to be low. When a number of factors are required from the host, the host range could be restricted. There are, as yet, no examples of high specificity arising in this way.

Features of the host which prevent infection

As well as the requirement that a pattern of certain components should be present in the environment, infection requires that damaging substances and damaging physical conditions should be absent. These features which protect the host by thwarting the process of infection may be simple, like a thick integument or a hairy coat, or they may be complex, like the toxic substances produced by some molluscs, which kill miracidia before infection has occurred. Physiological conditions in the alimentary canal may also prevent infection. Thus the scolices

TABLE XVII

Factors affecting the Excystment of Cestode Larvae in vitro (*from Rothman, 1959*)

Species	Hydrochloric acid	Pepsin-hydrochloric acid	Bile salts only	Trypsin only	Bile salts-trypsin	Room temp.	37°C
Taenia taeniaeformis	—	Essential for cyst digestion	Unessential	Unessential	Unessential	Excyst	Excyst
Oochoristica symmetrica	Unessential	Unessential	Excyst	No effect	Excyst	Excyst	Excyst
Hymenolepis diminuta	Enhances cyst digestion	Preliminary cyst digestion	Some excystment depending on age	No effect	Excyst	No effect	Excyst
Hymenolepis citelli	Enhances cyst digestion	Preliminary cyst digestion	Activation only	No effect	Excyst	No effect	Excyst
Hymenolepis nana	Enhances cyst digestion	Preliminary cyst digestion	Activation only	No effect	Excyst	No effect	Excyst
Taenia solium	—	Essential for cyst digestion	Excyst	No effect	Excyst	—	Excyst
Taenia pisiformis	—	Unessential	Excyst	—	—	Excyst	Excyst
Cysticercus bovis	—	—	Excyst	—	—	Excyst	Excyst
Cysticercus tenuicollis	—	—	Excyst	—	—	Excyst	Excyst

of larvae of *Oochoristica symmetrica* and *Taenia taeniaeformis* may reinvert and fail to attach to the mucosa if the intestinal contents of the host contain more than 0.1% bile salt. Many animals have intestinal juices which digest the scolices of larvae of *Echinococcus granulosus*; this is said to limit the host range of this parasite (Berberian, 1936). Stomach acidity and stomach and intestinal emptying times may also influence specificity (Larsh, 1947; Rothman, 1959).

Factors like these may be regarded as part of the natural resistance of animals and plants to parasites. As might be expected, natural resistance, whether it prevents infection or affects later stages of the parasites, seems to have a genetical basis (e.g. see Kartman, 1953; Whitlock and Madsen, 1957; Hoffman, 1958). Just how this is expressed in the phenotype is not known. Kartman (1953) found that different species of mosquitoes and their hybrids varied in their capacity to become infected with microfilariae of *Dirofilaria immitis* and it seemed that the critical factor was the speed of passage of the microfilariae through the midgut of the mosquito. Rapid clot formation in the midgut of *Aedes* and *Culex* impeded migration whereas slow clot formation in *Anopheles* was accompanied by the rapid disappearance of the microfilariae from the midgut. Kartman (1953) suggested that rapid migration might occur most efficiently in species possessing salivary anticoagulants, e.g. *Anopheles quadrimaculatus*, and showed that the addition of anticoagulants to the infective meal of mosquitoes lacking in salivary anticoagulant, e.g. *Aedes aegypti*, led to increased infection of the Malphigian tubules. Evidently some substance in the midgut of the mosquitoes, perhaps a digestive enzyme, had a harmful effect on the microfilariae and actually killed many of them if the period they spent in the midgut was prolonged.

Specificity in the Second Stage of the Association of the Parasite with the Host

In many species of parasites the infective stage, whether it is free-living or lives in a host, is protected from the environment and it does not feed or grow (see Chapter 3). As soon as the initial stages of infection have occurred, however, the invading organism, now truly parasitic, is fully exposed to its new environment. If the components of the environment needed by the parasite are present and if the natural resistance of the host (damaging physical and chemical factors in the environment) is not unfavourable, the parasite will grow, pass through the appropriate phase of the life cycle and reach maturity, or it will reach the infective stage. Presumably, it is possible that immunity, acquired in early stages of the life cycle, may interrupt later development and also influence specificity.

The complexity of the relationship between the parasite and the host during this stage of the association must, as a rule, be greater than in other stages, and it is here that events which are crucial in determining the range of hosts of the parasite must often occur. Though there are available many examples which support these views, explanations in terms of the chemistry of the system are difficult to find.

Requirements for the Growth and Migration of Parasites in the Host

Something of the nutritional needs of parasites is known (see Chapter 8) but there is little precise information to show how these needs may influence the specificity of parasites. This is possibly because the differences between host species are largely an expression of components of high molecular weight rather than those of low molecular weight and as yet we do not even know whether large molecules are important in the nutrition of metazoan parasites.

An example of how a small molecule, urea, may influence specificity in broad terms has been described by Read, Douglas and Simmons (1959; see Chapter 6). This substance occurs in high concentrations in the tissues and gut fluids of the Chondrichthyes; it is not toxic to these fish, and, in fact, it has in marine species a beneficent osmotic function of increasing the availability of water. It has the same action in adult cestodes from the spiral valve of these fish though it is toxic to cestodes from gulls and other vertebrates (Fig. 39).

The possibility that large molecules may influence the specificity of parasites in a broad way, or at least may determine the site in the host where the parasites may live, has been shown with blood flukes. These parasites will survive but show little growth in horse serum *in vitro* (Robertson, 1956). Even *in vivo* when they are placed in extravascular sites growth and the onset of sexual maturity are delayed (Moore and Meleney, 1955; Goodchild, 1958). This has been attributed to the lack of ingestion of blood of which the parasites certainly digest the haemoglobin, though they do not, apparently, absorb the haematin so formed (Rogers, 1940). The recent work of Timms and Bueding (1959) with *Schistosoma mansoni* strengthens this view. Timms and Bueding (1959) not only showed that the types and quantities of amino acids as they occur in globin had a pronounced effect on the survival of *Schistosoma mansoni in vitro*, but they also found that the parasites contained a protease which was more efficient in digesting haemoglobin than other proteins (Table XVIII). This suggests that blood flukes may have become so specialized that the products of hydrolysis of haemoglobin may be important nutrients. Clearly a requirement like this indicates the parasitic habit of an animal; but unless the protease showed specificity towards particular haemoglobins, this might not influence the host range. In fact the blood flukes can live in a number of different warm-blooded animals and they can be kept alive *in vitro* in medium lacking haemoglobin (see Chapter 8).

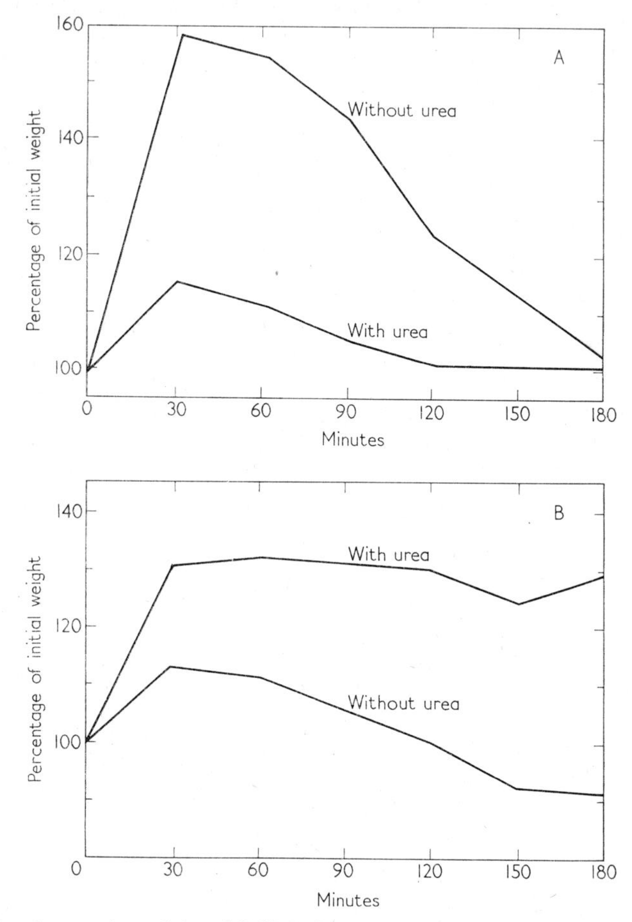

FIG. 39. The changes in weight of *Calliobothrium verticillatum* from the dogfish, *Mustelus canis* (A) and *Tetrabothrius erostris* from the gull, *Larus argentatus* (B) when incubated with and without 200mM urea in a medium containing sodium chloride (140mM), calcium chloride (5.1mM), potassium chloride (4.4mM) and magnesium chloride (2.9mM) (after Read *et al.*, 1959).

There is other evidence that the dietary needs of many parasites could not normally be met in the environments of free-living animals. The work of Read (1958, 1959) on the quality and quantity of carbohydrate needed by adult cestodes is the best example in this field. But here again it appears that the dietary needs of the parasite would only influence specificity in a broad way.

TABLE XVIII

The Specificity of a Proteolytic Enzyme from Schistosoma mansoni (*from Timms and Bueding, 1959*)

The results show the amounts of amino-nitrogen (μg) found in trichloracetic supernatants after incubating the different substrates with the purified enzyme under standard conditions

pH	Bovine haemo-globin	Bovine globin	Bovine serum γ-globulin	Pig serum γ-globulin	Bovine serum albumin	Bovine serum mercapt-albumin	Bovine serum glycoprotein fraction vi	Control haemoglobin pH 3.9
2.50	0.0	0.10	0.0	0.10	0.0	0.0	0.0	1.50
3.90	1.70	1.35	0.13	0.15	0.0	0.13	0.0	1.70
5.50	0.39	0.50	0.0	0.01	0.0	0.0	0.0	1.20
6.60	0.0	0.0	0.0	0.01	0.20	0.0	0.25	1.50
7.70	0.60	0.10	0.0	0.0	0.0	0.50	0.0	2.00

Hormones in host animals affect the growth and reproduction of metazoan parasites (see, for example, Sadun, 1951; Beck, 1952; Todd and Hollingsworth, 1952). Though it seems probable that the actions of the hosts' hormones on the parasites are indirect, there is as yet no clear indication of the mechanisms involved. It seems possible, however, that the endocrine systems of some species of potential hosts may influence their susceptibility to parasites. In hamsters, for instance, which are much more resistant to infection with *Nippostrongylus muris* than the normal host, the same dose of larvae gave infections in males some 25 times larger than those in females (Haley, 1958).

The Natural and Acquired Resistance of the Host

The features of the host that may form natural barriers and prevent the infective stage of a parasite gaining a foothold on or in the host seem obvious enough (Rogers, 1954). But the factors that prevent the growth of the parasite after the initial processes of infection have been completed are more difficult to visualize. As a rule we do not even know if the failure of a parasite to grow *in vivo* is due to lack of nutrients or to unfavourable chemical and physical features of the environment. And sometimes a factor needed by one parasite may be toxic for another; e.g. urea may be classed as a nutrient for some tapeworms whereas it is toxic to others.

The natural resistance of an organism to a parasite may be due to simple chemical or physical factors, or to complex features of the organism's physiology and anatomy. Some simple factors which might prevent the growth or survival of parasites are known; e.g. the higher temperature of homiothermic animals is often unfavourable for the development of parasites of invertebrates, or the size of animals may affect the host range of *Diphyllobothrium* (Becker, 1933). And, as mentioned above, the urea in elasmobranchs is toxic to many species of parasites. It is possible also that at least part of the natural resistance of dogs and pigs to *Ascaridia galli* may be due to toxic substances in the duodenal mucus of these animals (Eisenbrandt and Ackert, 1941).

Knowledge of the mechanisms that prevent the continued development of larvae in paratenic or abnormal hosts (Beaver, 1956) will no doubt aid our understanding of the processes that govern specificity. Larvae of some species in abnormal vertebrate or invertebrate hosts (Yoeli *et al.*, 1958) stop developing at the end of one or other of the larval stages as they do in true intermediate hosts, though not, of course, at an infective stage in the usual sense. This could be due, then, to the lack of a developmental stimulus provided by the abnormal hosts, or it could be due to natural resistance.

Sometimes the natural resistance of a host becomes apparent only as its age increases so that a young animal can be infected, though the adult, without previous experience of parasitism, is resistant. Changes of this sort may be associated with definite physiological and morphological changes in the host. Thus the skin of some species of tadpoles is penetrated by cercariae of *Diplostomum flexicaudum* and infection takes place; after metamorphosis, however, the skin of the frog is changed so that penetration cannot be effected (Davis, 1936). Similarly, the elimination of *Diphyllobothrium* from gulls occurs when a constant high temperature is established following the growth of feathers (Thomas, 1940). Resistance to *Ascaridia galli* in older chickens has a more gradual development and is associated with an increased secretion of a substance in the intestinal mucus which inhibits the growth of the parasite. The inhibiting substance is heat-stable and is soluble in physiological saline (Ackert, Edgar, and Frick, 1939; Frick and Ackert, 1948). In most hosts the development of age resistance, if it occurs, is a gradual process which does not become complete. It is reasonable to suppose, however, that the unfavourable features in the host that give rise to age resistance may often be similar to those which make an organism unsuitable as a host at any period during its life and so affect the range of hosts of parasites.

In some species of parasites, e.g. *Litomosoides carinii*, what seems to be the natural resistance of the abnormal host, in this instance the white laboratory rat, *Rattus norvegicus*, prevents the development of the early larval stages but does not inhibit the growth of the more mature parasite. Thus infection by the usual route in this host is not successful, but after early larval stages have been passed in the normal host (the cotton rat, *Sigmodon hispidus*) the worms transplanted into the abnormal host can develop to maturity and produce filariae (Olson, 1959). It appears that somewhere between the skin and the pleural cavity of white rats there exists or develops an environment which is unfavourable to the parasite. Because this effect is shown within a few days of infection Olson (1959) was inclined to regard it as natural resistance rather than acquired resistance.

A somewhat similar situation in infections of *Nippostrongylus muris* in white rats is generally regarded as due to resistance acquired by the host while the early larval stages of the parasite are developing. With this parasite infections in white rats that have not been previously infected last only for a short period and egg production may be appreciable only during the period 9 to 14 days after infection. Chandler (1936*a*) found that the transfer of larvae and young adults to a fresh host which had not been infected allowed the parasites to grow larger and produce more eggs (Fig. 40B). When the parasites were transferred to a host that had been infected before, growth and egg production were not increased (Fig. 40A). Other work (e.g. Chandler, 1936*b*) supported the suggestion that these results were due to the acquired resistance of the host. Thus parenterally induced immunity was communicated to the intestinal wall and affected the growth and reproduction of the parasite at this site. The mechanism by which the resistance of the host affects *Nippostrongylus muris* is unknown. Chandler (1935)

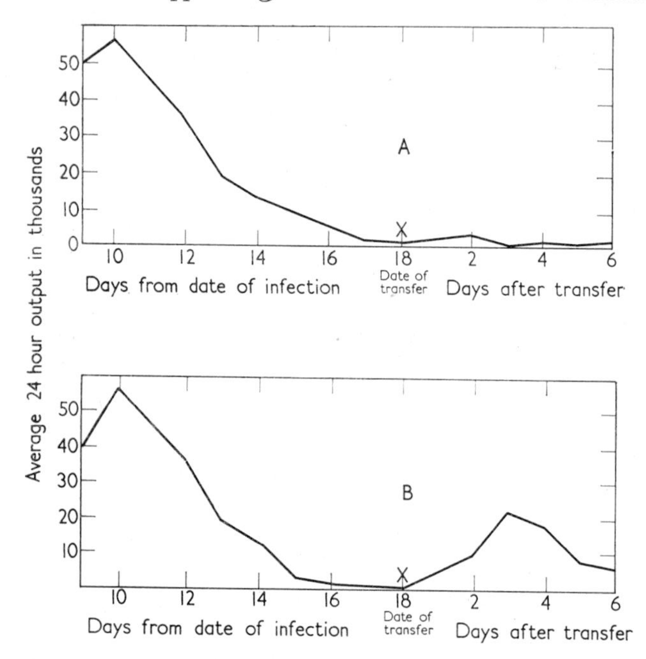

FIG. 40. A, the average egg output of *Nippostrongylus muris* in 13 infected rats from the 9th to the 18th day and the egg output of 6 of these rats to which the worms of the rest were transferred. B, the result of a similar experiment except that the worms were transferred to 6 fresh rats on the 18th day (after Chandler, 1936*a*).

thought it might be due to a failure in the nutrition of the worms due to inhibiting actions of the host. No clear-cut evidence has been obtained which supports or denies this view. However, it has been shown that the globulin fraction of the serum of rats increases during the development of an acquired immunity (Leland, Lindquist, and Lillevik, 1955). Moreover there is evidence that the protective action of immune serum may be due to antibodies (Thorson, 1954*a*, 1954*b*) and Thorson (1953, 1954*b*) has advanced the view similar to Chandler's that immunity acquired by rats against *Nippostrongylus muris* is due to the production by the host of substances that affect the parasites' enzyme systems and so interfere with the nutrition and movements of invading larvae.

In abnormal hosts the proportion of infective larvae of *Nippostrongylus muris* which reach maturity is greatly reduced (Lindquist, 1950; Haley, 1958). In hamsters this is largely due to the failure of the larvae to develop beyond the third stage so that it appears that the lungs form a barrier to the migrating larvae (Haley, 1958). Though the cellular reactions of abnormal hosts to single infections are similar to the reactions of hyperimmunized laboratory rats, Lindquist found that acquired immunity, as judged by the effects of sera on infective larvae *in vitro* (Sarles, 1938), was not greater in abnormal hosts, nor did it develop more rapidly. Moreover, he did not think that specific antibodies would be formed rapidly enough, in initial infections, to take part in cellular reactions. He suggested therefore that the resistance of these abnormal hosts was due to the slowing down of development of the parasite in an unfavourable environment so that the hosts' cells could isolate and encapsulate larvae in a "foreign body reaction". Lindquist's views have been supported by results obtained with *Nematospiroides dubius* (Cross, 1960). The primary factor in the natural resistance of the rat to this parasite seems to be the connective tissue reaction which surrounds the developing parasite in the intestinal wall. This prevents the parasite from re-entering the lumen of the intestine and causes its death. In rats treated with cortisone the inflammatory reaction in the intestinal wall does not occur and the parasites are able to complete their life cycles.

An interesting comment on the possibility that the specificity of the Monogenea might be influenced by blood-born antibodies has been made by Llewellyn (1957). Parasites of this group are usually highly specific; indeed many can infect one species of host only. An exception is *Benedenia melleni* which, though restricted to some families of the Perciformes, has a very wide range of hosts. It may be significant, then, that this parasite has the unusual characteristic of destroying the cornea of its hosts (MacCallum, 1927). The cornea, in mammals at any rate, is not vascularized and so does not react to antigenic material as do other tissues.

Specificity in the Third Stage of the Association of the Parasite with the Host

In some species of parasites the requirement of nutrients is qualitatively and quantitatively greater during reproduction (see Chapter 9). But it is possible that the host may affect the reproductive capacity of parasites in other ways, e.g. via natural resistance or resistance acquired during an earlier phase of the life cycle of the parasite. It is necessary that the eggs or larvae, produced by the reproduction of parasites within the host, should reach the sites where the continuance

TABLE XIX

A Summary of Features in the Host–Parasite Relationship that might affect Specificity of Metazoan Parasites

Stage of association	Factors affecting specificity	Stage of the parasite affected	Requirements that parasitism should occur
Stage I: contact with the host, infection	physical and chemical components of the free-living environment	free-living stages	geographical range of host and parasite must overlap
	behaviour of the host and the parasite	free-living and infective stages	infective stage must make contact with the host
	environment at the site of infection	infective stages	development of the first parasitic stage starts
Stage II: migration in the host, growth to maturity	physical and chemical components in the environment within the host	the developing parasite	parasite grows to maturity
	natural resistance of the host	do.	parasite must withstand unfavourable features of the environment
	acquired resistance of the host	do.	parasite must withstand antigenic and other toxic changes in the host
Stage III: reproduction of the parasites	physical and chemical components of the environment within the host	the mature parasite and the products of reproduction	reproduction must occur and infective agents become available to the next host
	natural resistance of the host	do.	do.
	acquired resistance of the host	do.	do.

of the life cycle is possible. Thus in some abnormal hosts, schistosomes produce eggs but these do not pass to the exterior and the life cycle cannot be completed without experimental intervention.

An organism in which the normal reproduction of a parasite does not take place, or which will not allow the normal completion of the life cycle, cannot be regarded as a true host. But as a rule it seems that deficiencies of these sorts in the host–parasite relationship would probably be less important than most other factors which influence the range of hosts of parasites even under natural conditions.

Summary

Specificity is dependent upon a whole series of factors in the relationship between the parasite and its host (Table XIX). The ecology and behaviour of the infective stage and of the host and the conditions that are necessary in the host for infection to take place affect specificity during the first stage of the association of the parasite with the host. However, it is probable that factors in the host that affect the growth and development of the parasite are of more general importance. These factors may be needed by the parasite, e.g. some tapeworms of elasmobranchs require urea; or they may be natural or acquired characters of the host that are unfavourable to the parasite, e.g. tissue reactions that prevent the growth of some nematodes in rodents. Specificity may also be influenced by factors which affect the reproduction of parasites. Little is known of this at present.

It seems that the ecology and behaviour of the parasite and the host, which influence the opportunity for contact, are important in determining specificity of organisms which have more recently assumed a parasitic mode of life, whereas physiological factors, such as the chemical and physical needs of the parasite and the natural or acquired resistance of the prospective host may be more important in organisms which have long been parasites. The relative importance of the components of the environment which determine phylogenetic specificity is unknown.

References

Ackert, J. E., Edgar, S. A. and Frick, L. P. (1939) *Trans. Amer. micr. Soc.* **58**, 81.
Anderson, R. C. (1956) *Canad. J. Zool.* **34**, 485.
Baer, J. G. (1934) *Bull. Soc. neuchâtel Sci. nat.* **58**, 57.
—— (1952) "Ecology of Animal Parasites". University of Illinois Press, Urbana.
—— (1957) *In* "First Symposium on Host Specificity among Parasites of Vertebrates". Paul Attinger, Neuchâtel.
Baylis, H. A. (1924) *J. Linn. Soc. (Zool.)* **36**, 13.
—— (1938) *In* "Evolution". (G. R. de Beer, ed.), Clarendon Press, Oxford.
Beaver, P. C. (1956) *Exp. Parasit.* **5**, 587.

Beck, J. W. (1952) *Exp. Parasit.* **1**, 109.
Becker, E. R. (1933) *Amer. J. trop. Med.* **13**, 505.
Berberian, D. A. (1936) *J. Helminth.* **14**, 21.
Bird, A. F. (1959) *Nematologica,* **4**, 222.
Calam, C. T., Todd, A. R. and Waring, W. S. (1949) *Biochem. J.* **45**, 513.
Caullery, M. (1952) "Parasitism and Symbiosis". Sidgwick and Jackson, London.
Chandler, A. C. (1932) *J. Parasit.* **18**, 135.
—— (1935) *Amer. J. Hyg.* **22**, 157.
—— (1936*a*) *Amer. J. Hyg.* **23**, 46.
—— (1936*b*) *Amer. J. Hyg.* **24**, 129.
Cross, J. H. (1960) *J. Parasit.* **46**, 175.
Culbertson, J. T. (1941) "Immunity against Animal Parasites". Columbia University Press, New York.
Davis, D. J. (1936) *J. Parasit.* **22**, 329.
Dickinson, S. (1959) *Nematologica,* **4**, 60.
Dubois, G. and Chabaud, A. (1957) *In* "First Symposium on Host Specificity among Parasites of Vertebrates". Paul Attinger, Neuchâtel.
Eisenbrandt, L. L. and Ackert, J. E. (1941) *J. Parasit.* **27**, Suppl. 36.
Ellenby, C. (1945) *Emp. J. exp. Agric.* **13**, 158.
—— (1954) *Euphytica,* **3**, 195.
—— (1958) *Nature, Lond.* **181**, 920.
—— and Gilbert, A. B. (1957) *Nature, Lond.* **180**, 1105.
—— (1958) *Nature, Lond.* **182**, 925.
Elton, C. (1947) "Animal Ecology". Sidgwick and Jackson, London.
Fairbairn, D. (1960) *In* "Host Influence on Parasite Physiology". (L. A. Stauber, ed.), Rutgers University Press, New Brunswick.
Faust, E. C. (1924) *J. Parasit.* **10**, 199.
—— and Khaw, K. (1925) *Proc. Soc. exp. Biol. Med.* **23**, 245.
—— (1927) *Monogr. Series, Amer. J. Hyg.* 8.
Franklin, M. T. (1951) "The Cyst-Forming Species of *Heterodera*". Commonwealth Bureau of Agricultural Parasitology (Helminthology), St. Albans.
Frick, L. P. and Ackert, J. E. (1948) *J. Parasit.* **34**, 192.
Goodchild, C. G. (1958) *Exp. Parasit.* **7**, 152.
Gordon, H. McL. (1948) *Aust. vet. J.* **24**, 17.
—— (1949) *Rep. Aust. Ass. Adv. Sci.* **27**, 131.
Haley, A. J. (1958) *Amer. J. Hyg.* **67**, 331.
Hoffman, G. L. (1958) *Exp. Parasit.* **7**, 23.
Hopkins, G. H. E. (1957) *In* "First Symposium on Host Specificity among Parasites of Vertebrates". Paul Attinger, Neuchâtel.
Hunter, W. S. and Chait, D. C. (1952) *J. Parasit.* **38**, 87.
Hyman, L. H. (1951) "The Invertebrates" Vol. III. McGraw-Hill Book Co., New York.
Kartman, L. (1953) *Exp. Parasit.* **2**, 27.
Larsh, J. E. (1947) *J. Parasit.* **33**, 79.
Leland, S. E., Lindquist, W. D. and Lillevik, H. A. (1955) *Exp. Parasit.* **4**, 208.
Lindquist, W. D. (1950) *Amer. J. Hyg.* **52**, 22.
Llewellyn, J. (1957) *In* "First Symposium on Host Specificity among Parasites of Vertebrates". Paul Attinger, Neuchâtel.
MacCallum, G. A. (1927) *Zoopathologica,* **1**, 291.
Marrian, D. H., Russel, P. B., Todd, A. R. and Waring, W. S. (1949) *Biochem. J.* **45**, 524.

Millemann, R. E. (1955). *J. Parasit.* **41**, 424.
Miller, H. M. and McCoy, O. R. (1930) *J. Parasit.* **16**, 185.
Mönnig, H. O. (1941) *J. S. Afr. vet. med. Ass.* **12**. 59.
Moore, D. V. and Meleney, H. E. (1955) *J. Parasit.* **41**, 235.
Nerhaus, W. (1953) *Z. Parasitenk.* **15**, 476.
Olson, L. J. (1959) *J. Parasit.* **45**, 182.
Read, C. P. (1955) *In* "Some Physiological Aspects and Consequences of Parasitism". (W. H. Cole, ed.), Rutgers University Press, New Brunswick.
—— (1958) *Rice Inst. Pamphl.* **45**, 36.
—— (1959) *Exp. Parasit.* **8**, 365.
——, Douglas, L. T. and Simmons, J. E. (1959) *Exp. Parasit.* **8**, 58.
—— and Millemann, R. E. (1953) *Univ. Calif. Publ. Zool.* **59**, 61.
Robertson, D. L. H. (1956) *J. Helminth.* **29**, 193.
Rogers, W. P. (1940) *J. Helminth.* **18**, 53.
—— (1954) *Rep. Aust. Ass. Adv. Sci.* **30**, 105.
—— (1958) *Nature, Lond.* **181**, 1410.
—— (1960) *Proc. roy. Soc. Lond.* **B152**, 367.
—— (1961) *J. Helminth.*
—— and Sommerville, R. I. (1960) *Parasitology*, **50**, 1.
Rothman, A. H. (1959) *Exp. Parasit.* **8**, 336.
Rothschild, M. and Clay, T. (1953) "Fleas, Flukes and Cuckoos". Collins, London.
Sadun, E. H. (1951) *Exp. Parasit.* **1**, 70.
Sandground, J. H. (1929) *Parasitology*, **21**, 227.
Sarles, M. P. (1938) *J. infect. Dis.* **62**, 337.
—— (1943) *J. Parasit.* **29**, 263.
Schneider, H. A. (1951) *Amer. J. trop. Med.* **31**, 174.
Spindler, L. A. (1934) *Bull. U. S. Dep. Agric.* No. 405.
Theodor, O. (1957) *In* "First Symposium on Host Specificity among Parasites of Vertebrates", Paul Attinger, Neuchâtel.
Thomas, L. J. (1940) *Anat. Rec. Suppl.* **78**, 104.
Thorson, R. E. (1953) *Amer. J. Hyg.* **58**, 1.
—— (1954*a*) *Exp. Parasit.* **3**, 9.
—— (1954*b*) *J. Parasit.* **40**, 300.
Timms, A. R. and Bueding, E. (1959) *Brit. J. Pharmacol.* **14**, 68.
Todd, A. C. and Hollingsworth, K. D. (1952) *Exp. Parasit.* **1**, 303.
Tracey, M. V. (1958) *Nematologica*, **3**, 179.
Whitlock, J. H. and Madsen, H. (1957) *J. Parasit.* **43**, Suppl. 11.
Wieser, W. (1956) *Proc. helm. Soc. Wash.* **23**, 59.
Winslow, R. D. (1953) *Ann. appl. Biol.* **40**, 225.
Wright, C. A. (1959) *Ann. trop. Med. Parasit.* **53**, 289.
Yoeli, M., Alger, N. and Most, H. (1958) *Exp. Parasit.* **7**, 531.

CHAPTER II

The Evolution of Parasitism

IN this chapter the way in which associations between organisms that have given rise to parasitism may have started and developed will be discussed. The adaptations to parasitism which are found in metazoan parasites are also examined. Of course these subjects cannot be discussed without referring to particular parasites, but as far as possible I am concerned with the evolution of parasitism rather than with the evolution of parasites. My interest is in the physiological aspects of the evolution of parasitism rather than in the taxonomic aspects of speciation of parasites.

Parasites have evolved from free-living ancestors and in some groups, such as the Nematoda, the modern free-living forms, which are in many respects similar to the parasitic forms, are available for comparative studies. This approach has not been used deliberately in search of experimental evidence about the factors which might influence the establishment of a parasitic mode of life; nor have many experiments been carried out to see if free-living forms might be adapted to live as temporary parasites. It is probable, of course, that those characters of the ancestral stock of nematodes which favoured parasitism are not present in modern free-living forms. Nevertheless an experimental study of the origins of parasitism in this group might be possible.

In groups such as the Acanthocephala and Cestoda adaptations to parasitism have proceeded so far that it is difficult to suggest the origins of these animals. Comparative studies with these and other groups of parasites will assist understanding of the evolution of parasitism because they will show how different groups have solved problems inherent in the life of a parasite. Thus parasites of the alimentary canal must have some mechanism which prevents them from passing down the gut of the host with the movement of the ingesta. This problem has been solved in the parasitic platyhelminths and Acanthocephala by the development of suckers and hooks. Presumably, the nematodes which live in the lumen of the gut maintain their position by the swimming movements which are seen in the free-living species. The extension of information like this to include physiological adaptation is necessary for understanding the evolution of parasitism.

A number of stages would be involved in the evolution of parasitism.

(a) The prospective parasite, usually in large numbers, must make contact with the prospective host.

(b) The prospective parasite must be able to penetrate at least some of the barriers against invading organisms in the prospective host.

(c) The two organisms must establish some sort of association leading directly or indirectly to a condition where one of the partners lives at the expense of the other.

(d) The host and parasite or their offspring must emerge from the association so that further generations may become associated in turn.

(e) The parasite becomes more closely adapted to its way of life so that the chance of associations forming during further generations would be increased and the exploitation of the host more efficient.

(f) The evolution of the parasite would take place in step with adaptations of the host to counter the unfavourable effects of the parasite so that a steady-state condition between the demands of the parasite and the reactions of the host would be maintained. This balance between host and metazoan parasite, which does not multiply within the host, would also be influenced strongly by the relation of the host to factors other than the parasite in its environment.

(g) The association of the parasite with the host might act as an isolating mechanism favouring speciation of the parasite to varying degrees in different species of hosts. This would lead to phylogenetic specificity.

The host–parasite relationship might be regarded as ultimately reaching a steady state in which two genotypes react to give a common phenotype on which selection might act. In response to selection a change in phenotype might react differently on the two genotypes though in this state they could not react independently. It is possible, of course, that a parasite could revert to a free-living form. But the probability that this could occur would get less as a parasite becomes more specialized.

There has been considerable speculation about the evolution of parasites and parasitism. This has concerned subjects such as the relative rates of evolution of parasites and their hosts, the significance of specificity in larval and adult parasites, the origins of complex life cycles, speciation, and the pathogenicity of parasites (Baylis, 1938; Ball, 1943; Chabaud, 1957; Manter, 1957; Schwartz, 1959). Here these different subjects are discussed only so far as they concern the central topic of the evolution of parasites.

Ecological Factors in the Origin of Parasitism

The probability that two organisms will become associated depends somewhat on their ecological and behavioural characteristics. Clearly organisms which do not meet will not become associated; those that do meet may form an association and, other things being equal, the more frequently they meet the greater the chance of association. This being so the potential parasite would be expected to find its hosts in organisms which occupy the same niche largely independently of their phylogenetic relationships. In fact the specificity of many parasites is based on the ecological relationship of the hosts, especially in groups which have only recently become parasitic. The digenetic trematodes, which are often regarded as recent parasites in the adult stage, are said to offer a perfect example of ecological specificity (Baer, 1952, p. 116) though this may not apply to all adult parasites in this group (Manter, 1955). It might be said that the range of hosts of many adult Digenea reflects the initial conditions under which cercariae or metacercariae were able to make contact and form an association with the prospective host.

Infection of the Prospective Animal Host

Various types of associations between organisms of different species may be formed (Baer, 1952, pp. 1–7; Caullery, 1952, pp. 1–30; Yonge, 1957; see Chapter 2). There seems to be doubt about the exact relationships between the different forms of association and about how parasitism might have evolved from different forms of association. Thus Baer stated that commensalism never leads to parasitism; Ball (1943) took a contrary view and Caullery regarded parasitism as developing through different stages of inquilinism. He defined inquilinism as a form of association in which one organism "lives within another but without feeding entirely at its expense although finding shelter and diverting for its own use a part of the food collected by its partner".

It seems to me that parasitism may have arisen in different ways in different groups of animals. In some it may have been preceded by some other form of association; in others it may have started by the accidental ingestion of organisms by the prospective host. Or the prospective host may have played a passive role so that parasitism developed in organisms which penetrated its integument or natural orifices either by their own activity or by the action of the intermediate host in which the organisms were already parasitic (Rogers, 1954). Whatever the precise mechanisms by which parasitism started it must always have involved some piercing of the hosts' barriers against invading organisms. The difficulty of achieving this must have varied greatly. It may have been relatively simple for some ectoparasites to gain a foothold on the prospective host, but for most prospective endoparasites features not commonly found in free-living organisms or in most ectoparasites would have been required to enable them to invade the prospective host even temporarily. The features of the prospective host which might prevent free-living organisms entering a parasitic life via its alimentary canal, for instance, would include mechanical barriers, osmotic pressure, temperature (in homiothermic animals), low oxygen pressures, digestive enzymes, and high hydrogen ion concentrations (in the stomachs of most vertebrates). Some of these features would also act as barriers against the change from an ecto- to endoparasitic mode of life.

Mechanical and Physical Barriers

Mechanisms concerned in the collection and physical treatment of food might often limit the type of organisms which could enter the alimentary canal. In both filter-feeders and animals in which grinding surfaces prepare food for chemical treatment the size of the organisms which could enter the gut would be limited. The mechanical action of the movement of ingesta along the gut of the host might also affect the establishment of parasitism; except in organisms already adapted to maintain their position in the gut of the host only a temporary parasitism could be achieved.

The temperature of warm-blooded animals may be one of their more important barriers against the casual invasion of free-living organisms. Thus many small free-living invertebrates and parasites of invertebrates die or become abnormal at these temperatures (see, for example, Sweetman, 1939; Stoll, 1953). There are exceptions however; occasional species, both free-living and parasites of invertebrates, can survive temperatures of 40°C or even more (Chapman *et al.*, 1926; Buxton, 1924; De Witt, 1955).

Physico-chemical Features

When fresh water or terrestrial free-living organisms enter the gut or tissues of a prospective host they move into a medium of higher osmotic pressure. With many free-living animals this is deleterious, but some, such as free-living nematodes, can resist quite large changes of this sort (Osche, 1952; see Chapter 4) and so have at least one of the basic physiological characters necessary for a parasitic mode of life.

A more severe challenge to organisms entering the gut of vertebrates is the high hydrogen ion concentration of the stomach which is sufficient to kill many free-living animals and parasites (Osche, 1952; Davey, 1938). However, the action of acid in the concentrations normally found in the stomach would be relatively slow, and it might be expected that many organisms would survive the changes in pH involved in the development of parasitism in the alimentary tract provided that retention in the stomach was short. Further it seems that those saprophytic organisms which live in media in which decay or autolysis leads to an increased hydrogen ion concentration would be favourably placed to survive some of the initial changes involved in parasitism of the gut. Thus the saprophyte *Rhabditis pellio* can often survive passage through the stomach of man, and in the frog may even become a temporary parasite.

Other physico-chemical conditions, such as the oxidation-reduction potentials in the gut, differ from those found in most of the environments of free-living animals but the effects of these on survival have not been studied.

The Host's Digestive Enzymes

The cuticles of many parasites contain substances which are not hydrolysed by pepsin and trypsin (Chitwood, 1936) though they are attacked by proteases of the papain bromelin group (Berger and Asenjo, 1939). This property of the cuticle has been regarded as the major feature which protects nematode parasites from the action of host enzymes (McCoy, 1935). There may be other explanations however. Thus conditions unfavourable for the action of proteases may be actively maintained by the cellular mechanisms of tissues underlying the cuticle. For example, tissue cathepsins show no gross proteolytic activity until the cells that contain them die. Thereafter changes in pH and Eh might give conditions favourable for proteolytic activity. This suggests that an ability of a prospective parasite to resist the actions of the hosts' digestive enzymes might depend upon its ability to survive other unfavourable conditions in the new environment. The fact that many parasites which are killed *in vivo* by the action of anthelmintics are then attacked by digestive enzymes lends some support to this suggestion. However, it is possible that the anthelmintic itself might cause changes in the cuticle by making it susceptible to hydrolysis. Thus the changes in the property of the cuticle might not be attributed directly to the death of the parasite.

Anti-proteolytic substances are produced by *Ascaris lumbricoides* (Sang, 1938; Collier, 1941) and are said to have some protective functions. It is doubtful if such substances are important *in vivo*, and, in particular, it is unlikely that they would be produced by free-living organisms. Adaptations of this sort and the development of the thick protective cuticle found in adult parasitic nematodes and digenetic trematodes would most likely occur after the establishment of parasitism.

Oxygen Pressures in the Gut

Oxygen is available in most regions of the bodies of animals though the pressures may be low in damaged tissues, and in the bulk of the contents of the alimentary canal oxygen may be absent. However, this may not form a serious barrier against the entry of some free-living organisms. Many of them, especially many free-living nematodes (von Brand, 1946), can survive at low pressures of oxygen, which indeed is often a feature of the environments of saprophytes. Moreover, appreciable oxygen tensions exist close to the mucosa in the less voluminous parts of the gut (Rogers, 1949*a*, 1949*b*; see Chapter 6).

It appears that, within certain limits, the change in oxygen pressure experienced by many organisms entering the prospective host would not prevent the establishment of a parasitic mode of life. Nevertheless there is some justification in regarding a facultative anaerobic free-living nematode as being advantageously placed for development as a parasite. Such an organism could not only withstand the initial difficulty of change in oxygen tension but it could become specialized in the new environment by emphasis on either aerobic or anaerobic mechanisms. The small size, shape and swimming movements of free-living nematodes would enable them to maintain a position close to the mucosa of the hosts' gut where more oxygen would be available and where they could more easily resist the movements of the ingesta.

Diet and Feeding Mechanisms

When free-living organisms entered the gut of a prospective host the diet would change whether they fed on gut contents or on the mucosa. The unspecialized organism with adequate digestive enzymes would certainly find within the host all the nutrients it needs, but under some circumstances these might not be available. Thus the high hydrogen ion concentration would interfere with digestive and absorptive processes of invading organisms ingesting the contents of the stomach. On the other hand the obtaining of adequate nutrient from the contents of the intestine or the mucosa throughout most of the alimentary canal might present little difficulty to saprophytes, especially those which could effectively close off their digestive cavities from the external environment.

The powerful sucking action by which food is obtained by many saprophytic nematodes would help prospective parasites to obtain food in the host whether they entered via the alimentary canal or via the body surface. There seems little doubt that the more elaborate feeding mechanisms associated, for example, with the armoured buccal capsule in nematodes would be adaptations developed after parasitism had been established.

Unspecific Reactions of the Host

It seems possible that invading organisms might stimulate unspecific reactions in the prospective host which would prevent the development of parasitism. If the tissues were invaded, reactions to trauma, or inflammation, might repel some organisms. In the gut simple mechanical irritation might lead to host reactions such as increased secretion of intestinal glands or increased peristalsis. Reactions like these might prevent large or very active free-living organisms from assuming a parasitic mode of life.

Infection of the Plant Host

The variety of metazoan parasites of plants is very much restricted in comparison with the variety which parasitize animals. This suggests that the barriers preventing the association of free-living animals with plants are more effective than those in the prospective animal host. The greatly increased importance of nematodes over most other metazoa as parasites of plants suggests that nematodes were unusual in possessing features which allowed them to attack both animals and plants. Even closely related species of nematodes occupy different niches. Thus some species of *Aphelenchoides* are obligate parasites of plants, others live in the body cavities of beetles; some are saprophytes or live on fungi, others are predators of free-living nematodes. Only the arthropods rival the nematodes in the wide range of hosts they can attack throughout the plant and animal kingdoms. This may be largely the outcome of ecological relationships. Thus the number of free-living nematodes in soil is very large. In many localities their weight per square metre about equals that of earthworms, and their metabolism, measured by oxygen consumption, is ten times greater (Overgaard Nielson, 1949). The chances, then, that free-living nematodes will form associations with underground structures of plants are greater than in most other groups. The importance of ecological factors in the development of plant parasitism in nematodes is supported by the wide host ranges of the majority of species and the recent development of this type of parasitism (Filipjev and Schuurmans Stekhoven, 1941, p. 199).

Though some nematodes which are found in association with plants are known under some conditions to have beneficial effects on the host if the numbers present are not great (Chitwood, 1951; Chitwood, Specht and Havis, 1952) most nematodes found under these circumstances are true parasites. Many, indeed, have pronounced pathological effects (Dropkin, 1955). It would thus appear that parasitism in plant parasitic nematodes probably started directly rather than evolving from other forms of association. The free-living nematodes in the soil which normally obtained their food in decaying vegetable matter may well have become parasitic directly as the result of casual contact with the host. Many free-living nematodes feed on micro-organisms in decaying material rather than on the material itself and so presumably are equipped with enzymes which attack bacterial cell walls. Features of this sort would help free-living nematodes to become parasites of plants without involving intermediate associations.

Barriers against the Development of Parasitism in Plants

Infection of plants takes place usually at special regions of the host: at growing regions of the root, through cracks and damaged tissues or even through stomata to which infective agents migrate in a film of water (Weber, 1927; Linford, 1939; Wieser, 1956). The method of entering the host may be elaborate and may involve the actions of attractants and repellents, actions such as adhesion to a hydrophobic surface and the mechanical rupture of cell walls as well as the secretion of enzymes attacking intra- and intercellular materials (Wieser, 1956; Tracey, 1958; Dickinson, 1959). The complex processes involved in entering the plant host suggest that the outer surface of the plant may have been an important barrier against the development of parasitism.

Though the physical and chemical nature of plant surfaces is probably the main barrier against the invasion of prospective parasites, other features, such as the production of substances which are toxic to some species of nematodes (Oostenbrink, Kuiper, and s'Jacob, 1957), may have limited the development of parasitism in plants.

Adaptations in Parasites and their Hosts

A free-living organism which has penetrated the host's initial barriers will have certain features which predispose it towards parasitism. But invasion of the host may not lead to parasitism; the mere action of entering the host may cause it to react unfavourably towards the presence of the foreign organism. The reactions may be local or they may lead to the formation of antibodies which have immediate effects on the parasite; or the host may slowly become adapted either towards the rejection of the parasite or to the effects of parasitism. At the same time the parasite may become adapted to live more efficiently and to resist the unfavourable changes in the host.

Knowledge of the genetics of the interaction of metazoan parasites and their hosts is necessary for an understanding of the evolution and maintenance of parasitism and is also basic to our understanding of the physiological relationship between individual parasites and their hosts.

Information of this sort about metazoan parasites and their hosts is not available but work on obligate fungal parasites of plants indicates the general importance of this approach to the study of parasitism (see, for example, Flor, 1955, 1956; Schaller and Briggs, 1955*a*, 1955*b*). The flax rust, *Melampsora lini*, and its host *Linum usitatissimum*, have been studied in most detail. Adaptation to parasitism has reached a high degree in both parasite and host; specificity is high so that certain strains of the parasite can grow only in certain strains of the host. The basis of this specificity lies in the complementary genetic systems of the host and the parasite in which a gene in the system of the host reacts specifically with a corresponding gene in the system of the parasite to give a common phenotype of resistance or susceptibility of the host. The fungus and its host have at least 25 such corresponding or oppositional genes; each pair of oppositional genes reacts independently of all other pairs to give a common phenotype on which selection acts. It is apparent that the effect of this selection can only be considered in the context of the population of the parasites and the population of the hosts existing together under natural conditions; and it is the effect of this selection which determines the further evolution of the association between the parasite and its host.

With this information, models for the relationship of the evolution of the parasite and its host, which might be applied to metazoan parasites, have been constructed. Assuming that the genetic structure of the hosts and parasites had evolved under a system of random mating, and that the parasites had evolved with their hosts, Mode (1958) showed that the complementary genetic systems would ultimately give rise to a condition of stable equilibrium in the host–parasite relationship. This equilibrium would not only favour the continued existence of the host and its parasite but indeed might be a necessary condition for their coupled evolution.

Genetical information about metazoan parasites and their hosts of the sort used by Mode in his analysis of evolutionary relationships between hosts and their fungal parasites is not yet available. Clearly, however, mechanisms that maintain the balance between metazoan parasites and their hosts must have evolved, though under present day conditions the balance in some species may have been disturbed. These mechanisms in metazoan parasites may be somewhat different from those in other sorts of parasites in which resistance must often be directed towards the limitation of the multiplication of the parasites within the host. In metazoan parasites, though host resistance might often be directed towards countering the virulence of the parasite, the balance between the partners which leads to a stable condition may have been obtained from adaptations in the parasite or in the host which influence the number of infective agents entering the host. Thus changes in behaviour of the host or infective agents and changes in the fertility of the parasites all affect the chances of infection, so that selection pressure could act against those parasites in a population of which infective agents reached hosts in such large numbers that the hosts were killed, or against those hosts in a population which had features that exposed them unduly to the risk of infection. In this way a single species of parasite might approach a condition of stable equilibrium with a variety of hosts linked largely by common ecological characters—a situation not uncommon among metazoan parasites. With increasing specialization of the different species of hosts and of the parasite the host range would become narrowed. This might occur by the elimination of the parasite from some species of host, or by the isolation of the parasite in different hosts to a degree which might give rise to speciation. In this way phylogenetic specificity in which the parasite is closely adapted to one species of host or a few related species of hosts, might arise.

A process which helps to maintain the balance in host–parasite relationships is seen in some plant parasitic nematodes. For instance heavy infections of *Heterodera rostochiensis* tend to have a high proportion of males. The mechanism by which this is achieved is unknown though it is not due to differential mortality (Ellenby, 1954). It clearly has a stabilizing effect by reducing egg production. A fall in egg production per female parasite occurs in heavy infections of animals (Rogers, 1939).

Most of the adaptations which are found in parasites occur in free-living animals as well. Some, however, are unusual because they are responses to unusual components in the parasites' environment such as antibodies produced by the host. Thus the changes in antigenic structure which some trypanosomes undergo during the course of infection (Browning, Adamson and Keppie, 1953) are adaptations of a sort which are not likely to be found in free-living animals. Again the adaptation which makes high concentrations of some form of carbon dioxide necessary as a stimulus for the exsheathment of larvae of *Haemonchus contortus* is unusual. But adaptations of these sorts are not entirely restricted to parasites—for instance, carbon dioxide stimulates developmental changes in *Hydra* (see Chapter 4).

Adaptations to parasitism in metazoan parasites and their hosts have been discussed in detail by many writers (see, for example, Baer, 1952, pp. 11–139; Caullery, 1952, pp. 40–65, pp. 154–171; Becker, 1953; Lapage, 1958, pp. 111–219). In the sections that follow, therefore, there will be discussed only a few aspects of this subject, and then only in general terms.

Morphological Changes associated with Parasitism

A variety of morphological features in parasites can be regarded as adaptations to a parasitic mode of life. Examples usually given here are: organs of adhesion such as suckers and hooks; the replacement of a surface epithelium by a resistant cuticle; the development of special feeding devices for sucking blood and cutting tissues; and changes in size and shape of the body and organs, usually associated with changes in reproductive activity. Many of these features were present in the free-living ancestors of parasites; their increased development is an adaptation which allows parasites to exploit a new environment effectively.

Though the infective agents of parasites are small, adult parasites, except in some groups like the plant parasitic nematodes, grow larger than their free-living relatives. This is clearly seen in nematode parasites of animals; in this group the adults, though not often reaching the dimensions of *Ascaris lumbricoides* or *Dioctophyme renale*, are nevertheless usually larger than free-living species. The advantages of large size are not at all obvious. Presumably increased size may result from a variety of adaptations, some concerned with particular organs, like the reproductive system, others concerned with the whole organism.

Increases in size would involve changes in metabolism of parasites and changes in their relations to the host. Increased efficiency in the transport of substrates and excretory products would be needed. And unless associated with adaptations for a greater predominance of anaerobic mechanisms the larger parasite would have difficulty in obtaining sufficient oxygen for internal tissues. Pathogenicity due to physical causes such as obstruction, pressure and movement would be increased. But other forms of pathogenicity might be decreased. Thus a number of small parasites in the intestine equivalent in weight to an infection with *Ascaris lumbricoides* or *Taenia saginata* might well be more pathogenic. Again unfavourable host reactions may be less effective on organisms with a small surface/volume ratio. An important advantage of large size in a parasite might be that infection—always a hazardous point in the life cycle—resulting from a minimum number of eggs or larvae can give rise to very large output of infective agents for the next generation. Offsetting this would be the disadvantage of a partly anaerobic metabolism in the larger parasites.

Many morphological changes must have been associated with physiological adaptations. For example the morphological changes in the loss of the gut must have been preceded by development of other absorptive areas. These adaptations must have taken place after the parasitic mode of life had been established.

Physiological Changes associated with Parasitism

Physiological adaptation has been defined as "any alteration or response of an organism which favours its survival in a changed environment, hence is 'useful' in a strictly objective sense" (Prosser, 1958). Adaptations may occur in individuals in association with changes in the environment, e.g. some *Daphnia* when exposed to low oxygen tensions have increased concentrations of haemoglobin in their tissues. Or adaptations may be genetically determined and occur in populations of organisms or in species.

I have argued in earlier chapters that an important adaptation to parasitism is the suspension of development in the infective stage and the requirement that the host should provide a stimulus for its resumption. A mechanism of this sort exists in some nematodes and has a selective value because it ensures that the protective features of infective larvae would not be discarded until an environment which favoured further development was reached. Adaptations of this sort probably have an evolutionary relationship to mechanisms concerned in the dispersal of some free-living forms. Thus "dauer" larvae, or the third-stage larvae of *Rhabditis coarctata*, may require a stimulus before development is resumed (see Chapter 3).

The loss of sense organs is a common feature of parasitism. These organs are replaced by mechanisms which allow the infective stage to "recognize" its host. Thus the "receptor" which responds to the stimulus in the rumen of the sheep and causes the exsheathment of larval nematodes is, in some respects, a sense organ, though it acts as a physiological "trigger" (Bullock, 1957) rather than as a conventional sense organ.

Many metazoan parasites have undergone changes in their metabolism during their evolutionary history. However, these adaptations have not coupled them closely with the metabolism of the host as in viruses for instance, and basically the metabolism of metazoan parasites is probably similar to that in their free-living ancestors. The basic metabolic routes of cellular respiration seem to be the glycolytic reaction sequence, the pentose phosphate pathway, the Kreb's tricarboxylic acid cycle and the cytochrome system. Of these, glycolysis, though receiving more emphasis in some parasites than others, seems largely unchanged. The tricarboxylic acid cycle and the cytochrome system, however, have evidently been modified considerably in some species; parts of it have been lost, and unusual mechanisms, both aerobic and anaerobic, have often been added. Mitochondria which are morphologically similar to those in vertebrate tissues are found in regions of some parasites which are poorly supplied with oxygen (Prestage, 1960). Those in the testis of *Parascaris equorum* are dense and abnormal (Hovasse, 1959). It is not known if any of these mitochondria are normal in their biochemical activities.

An adaptation associated with oxidative metabolism is the presence of haemoglobin in the tissues of many nematode parasites and some platyhelminth and arthropod parasites (see Chapter 6). This is more common among parasites of the alimentary canal where oxygen pressures are generally low so that pigments of suitable physical properties would have selective value. It is probable that this adaptation is genetically based, though the possibility that it is environmentally induced as in some free-living species has not been disproved. There is evidently considerable variation in the amounts of pigment in individuals of the same species.

Adaptation to live at higher temperatures is an important feature of many metazoan parasites and indeed it is a determining factor in the broader categories of specificity (see Chapter 10). It influences the evolution of parasites in several ways. Thus it can lead to changes in life cycles as in *Hymenolepis nana* where the capacity of the cysticercoid to develop at the temperature of the definitive host is at least partly responsible for the evolution of the direct life cycle (Heyneman, 1958). Changes in temperature would also affect the metabolism of parasites entering warm-blooded hosts. But these effects could be unfavourable as well as favourable. Thus the increased temperature would lead to a higher respiratory rate and a greater need for oxygen. This would be unfavourable for organisms entering the alimentary canal where oxygen pressures may be low. It is known that in some organisms the adaptation to higher temperatures is associated with a decrease in the proportion of cytochrome-mediated respiration and an increased importance in iodoacetate-sensitive routes (Eckberg, 1958). Changes like these might be beneficial to organisms entering the alimentary canal of a prospective host.

These and most other physiological adaptations which occur in metazoan parasites are similar to those found in free-living animals. Adaptations that are more characteristic of parasitism will be those concerned with the more unusual features of the parasites' environment, e.g. those adaptations which allow parasites to counter the more complex biological attacks of the host. Little is known about these (Becker, 1953).

Adaptations that increase the Chances of Infection

The chances of a parasite's making contact with the host may be increased in a variety of ways. Chief of these is the increased production of infective agents. This may be achieved, for example, by (a) producing more eggs; (b) more efficient means of fertilization as in the

Strongyloidea; (c) parthenogenesis and asexual reproduction. More efficient protection of infective agents against unfavourable features of the environment by the thickening of egg-shells and cuticles, changes in the life cycle and behaviour of infective larvae (see Chapter 3), and adaptations in the process of infection (see Chapter 5) all increase the chances of infection.

Adaptations like these, in organisms that had established a parasitic mode of life, must have occurred in step with changes in the host which decreased the possibility of overwhelming infections.

Changes in the life cycles which have occurred during the evolution of parasites may, in some species at least, have had selective advantage because they increased the chances of infection. Thus the acquisition of a suitable intermediate host may aid the infective form to reach the definitive host. And the acquisition of a definitive host may lead to increased production of infective agents. The advantages of the more complex life cycles are, however, difficult to fathom. Indeed Hyman (1951, p. 419) took the view that "the chances of offspring reaching the definitive host and maturing to the reproductive stage would seem to be greatly reduced by this roundabout way of reaching adulthood".

Presumably life cycles have become more complex during the course of evolution though, in old-established parasites, they have also become more simple. Complexity would increase as new hosts became available. Thus it has been suggested that the digenetic trematodes were originally parasites of molluscs and had free-swimming adults (Baylis, 1938). Later, vertebrate hosts became available and this led to more complex life cycles. On the other hand it seems that the life cycles of some cestodes and nematodes may, in the later phases of evolution, become simplified by the loss of a host (Baer, 1952, p. 148; Schwartz, 1959).

Adaptations of the Host to Parasitism

Though there is little doubt that genetically determined adaptations in host organisms have been concerned in developing the balance in host–parasite relationships, the genetics of these processes and their mode of expression in the phenotype are largely unknown. Work in this field is just beginning (see, for example, Whitlock and Madsen, 1957). Adaptations might allow a host species to reject a parasite, so narrowing its host range, or they might lead to a balance by allowing a host to eliminate or to avoid some of the individual parasites of a virulent species so that the pathological effects are reduced, or they might allow the host to withstand the effects of the parasite. These adaptations might take different forms.

(i) Morphological changes such as the thickening of epidermis might reduce the number of parasites entering the host.

(ii) Changes in behaviour; e.g. changes in feeding habits of *Dipodomys merriami merriami* may have taken place which prevent its infection, under natural conditions, with *Oochoristica deserti* (Read, 1958).

(iii) Metabolism might change so that a substance needed by the parasite was no longer available, or toxic substances might be produced; e.g. a root diffusate which is toxic to *Tagetes* spp. is produced by some plants (Oostenbrink, Kuiper, and s'Jacob, 1957).

(iv) Changes might occur in the capacity to synthesize protective substances concerned in antigen-antibody or similar reactions; e.g. the production of substances which neutralize the salivary secretions of parasites (Liao and Dunlap, 1950), or which cause "self-cure" (Soulsby, 1958*a*).

With the information at present available it is difficult to decide how far immune reactions of the sort developed against micro-organisms might influence the evolution of metazoan parasites. In some, like nematodes, antibodies produced by the host would have to act via the alimentary canal of the parasite or through its protective cuticle. This might be difficult except during certain times in the life cycle such as moults or metamorphoses. Certainly there is evidence that antibody production is increased at such times (Soulsby, 1958*b*). Moreover, immunity of the host sometimes has the action of delaying the passage of a nematode through a moult.

Many adaptations concerned with the fitness of host organisms in their external environment must have influenced the evolution of host–parasite relationships which took place under conditions approaching balanced polymorphism. Some variations in host organisms, though selectively favourable overall, may have increased parasitism. For example the capacity for close grazing may have been advantageous in some herbivores though it may have led to increased chances of infection. On the other hand, some variations may have had selective advantage only because they were unfavourable to parasites. Thus sickle cell anaemia in man has a selective advantage only in areas where malaria is endemic.

Pathogenicity and Parasitism

Presumably during the evolution of parasites occasions may have arisen where the survival of a parasite, or the host and its parasite, was threatened by increased resistance of the host or increased virulence of the parasite. This may have led to the extinction of local populations of either parasites, or their hosts, or both.

It has frequently been asserted that high pathogenicity is evidence of recent and still imperfect host–parasite relationships (Hegner, 1926; Fantham, 1936; Chandler, 1940). This does not seem unreasonable. Thus, in the invasion of a new host by a prospective parasite, selection would act against the more pathogenic individuals among the parasite species and the less resistant individuals in the host species. This would lead to a more stable host–parasite relationship. The condition in which a high pathogenicity indicates a newly established parasite might be expected if parasitism arose directly (Rabaud, 1928; Baer, 1952) and not from a more benign association. This may be true for some species but there is also evidence which suggests that parasitism may have arisen through intermediate conditions like commensalism (Wenrich, 1935; Caullery, 1952). As Ball (1943) has pointed out, if this is true the view that high pathogenicity indicates a newly established parasite is less plausible. In fact, examples which indicate that high pathogenicity can occur in both newly established and old parasites are known (Ball, 1943). It seems, then, that generalizations about the evolution of parasites based on pathogenicity should be avoided until more data are available.

SUMMARY

I have suggested that the evolution of parasitism involves several steps. The chance that parasitism might be established must first depend on ecological factors—the prospective parasite must meet the host and, other things being equal, the more frequently they meet the more likely an association would be formed. But not all the organisms contacting the prospective host could penetrate its initial morphological and physiological barriers. Where this did occur, commensalism, which could give rise to parasitism, might result, or ecto- or endo-parasitism might arise directly. In order that parasitism might persist a balanced condition between the host and its parasites must develop. This would involve a series of adaptations concerned primarily with the chances of infection, the virulence of the parasite and the resistance of the host to the parasite or its pathogenic effects. In addition, the adaptation of the host to factors in its environment other than parasites would have an important bearing on the evolution of parasitism. This complex of interactions between parasite, host and the host's environment would lead to a condition in which the disadvantages of parasitism to the host would be balanced against advantages obtained by the host from its environment during exposure to parasitism.

As a host evolves, its own isolation may lead to the isolation of some of its parasites. This would lead to the speciation of the parasite and the development of phylogenetic specificity.

REFERENCES

Baer, J. G. (1952) "Ecology of Animal Parasites". University of Illinois Press, Urbana.
Ball, G. H. (1943) *Amer. Nat.* **77**, 345.
Baylis, H. A. (1938) *In* "Evolution". (G. R. de Beer, ed.), Clarendon Press, Oxford.
Becker, E. R. (1953) *J. Parasit.* **39**, 467.
Berger, J. and Asenjo, C. F. (1939) *Science,* **90**, 299.
Browning, C. H., Adamson, H. and Keppie, A. A. N. (1953) *J. Path. Bact.* **65**, 137.
Bullock, T. H. (1957) *In* "Physiological Triggers and Discontinuous Rate Processes". (T. H. Bullock, ed.), American Physiological Society, Washington, D.C.
Buxton, P. A. (1924) *Proc. roy. Soc.* **B96**, 123.
Caullery, M. (1952) "Parasitism and Symbiosis". Sidgwick and Jackson, London.
Chabaud, A. G. (1957) *In* "First Symposium on Host Specificity among Parasites of Vertebrates". Paul Attinger, Neuchâtel.
Chandler, A. C. (1940) "Introduction to Parasitology". J. Wiley and Sons, New York.
Chapman, R. N., Mickel, C. E., Parker, J. R., Miller, G. E. and Kelly, E. G. (1926) *Ecology*, **7**, 416.
Chitwood, B. G. (1936) *Proc. helm. Soc. Wash.* **3**, 39.
—— (1951) *Plant & Soil*, **3**, 47.
——, Specht, A. and Havis, L. (1952) *Plant & Soil*, **4**, 77.
Collier, H. B. (1941) *Canad. J. Res.* **B19**, 91.
Davey, D. G. (1938) *J. exp. Biol.* **15**, 217.
De Witt, W. B. (1955) *Exp. Parasit.* **4**, 271.
Dickinson, S. (1959) *Nematologica*, **4**, 60.
Dropkin, V. H. (1955) *Exp. Parasit.* **4**, 282.
Eckberg, D. (1958) *Biol. Bull., Woods Hole,* **114**, 308.
Ellenby, C. (1954) *Nature, Lond.* **174**, 1016.
Fantham, H. B. (1936) *Scientia*, **59**, 316.
Filipjev, I. N. and Schuurmans Stekhoven, J. H. (1941) "A Manual of Agricultural Helminthology". E. J. Brill, Leiden.
Flor, H. H. (1955) *Phytopathology*, **45**, 680.
—— (1956) *Advanc. Genet.* **8**, 29.
Hegner, R. (1926) *Quart. Rev. Biol.* **1**, 393.
Heyneman, D. (1958) *Exp. Parasit.* **7**, 374.
Hovasse, R. (1959) *Proc. 15th Int. Congr. Zool. Lond., 1958*, 708.
Hyman, L. H. (1951) "The Invertebrates" Vol. II. McGraw-Hill Book Co., New York.
Lapage, G. (1958) "Parasitic Animals". Heffer and Sons, Cambridge.
Liao, S. C. and Dunlap, A. A. (1950) *Phytopathology*, **40**, 416.
Linford, M. B. (1939) *Proc. helm. Soc. Wash.* **6**, 11.
McCoy, O. R. (1935) *Physiol. Rev.* **15**, 221.
Manter, H. W. (1955) *Exp. Parasit.* **4**, 62.
—— (1957) *In* "First Symposium on Host Specificity among Parasites of Vertebrates". Paul Attinger, Neuchâtel.
Mode, C. J. (1958) *Evolution*, **12**, 158.
Oostenbrink, M., Kuiper, K. and s'Jacob, J. J. (1957) *Nematologica*, **2**, Suppl. 424.
Osche, G. (1952) *Z. Morph. Ökol. Tiere*, **41**, 54.
Overgaard Nielson, C. (1949) *Proc. 4th Int. Congr. Microbiol., Copenhagen, 1947*, 483.
Prestage, J. J. (1960) *J. Parasit.* **46**, 69.
Prosser, C. L. (1958) *In* "Physiological Adaptation". (C. L. Prosser, ed.), American Physiological Society, Washington, D. C.

Rabaud, E. (1928) *Revue-Philosophique,* **106**, 18.
Read, C. P. (1958) *Rice Inst. Pamphl.* **45**, 36.
Rogers, W. P. (1939) *J. Helminth.* **17**, 151.
—— (1949*a*) *Aust. J. sci. Res.* **B2**, 157.
—— (1949*b*) *Aust. J. sci. Res.* **B2**, 399.
—— (1954) *Rep. Aust. Ass. Adv. Sci.* **30**, 105.
Sang, J. H. (1938) *Parasitology*, **34**, 141.
Schaller, C. W. and Briggs, F. N. (1955*a*) *Agron. J.* **47**, 181.
—— (1955*b*) *Genetics*, **41**, 421.
Schwartz, B. (1959) *Amer. J. vet. Res.* **20**, 7.
Soulsby, E. J. L. (1958*a*) *Vet. Revs. Annotations*, **4**, 1.
—— (1958*b*) *Nature, Lond.* **181**, 465.
Stoll, N. R. (1953) *J. Parasit.* **39**, 422.
Sweetman, H. L. (1939) *J. econ. Ent.* **32**, 698.
Tracey, M. V. (1958) *Nematologica,* **3**, 179.
von Brand, T. (1946) "Anaerobiosis in Invertebrates". Biodynamica, Normandy, Missouri.
Weber, H. (1927) *Forsch. Pflkr., Berl.* **3**, 129.
Wenrich, D. H. (1935) *Proc. Amer. phil. Soc.* **75**, 605.
Whitlock, J. H. and Madsen, H. (1957) *J. Parasit.* **43**, Suppl. 11.
Wieser, W. (1956) *Proc. helm. Soc. Wash.* **23**, 59.
Yonge, C. M. (1957) *Mem. geol. Soc. Amer.* **67**, vol. 1, 429.

Author Index

Numbers in italics refer to the pages on which references are listed at the end of each chapter.

A

Ackert, J. E., 169, 173, 174, 176, *189, 190, 192,* 234, 235, *239, 240*
Adamson, H., 16, *23,* 251, *258*
Addis, C. J., 186, *189*
Agosin, M., 100, 120, 121, 122, *130,* 161, 162, *164*
Aldrich, D.V., 123, *130,* 187, 189, *189*
Alexander, A. E., 118, *130*
Alger, N., 234, *241*
Alicata, J. E., 31, 32, 33, 34, 35, 38, 43, *46,* 77, *93*
Allee, W. C., 14, *23*
Allen, M. W., 209, *218*
Alt, H. L., 121, *130*
Ammon, R., 202, *217*
Anderson, R. C., 223, *239*
Andrewartha, H. G., 14, *23*
Aravena, L. C., 100, 120, 121, *130*
Archer, V. W., 159, *164*
Artemov, N. M., 125, *130*
Asenjo, C. F., 115, *130,* 174, *191,* 246, *258*
Augustinsson, K. B., 125, *130*
Axmann, M. C., 64, *66,* 187, *189*

B

Bacq, Z. M., 126, *130*
Baer, J. G., 13, *23,* 29, 45, *46,* 49, *66,* 122, *131,* 161, *165,* 183, *191,* 219, 220, 223, *239,* 244, 251, 255, 257, *258*
Bahl, K. N., 108, *130*
Bair, T. D., 54, 56, 63, *66*
Baldwin, E., 112, 113, 114, 117, *130*
Ball, G. H., 176, *191,* 243, 244, 257, *258*
Barrington, E. J. W., 71, *93*
Baylis, H. A., 220, 222, 223, *239,* 243, 255, *258*
Beach, T. D., 215, *217*
Beaver, P. C., 234, *239*
Beck, J. W., 234, *240*
Becker, E. R., 219, 234, *240,* 251, 254, *258*
Becker, M., 207, *218*
Berberian, D. A., 230, *240*
Bergeim, O., 71, *93*
Berger, J., 115, *130,* 246, *258*
Berkhina, R. A., 145, *164*
Berl, S., 105, *130,* 144, *164*
Berry, L. J., 140, *166*
Bingley, W. J., 180, *192*
Birch, L. C., 14, *23*
Bird, A. F., 85, *93,* 115, 116, 118, *130,* 151, *164,* 227, *240*
Bishop, A., 91, *93*
Bishop, D. W., 141, *164*
Blower, G., 213, *217*
Bovet, P., 111, *132,* 201, *218*
Bowen, R. H., 200, *217*
Brand, T. von., 16, 18, *23,* 55, 64, *67,* 71, *94,* 100, 102, 106, 108, 119, 120, 121, 122, 123, *130, 133,* 135, 136, 137, 138, 139, 140, 141, 142, 143, 144, 145, 146, 147, 148, 149, 153, 155, 157, 160, 161, 162, *164, 166,* 174, 175, 177, 178, 179, 180, 181, 186, 187, *192, 193,* 214, *217,* 247, *259*
Brante, G., 183, *189*
Bretschneider, L. H., 106, *132,* 169, *190*
Briggs, F. N., 250, *259*
Brody, G., 173, *189*
Brown, C. H., 115, *130,* 213, *217*
Brown, H. W., 52, 53, *66*
Browne, H. G., 168, 172, *189*
Browning, C. H., 16, *23,* 251, *258*
Bueding, E., 100, 102, 103, 105, 114, 120, 121, 122, 125, 128, *130, 131, 132,* 137, 139, 140, 141, 143, 144, 145, 147, 148, 149, 160, 161, 162, *164, 165, 166,* 177, 178, 179, 180, 181, 185, 187, 189, *189, 192,* 231, 233, *241*
Bullock, T. H., 253, *258*
Buxton, P. A., 245, *258*

C

Calam, C. T., 89, *93,* 226, *240*
Campbell, J. W., 189, *189*
Campbell, P. L., 204, *217*

Carpenter, M. F. P., 169, *189*
Carter, G. S., 152, *165*
Caullery, M., 12, *24,* 219, *240,* 244, 251, 257, *258*
Cavier, R., 100, 108, 110, 111, *131,* 169, 179, 180, *189*
Chabaud, A., 221, *240,* 243, *258*
Chait, D. C., 86, *93,* 184, *191,* 228, 240
Chance, M. R. A., 180, *189*
Chandler, A. C., 33, 43, *46,* 123, 126, *130, 131,* 181, 182, 186, 187, 189, *189, 190,* 221, 235, 236, *240,* 257, *258*
Chang, P. C. H., 215, *217*
Chapman, R. N., 245, *258*
Charms, B., 102, 105, *130*
Chin, C., 102, *131,* 149, *165*
Chitwood, B. G., 12, *24,* 35, *47,* 90, *93,* 111, 115, *131,* 168, 169, 173, *190,* 200, 201, 202, 203, 204, 205, 207, 208, 209, 210, *217,* 246, 248, *258*
Chitwood, M. B., 33, 35, 43, *46, 47,* 111, 115, *131,* 168, *190,* 200, *217*
Chowdhury, A. B., 168, 172, *189*
Christenson, R. O., 210, 211, *217*
Christie, J. R., 171, *190,* 214, *217*
Chu, H. J., 176, *191*
Clapham, P. A., 173, 174, *196*
Clarke, A. S., 72, *93*
Clay, T., 223, *241*
Clegg, J. A., 212, 213, *217, 218*
Clifton, C. E., 135, *165*
Colas, J., 200, 206, *217*
Collier, H. B., 17, *24,* 246, *258*
Cort, W. W., 215, *217*
Costello, L. C., 54, 55, 58, *66*
Courtois, A., 116, *131*
Crawford, N. Z., 173, *189*
Crites, J. L., 203, 204, 205, 207, 208, *217*
Crofton, H. D., 9, *11,* 36, *47,* 51, *66,* 111, 114, 118, *131,* 152, 153, *165*
Cross, J. H., 237, *240*
Culbertson, J. T., 219, *240*

D

Daugherty, J. W., 123, *130, 131,* 187, 189, *189, 190*
Davenport, H. E., 153, 154, 155, 156, 157, *165*
Davey, D. G., 16, 17, *24,* 119, *131,* 146, 147, 155, 160, *165,* 176, *190,* 245, *258*
Davis, C. C., 43, *47*
Davis, D. J., 235, *240*
Dawes, B., 45, *47,* 88, *93,* 124, *131,* 181, 184, 186, *190,* 212, 215, *217*
Day, M. F., 71, *93*
de Beer, E. J., 112, 114, *132*
Debusmann-Morgenroth, M., 202, *217*
Delaunay, H., 108, *131*
De Ley, J., 121, *131*
Dennell, R., 213, *217*
Deutsch, K., 115, 118, *130,* 151, *164*
de Waele, A., 87, *93*
Dewey, D. W., 71, *93*
De Witt, W. B., 245, *258*
Dickinson, S., 90, *93,* 227, *240,* 249, *258*
Dinnick, J. A., 52, 53, *66*
Dinnick, N. N., 52, 53, *66*
Dirnhuber, P., 180, *190*
Dixon, K. C., 142, *165*
Donaldson, A. W., 174, *190*
Dougherty, E. C., 176, *190*
Douglas, L. T., 126, 127, *133,* 231, 232, *241*
Dresel, E. I. B., 108, *131*
Dropkin, V. H., 62, *66,* 89, *93,* 171, 173, *190,* 248, *258*
Dubois, G., 221, *240*
Dubos, R. J., 6, 7, *11,* 167, *190*
Duchateau, G., 110, 123, *131*
Dunlap, A. A., 256, *258*
Dusanic, D., 88, *94*
Duval, M., 116, *131*

E

Ebel, J. P., 200, 206, *217*
Eckberg, D., 254, *258*
Eden, A., 108, 116, 117, 118, *132*
Edgar, S. A., 87, *93,* 235, *239*
Eisenbrandt, L. L., 234, *240*
Eisma, M., 59, *66*
Ellenby, C., 16, *24,* 89, *93,* 214, *217,* 226, 227, *240,* 251, *258*
Elliot, A., 49, 51, *66*
Elton, C., 223, *240*
Emerson, A. E., 14, *23*
Entner, N., 101, 103, *130, 131,* 177, *190*
Epps, W., 144, *165*
Ernberg, T., 183, *189*
Esserman, H. B., 170, *190*
Evans, A. S., 68, *93*

F

Fairbairn, D., 13, 16, *24,* 49, 50, 51, 53, 54, 56, 57, 63, *66,* 72, 77, 89, 91, *93, 94,* 100, 101, 105, 106, 108, 110, 111, 115, 116, *131, 132,* 139, 143, 144, 145, *165,* 180, *190,* 200, 201, 207, 211, 215, *217, 218,* 225, *240*
Fantham, H. B., 257, *258*
Farber, E., 103, *130*
Farrow, G. W., 102, 114, *130*
Fauré-Fremiet, E., 49, 53, 56, *66,* 115, *131,* 200, 201, 205, 206, 207, 211, *217*
Faust, E. C., 33, *47,* 86, *93,* 214, 215, *217,* 223, 228, *240*
Feng, L. C., 168, 176, *190, 191*
Fenn, W. O., 149, *165*
Fenwick, D. W., 176, *190*
Ferguson, M. S., 86, *93,* 184, *190*
Ferreol, G., 50, *67,* 207, *218*
Filhol, J., 201, *217*
Filipjev, I. N., 31, *47,* 248, *258*
Flor, H. H., 250, *258*
Florkin, M., 110, 123, *131*
Flury, F., 115, *131,* 207, *217*
Follansbee, R., 71, *93*
Foster, W. B., 123, *131,* 189, *190*
Foster, W. D., 207, *218*
Franklin, M. T., 89, *93,* 227, *240*
Frick, L. P., 235, *239, 240*
Friedheim, E. A. H., 122, *131,* 161, *165*
Fouquey, C., 50, *66, 67,* 207, *217, 218*
Fülleborn, F., 54, *66*

G

Gaafar, S. M., 173, 174, *190*
Garoian, G., 170, *190*
Garrault, H., 115, *131*
Gerard, R. W., 149, *165*
Gettier, A., 128, *131,* 186, *190*
Gilbert, A. B., 16, *24,* 89, *93,* 226, 227, *240*
Giovannola, A., 49, 51, *66*
Giroud, A., 180, *190*
Girth, H. B., 175, *190*
Glaser, R. W., 51, *66,* 175, 176, *190*
Glocklin, V. C., 105, *131,* 139, 143, 144, 145, *165*
Goddard, D. R., 137, 140, *165*
Godfried, E. G., 109, *131*
Goil, M. M., 123, *131*
Goldberg, E., 102, *131,* 180, *190*
Gonzalez, C., 101, *131,* 177, *190*
Goodchild, C. G., 124, *131,* 184, 189, *190,* 231, *240*
Gordon, H. McL., 222, *240*
Gothié, S., 211, *217*
Gräsbeck, R., 183, *191*
Graham, G. L., 210, 215, *217*
Grembergen, G. van., 122, 123, 126, *132, 133,* 154, 161, 163, *166*
Gresson, R. A. R., 181, *190*
Grollman, S., 54, 55, 58, *66*
Guzman, Barron, E. S., 102, *132*

H

Haley, A. J., 234, 237, *240*
Hankes, L. V., 115, *131, 133,* 179, *190, 192*
Hansen, E. L., 176, *190*
Hansen, M. F., 73, *93*
Harnish, O., 161, *165*
Harris, J. E., 9, *11,* 36, *47,* 111, 114, 118, *131,* 152, 153, *165*
Hartridge, M. D., 158, *165*
Haskins, W. T., 37, *47,* 58, 59, *66, 67,* 107, 109, 123, *131*
Havis, L., 12, *24,* 248, *258*
Hawking, F., 15, *24,* 167, 176, *190*
Hedrick, R. M., 122, *131*
Hegner, R., 257, *258*
Hemenway, M., 86, *93*
Henry, H., 79, *93*
Henseleit, K., 110, *132*
Herfs, A., 128, *132*
Heyneman, D., 254, *258*
Higashi, A., 160, *166*
Hill, A. V., 149, *165*
Hill, G. R., 180, *192*
Hirsch, G. C., 106, *132,* 169, *190*
Hirschmann, H., 116, *132*
Hobson, A. D., 71, *93,* 108, 116, 117, 118, *132,* 137, *165,* 169, *190*
Hodgetts, V. E., 71, *94*
Hönig, G., 60, *66,* 202, 203, 204, 205, 206, 207, 208, 209, 213, *218*
Hoeppli, R., 168, 176, *190*
Hoffman, G. L., 86, *93,* 230, *240*
Hollingsworth, K. D., 189, *192,* 234, *241*
Hopkins, C. A., 54, *66,* 161, 162, 163, *165,* 187, *191*

Hopkins, G. H. E., 220, *240*
House, L. H., 181, *191*
Hovasse, R., 254, *258*
Hsü, H. F., 155, *165,* 169, 172, 181, *191*
Hubbard, J. A., 103, 104, 106, *133*
Huff, G. C., 53, 56, *66,* 173, *191*
Hunter, W. S., 57, 65, *66, 67,* 86, *93,* 161, *165,* 184, 187, *191, 192,* 228, 240
Hyman, L. H., 34, *47,* 124, 126, *132,* 155, *165,* 181, *191,* 215, *217,* 222, *240,* 255, *258*

I

Ingersoll, E. M., 186, *191*
Ishii, K., 206, *218*

J

Jacobs, L., 169, *190,* 201, 203, 204, 205, 206, 207, 208, 209, 211, *217*
Janicki, M. J., 155, *165,* 169, *191*
Jarman, M., 112, *132*
Jaskoski, B. J., 53, 56, *66,* 211, *217*
Johnson, R. W., 62, *66*
Jones, C. A., 51, 58, *66,* 100, *132*
Jones, M. F., 7, *11,* 51, *67,* 175, 176, 179, 180, *193,* 203, 204, 205, 206, 207, 208, 209, 211, 216, *217, 218*
Joyeux, C., 183, *191*

K

Kartman, L., 230, *240*
Kates, K. C., 51, *66,* 215, *217*
Keilin, D., 153, 154, 155, *165*
Keith, D. F., 176, *190*
Kelley, G. W., 216, *217*
Kelly, E. G., 245, *258*
Kent, H. N., 124, *132,* 187, *191*
Keppie, A. A. N., 16, *23,* 251, *258*
Khaw, K., 86, *93,* 228, *240*
Kikuchi, G., 102, *132*
Kirch, E. R., 71, *93*
Kleinberg, J., 71, *93*
Koletsky, S., 162, *165*
Krebs, H. A., 110, *132*
Kreis, H. A., 214, 215, *217*
Kreuzer, L., 202, 203, 205, 209, *217*
Krogh, A., 149, *165*
Krotov, A. I., 112, 113, *132*
Krüger, F., 138, 139, 146, *165*
Kuiper, K., 249, 256, *258*

L

Lams, H., 211, *217*
Lamson, P. D., 115, *133*
Lapage, G., 35, 45, *47,* 51, 53, *66,* 80, *93,* 176, *191,* 251, *258*
Larsh, J. E., 72, *93,* 230, *240*
Laser, H., 102, *132,* 141, 142, 145, *165*
Latchford, W. B., 55, *67,* 107, *133,* 139, 154, *166*
Laurie, J. S., 121, 122, *132,* 187, 188, *191*
Lawrence, J. J., 51, *66,* 176, *191*
Lazarus, M., 21, *24,* 100, 101, 118, 121, *132, 133,* 138, 161, *165,* 169, 170, 171, 177, *192*
Lederer, E., 50, *66, 67,* 207, *217, 218*
Lee, C. L., 88, *93*
Lee, H. J., 71, *93*
Lee, K. L., 185, *191*
Leland, S. E., 236, *240*
Leuckart, R., 33, *47*
Levitas, N., 162, *166*
Lewert, R. M., 88, *93, 94*
Lewis, R. W., 8, *11*
Li, S. Y., 169, 181, *191*
Liao, S. C., 256, *258*
Lillevik, H. A., 236, *240*
Lindquist, W. D., 236, 237, *240*
Linford, M. B., 89, *94,* 249, *258*
Linkous, W. H., 174, *192*
Llewellyn, J., 237, *240*
Loomis, W. F., 15, *24,* 91, *93*
Looss, A., 35, 36, 38, *47,* 61, *66,* 88, *93*
Lorincz, A. C., 87, *93*
Lucker, J. T., 51, 54, *66*
Lure, R. N., 125, *130*
Lwoff, A., 15, *24*

M

MacCallum, G. A., 237, *240*
McConnachie, E. W., 91, *93*
McCoy, E. E., 175, *190*
McCoy, O. R., 51, 52, 53, 54, 55, *66, 67,* 107, *133,* 139, 154, *166,* 176, *191,* 223, *241,* 246, *258*
McEntegart, M. G., 176, *191*
McIlvaine, M. F., 173, *189*
McKee, R. W., 167, *191*
MacKinnon, J. A., 120, *130*
McLeod, J. A., 124, *133,* 181, 186, *193,* 212, 213, *218*
McMahon, P., 121, 122, *130,* 161, *164*

Madsen, H., 230, *241*, 255, *259*
Maggenti, A. R., 209, *218*
Makidono, J., 146, *165*
Maldonado, J. F., 174, *191*
Malkani, P. G., 87, *93*
Mandlowitz, D., 88, *94*
Mansour, T. E., 120, 121, 124, *132*, 161, 162, *165*, 181, *191*
Mansour-Bek, J. J., 71, *94*
Manter, H. W., 243, 244, *258*
Mao, S. P., 185, *191*
Maplestone, P. A., 210, *218*
Marrian, D. H., 89, *93*, 226, *240*
Marston, H. R., 71, *93*
Martin, C. J., 21, *24*, 216, *218*
Martin, G. C., 62, *66*
Massey, V., 102, *132*, 177, *191*
Maupas, E., 31, *47*
Meeuse, B. J. D., 137, 140, *165*
Mehlman, B., 64, *66*, 102, 106, *130*, 143, 145, 148, 149, *166*, 179, *193*
Meleney, H. E., 231, *241*
Mellanby, H., 114, *132*
Mendes, M. V., 137, 140, *165*
Michajlova, E., 31, *47*
Mickel, C. E., 245, *258*
Millemann, R. E., 88, *94*, 224, *241*
Miller, G. E., 245, *258*
Miller, H. M., 223, *241*
Mishchenko, O. S., 145, 163, *165*
Mode, C. J., 250, *258*
Mönnig, H. O., 224, *241*
Monné, L., 60, *66*, 202, 203, 204, 205, 206, 207, 208, 209, 213, *218*
Moore, D. V., 162, *165*, 231, *241*
Moorthy, V. N., 37, 38, *47*
Most, H., 120, 121, *130*, 137, *165*, 180, 181, 185, 189, *189*, 234, *241*
Mountain, W. B., 176, *191*
Moyle, V., 108, 112, 113, 114, *130*, *131*
Mueller, J. F., 118, *132*, 169, 183, *191*
Muller, R., 184, *190*

N

Nachmansohn, D., 125, *130*
Nerhaus, W., 223, *241*
Newsome, J., 185, *191*
Nicholas, H. O., 126, *131*, 182, *190*
Nicholas, W. L., 176, *191*
Nicholson, A. J., 14, *24*
Nigon, V., 111, *132*, 201, *218*
Nishi, M., 171, *191*
Nisman, B., 135, *165*
Nolf, L. O., 53, *66*, 173, *189*
Norton, S., 112, 114, *132*
Nyberg, W., 180, 183, *191*

O

Ochoa, A., 57, *66*
Ogren, R. E., 212, *218*
Oldham, J. N., 34, 35, 41, *47*
Oliver-Gonzalez, J., 143, 144, *165*
Olivier, L., 64, *66*, 123, *131*
Olson, L. J., 235, *241*
Oostenbrink, M., 249, 256, *258*
Osborn, H. L., 128, *132*
Osche, G., 245, *258*
Oteifa, B. A., 90, *93*, 173, *190*, *191*
Otto, G. F., 174, 178, *190*, *192*
Oury, A., 126, *130*
Overgaard Nielson, C., 248, *258*

P

Painter, T. S., 211, *218*
Panijel, J., 111, *132*, 201, *218*
Panikkar, N. K., 18, *24*, 116, 117, 118, 119, *132*
Park, O., 14, *23*
Park, T., 14, *23*
Parker, J. R., 245, *258*
Passey, B. I., 207, *217*
Passey, R. F., 49, 50, 51, 53, 54, 56, 57, 63, *66*, 91, *94*, 116, *131*, 211, *218*
Pasteels, J., 111, *132*
Payne, F. K., 37, *47*, 52, *66*, 68, *94*
Pennoit-DeCooman, E., 123, 126, *131*, *132*
Pepler, W. J., 125, *132*
Peters, L., 160, 162, *165*, *166*
Peterson, C. H., 159, *164*
Petrova, M. I., 201, *218*
Phifer, K., 120, *132*, 182, 187, *191*, *192*
Picken, L. E., 115, *132*
Pitts, T. D., 176, *191*
Pollack, J. K., 110, 111, *132*, 200, *218*
Polonsky, J., 50, *66*, *67*, 207, *217*, *218*
Premvati, 215, *218*
Prestage, J. J., 140, *165*, 200, *218*, 253, *258*
Price, N. O., 174, *192*
Price, W. H., 174, *191*

Prosser, C. L., 140, *165,* 253, *258*
Pryor, M. G. M., 115, *132,* 213, *218*

R

Rabaud, E., 257, *259*
Rakato-Ratsimananga, A., 180, *190*
Ramirez, J., 102, *132*
Ransom, H. B., 207, *218*
Rathbone, L., 100, 101, 102, *132,* 177, *191*
Raven, B., 59, *67*
Read, C. P., 15, 17, *24,* 71, *94,* 120, 121, 122, 126, 127, *131, 132,* 135, 136, 161, 162, 163, 164, *165, 166,* 182, 187, 188, *190, 191, 192,* 221, 224, 228, 231, 232, *241,* 256, *259*
Rees, K. R., 100, 101, *132,* 177, *191*
Reid, W. M., 177, 178, *192*
Resnitschenko, M. S., 91, *94*
Rhoades, H. L., 89, *94*
Ribiero, L. P., 155, *166*
Richards, A, Glenn, 213, *218*
Richardson, H. B., 56, *67*
Rico, J. T., 113, *133*
Riedel, B. B., 174, *192*
Rietschel, P. E., 124, *133*
Rivera, G. F., 121, 122, *130,* 161, *164*
Robertson, D. L. H., 185, *191, 192,* 216, *218,* 231, *241*
Robbins, B. H., 115, *133*
Rogers, R. A., 202, 204, 206, 209, *218*
Rogers, W. P., 8, *11,* 16, 17, 19, 21, *24,* 35, 37, 42, 44, *47,* 49, 51, 52, 53, 54, 55, 56, 57, 63, *67,* 68, 69, 71, 72, 73, 74, 75, 76, 77, 80, 81, 82, 83, 84, 85, 89, *93, 94,* 100, 101, 102, 107, 109, 110, 111, 118, 119, *132, 133,* 136, 138, 139, 154, 156, 157, 158, 159, *166,* 169, 170, 171, 172, 177, 180, *191, 192,* 225, 226, 231, 234, *241,* 244, 247, 251, *259*
Rohrbacher, G. H., 186, *192*
Ross, E., 18, *24,* 128, *133,* 186, *192*
Ross, I. C., 21, *24,* 216, *218*
Ross, O. A., 147, 148, *166,* 185, *192*
Rothman, A. H., 15, *24,* 87, *94,* 121, *133,* 182, 187, 188, *191, 192,* 228, 229, 230, *241*
Rothschild, M., 86, *94,* 186, *192,* 223, *241*
Roughton, F. J. W., 158, *165*
Rowan, W. B., 65, *67,* 79, *94*
Ruppender, H., 120, *130*
Russel, P. B., 89, *93,* 226, *240*
Ruud, J. T., 137, *166*

S

Sadun, E. H., 234, *241*
Sambell, P. M., 170, *190*
Sandground, J. H., 219, 221, *241*
Sang, J. H., 246, *259*
Sarles, M. P., 222, 237, *241*
Savel, J., 100, 106, 107, 108, 109, 110, 111, 115, *131, 133,* 169, 179, 180, *189, 192*
Saz, H. J., 103, 104, 106, 114, *130, 133*
Schalimov, L. G., 206, *218*
Schaller, C. W., 250, *259*
Schiller, E. L., 187, *192*
Schmidt, K. P., 14, *23*
Schmidt, W. I., 205, *218*
Schneider, H. A., 221, *241*
Schopfer, W. H., 108, 116, 118, 126, *133*
Schulz, F. N., 207, *218*
Schulze, P., 205, *218*
Schuurmans Stekhoven, J. H., 31, *47,* 59, *67,* 248, *258*
Schwabe, C. W., 54, 56, 58, 59, *67*
Schwartz, B., 243, 255, *259*
Scott, J. K., 137, *166*
Senft, A. W., 185, *192*
Seurat, L. G., 31, *47*
Silverman, P. H., 7, *11,* 51, *67,* 79, 80, *94,* 176, *192,* 216, *218*
Simmonds, R. A., 116, *133*
Simmons, J. E., 126, 127, *133,* 182, *192,* 231, 232, *241*
Simpson, W. F., 18, *23,* 108, 119, *130,* 135, 142, 143, 147, 148, 160, *166,* 174, 175, 179, *192, 193*
s'Jacob, J. J., 249, 256, *258*
Slater, W. K., 146, *166*
Slijper, E. J., 71, *94*
Smith, H. W., 108, *133*
Smyth, J. D., 17, 21, *24,* 72, 87, *94,* 124, 126, 127, *133,* 163, *166,* 180, 181, 183, 184, *192,* 212, 213, 216, *218*
Sommerville, R. I., 16, 17, 19, *24,* 35, 42, 44, *47,* 80, 84, *94,* 225, *241*
Soulsby, E. J. L., 256, *259*
Specht, A., 12, *24,* 248, *258*
Spector, W. S., 71, *94*
Spindler, L. A., 173, *189,* 222, *241*

Sproston, N. G., 18, *24,* 116, 117, 118, 119, *132*
Stacey, M., 79, *93*
Stannard, J. N., 55, *67,* 107, *133,* 139, 154, *166*
Stavitsky, A. B., 120, *132*
Stephenson, W., 18, *24,* 108, 116, 117, 118, 120, 128, *132, 133,* 163, *166,* 181, 186, *192,* 212, *218*
Stirewalt, M. A., 68, *93*
Stoll, N. R., 36, 42, *47,* 51, *66,* 175, 176, *190, 192,* 216, *218,* 245, *259*
Stoner, R. D., 115, *131, 133,* 179, *190, 192*
Stoughton, R. B., 87, *93*
Stunkard, H. W., 64, *67,* 80, *94,* 183, *192*
Sturkie, P. O., 71, *94*
Swann, M. M., 115, *132*
Sweetman, H. L., 245, *259*
Szidart, L., 181, *192*

T

Tanner, W.A., 176, *189*
Taylor, A. E. R., 176, *192*
Taylor, E. L., 80, *94*
Terhaar, C. J., 73, *93*
Theodor, O., 220, *241*
Thomas, A. P. W., 45, *47*
Thomas, L. J., 235, *241*
Thonard, J. C., 88, *94*
Thorson, R. E., 88, *94,* 168, *192,* 236, *241*
Threadgold, L. T., 181, *190*
Threlkeld, L. N. L., 174, *192*
Timm, R. W., 207, *218*
Timms, A. R., 185, 189, *192,* 231, 233, *241*
Tiner, J. D., 176, *192*
Tischer, D. A., 121, *130*
Todd, A. C., 176, 189, *189, 192,* 234, *241*
Todd, A. R., 89, *93,* 226, *240*
Toryu, Y., 143, 144, 147, 148, *166,* 178, *192*
Tracey, M. V., 90, *94,* 171, *192,* 227, *241,* 249, *259*
Travassos, L., 33, *47*
Triffit, M. J., 34, 35, 41, *47*
Trim, A. R., 116, 118, *130, 133*
Turner, A. W., 71, *94*
Turner, D. S., 73, *93*
Twohy, D. W., 42, *47*
Tyler, J., 214, *218*

V

Valk, A., 160, *166*
Van Cleave, H. J., 18, *24,* 128, *133,* 182, 186, *192*
van Grembergen, G., 122, 123, 126, *132, 133,* 154, 161, 163, *166*
van Niel, C. B., 135, *166*
Varley, G. C., 14, *24*
Veglia, F., 35, 36, 38, *47,* 61, *67*
Venard, C. E., 80, *94*
Vercruysse, R., 121, *131*
Vernberg, W. B., 57, 65, *66, 67,* 161, *165,* 187, *192*
Vidrine, A., 103, 104, 106, *133*
Villela, G. G., 155, *166*
von Bonsdorff, B., 183, *192*
von Brand, T., 16, 18, *23,* 55, 64, *67,* 71, *94,* 100, 102, 106, 108, 119, 120, 121, 122, 123, *130, 133,* 135, 136, 137, 138, 139, 140, 141, 142, 143, 144, 145, 146, 147, 148, 149, 153, 155, 157, 160, 161, 162, *164, 166,* 174, 175, 177, 178, 179, 180, 181, 186, 187, *192, 193,* 214, *217,* 247, *259*
Vonk, H. J., 71, *94*
Vora, D. D., 145, *166*
Vorobieva, E. I., 201, *218*

W

Walton, A. C., 200, 211, *218*
Wang, Y. L., 155, *165*
Ward, H. L., 122, *133,* 161, *166*
Wardle, R. A., 124, 126, *133,* 181, 186, 187, 188, *193,* 212, 213, *218*
Waring, W. S., 89, *93,* 226, *240*
Waterhouse, D. F., 71, *93*
Watt, J. Y. C., 173, *193*
Weber, H., 249, *259*
Weil, A., 104, *133*
Weinbach, E. C., 102, 106, *130,* 143, 145, 148, 149, *166,* 179, *193*
Weiner, M., 144, *165*
Weinland, E., 120, *133,* 147, *166*
Weinstein, P. P., 7, *11,* 37, *47,* 51, 58, 59, *66, 67,* 102, 106, 107, 109, *130, 131,* 143, 145, 148, 149, *166,* 175, 176, 179, 180, *193,* 216, *218*
Weise, W., 16, *23,* 71, *94*
Welch, A. D., 160, *166*
Weller, T. H., 176, 185, *192, 193*
Wells, H. S., 171, 172, *193*

Wells, O. C., 124, *131*, 189, *190*
Wenrich, D. H., 257, *259*
Wetzel, R., 172, *193*
Wharton, G. W., 154, 155, 157, 163, *166*
Whitlock, J. H., 169, *189*, 230, *241*, 255, *259*
Wieser, W., 89, *94*, 227, *241*, 249, *259*
Wigglesworth, V. B., 41, 44, *47*
Wilmoth, J. H., 162, *166*
Wilson, P. A. G., 60, 61, 62, *67*, 92, *94*
Winslow, R. D., 227, *241*
Wottge, K., 201, 202, 203, 204, 205, 207, 208, 209, 211, *218*
Wright, C. A., 223, *241*
Wykoff, D. E., 86, *94*

Y

Yale, H. W., 100, *130*, 144, *165*, 177, *189*
Yamao, Y., 180, *193*
Yanagisawa, T., 200, 202, 206, 207, 211, *218*
Yoeli, M., 234, *241*
Yogore, M., 161, *166*
Yokogawa, S., 42, *47*
Yonge, C. M., 244, *259*
Yorke, W., 210, *218*

Z

Zaiman, H., 174, *193*
Zawadowsky, M. M., 201, 206, *218*
Zimmerman, J. F., 140, *166*

Subject Index

A

Absorption of nutrients, 123, 169, 172, 179, 181–3
Absorption spectra of haemoglobins, 154–6, 158
Acanthocephala (see also generic names)
body surface, 181
cuticle, 126
cytochrome system, 122
egg production, 215
egg-shells, 69, 213–5
evolution, 242
glycogen, 161
infective stage, 48
intermediary metabolism, 119–22
metamorphosis, 45
nutrition, 180–2
osmoregulation, 126
Pasteur effect, 121, 161
process of infection, 79
spines, 182
use of carbohydrates, 187
Acetaldehyde
in *Ascaris,* 106
in *Litomosoides,* 106
Acetic acid
produced by Acanthocephala, 122
produced by cestodes, 122
produced by nematodes, 105, 144
Acetylcholine
effect on *Ascaris,* 114
in nematodes, 111, 114
in *Schistosoma,* 125
in *Taenia,* 125
Acetylcholine esterase
in *Ascaris,* 114
in *Litomosoides,* 114
n-Acetylglucosamine
in egg-shells, 205
in synthesis of egg-shells, 177
hatching of eggs, 78
Acetylmethylcarbinol
excretion by nematodes, 105, 144
synthesis in nematodes, 106
Aconitase in *Trichinella*, 102
Acquired immunity, 9, 16, 221, 230, 234–8, 249, 256
Acrosome
in nematode sperm, 200, 201
Adaptation to parasitism, 199, 220, 242–55
in infection, 27, 29, 30, 34, 41–4, 63, 64, 91
in life cycles, 27–44, 60
in oxygen requirements, 54
Adnenaline
effect on *Ascaris,* 113, 114
Adenosine triphosphate
in *Hymenolepis,* 120
in nematodes, 100, 177
nutrition of parasites, 14
Adrenylic aid
metabolism in nematodes, 110
Adhesive organs, 252
Aedes aegypti
susceptibility to *Dirofilaria,* 230
Aerobic metabolism, 54–8, 65, 102, 103, 105, 121, 122, 140–4, 159–61, 177, 252, 253
Age resistance, 235
Alanine
excreted by nematodes, 109
in egg membranes, 202, 209
metabolism, 110
uptake by nematodes, 111, 179
Aldolase
in *Taenia,* 120
Alimentary canal
and specificity of parasites, 9, 224, 225
barrier to infection, 9, 245–7
chitinase, 78
in nematodes, 168, 169
oxygen in, 16, 71, 136, 137, 139, 140, 245, 247
properties of contents, 71, 72
in trematodes, 181, 182
Allantoin
metabolism of, 110
Allassostoma magnum
haemoglobin, 163

Amines
excreted by nematodes, 58, 59, 109
excreted by platyhelminths, 123
detoxication, 134
in infective eggs, 64
Amino acids
absorption, 179
excreted by nematodes, 58, 109
excreted by platyhelminths, 123
in egg-shells, 202, 209
in gut contents, 72
in 'hyaline spheres', 206
in larval sheaths, 85
metabolism, 110
nutrients, 178, 179, 185, 187, 189, 231
synthesis, 110, 123
Amino acid oxidase, 110, 123
p-Aminobenzoic acid
as nutrient, 167
α-Aminobutyric acid
in egg-shells, 202
Ammonia
excreted by nematodes, 37, 58, 64, 108, 110
excreted by platyhelminths, 123
toxicity, 135
Ammonotelism, 108
Amphibia
metamorphosis in, 31, 235
Anaerobic metabolism, 58, 100, 101, 103, 105, 120–2, 139, 140, 142, 144, 149, 160, 177
and oxygen debt, 141
and size, 252, 253
Anaerobes, 138
Anaerobiosis
effect on haemoglobins, 155, 156
hatching of eggs, 52
oxygen uptake, 141–4
survival of parasites, 145, 146, 160–3
Ancestral stock of parasites, 252
Ancylostoma spp.
culture, 52
penetration of tissue, 87
Ancylostoma caninum
blood intake, 171
glycogen, 177
nutrition, 170, 172
oxygen requirements, 63
process of infection, 87
water balance, 59
Ancylostoma duodenale
hatching of eggs, 61
life cycle, 36
moults, 35
process of infection, 88
Angusticaecum spp.
water relations, 116, 117, 119
Annelids
Pasteur effect, 160
Anthelmintics, 106, 118, 159–63, 246
Antibodies, 16, 236, 237, 249, 256
Anticoagulants
in nematodes, 168
resistance to infection, 230
Antigens
cornea, 237
in trypanosomes, 16, 251
Antiprotease, 246
Anopheles quadrimaculatus
susceptibility to *Dirofilaria*, 230
Aphelenchoides spp.
parasites, 248
predators, 248
saphrophytes, 248
Arginase, 110, 123
Arginine
in egg-shells, 202
Arginine phosphate, 58, 100, 121
Arthropoda
and life cycle of *Rhabditis*, 41
egg-shells, 211
metamorphosis, 31, 33, 44
moulting, 39, 44
nutrition, 181
Ascaridia galli
aerobic metabolism, 140
amino acid excretion, 109
ammonia excretion, 110
egg-shells, 203, 205, 208
feeding habits, 21
glycogen, 177
glycolysis, 101
hatching of eggs, 75, 76
host resistance, 235
nitrogen excretion, 37, 109, 110
nutrition, 21, 170, 174
peptide excretion, 109
process of infection, 72, 75, 76
purine metabolism, 110
specificity, 225, 234

Ascaridine
composition of, 201
Ascaris lumbricoides
absorption of monosaccharides, 179
acid production, 103–5, 144
aerobic metabolism, 140
amines in vitelline fluid, 58, 109
amino acid excretion, 109
amino acid synthesis, 200
antiprotease, 246
ascarosides, 50
body fluid, 118, 152
carbon dioxide fixation, 56
carbohydrate metabolism, 49, 50, 56
culture *in vitro,* 176, 179, 180
cuticle, 36, 113, 115, 116, 118, 151, 169
cytochrome system, 57, 58, 102
egg production, 23, 29, 215, 216
egg-shell, 91, 202–9, 211
feeding habits, 172
food reserves, 49, 50
glycogen, 56, 118, 148. 177
glycolysis, 101
hatching of eggs, 73–8
hatching fluid, 73, 77, 78
haemoglobin, 153–7
infectivity, 72
life cycle, 34
lipids, 50, 106
lipid metabolism, 103–5, 144, 145
mitochondria, 103, 140
movements, 146, 148, 153, 159
neuro-muscular physiology, 111–4
nitrogen excretion, 37, 108, 109
oöcytes, 200
osmoregulation, 115–9
oxygen debt, 141, 142
oxygen toxicity, 145
oxygen transport, 151–3
oxygen uptake, 52–4, 56, 63, 138, 139, 146–8
Pasteur effect, 142–4
pathogenicity, 252
pentose phosphate pathway, 101
peptide excretion, 109
permeability of egg-shells, 91
process of infection, 72, 73, 75, 76
purine metabolism, 110
respiratory quotient, 56, 64
size, 252
specificity, 225
succinic acid, 103
succinic oxidase, 103
survival *in vitro*, 146, 148
trehalose, 50, 56
vitamins, 180
vitelline fluid, 58, 109,
volatile fatty acids, 101, 103–5, 144, 145
water relations, 108, 116–9
Ascaroidea
egg-shells, 206, 208
infective stage, 38, 43
life cycle, 43
Ascarosides
nature of, 50, 207
Ascaryl alcohol
nature of, 207
Ascorbic acid
effect on eggs, 75, 76, 186
effect on larvae, 83
in parasites, 180
Asexual reproduction, 199, 214, 255
Aspartic acid, 109, 110, 201, 209
Aspicularis sp.
egg-shell, 203, 205
Atractis spp.
life cycle, 49
Atropine
effect on *Ascaris*, 113
Azide ions
effect on eggs, 57, 91

B

Bacteria
amines produced by, 109, 110
food for larvae, 51, 52, 176
infectiousness, 5, 167
metabolism, 6, 7
nutrition, 8, 168
specificity, 168
Balance
hypothesis of parasitism, 9, 10
of host and parasite, 197, 250, 251, 255, 256
Balanced polymorphism, 197, 256
Behaviour
and infection, 30, 48, 51, 251, 256
and specificity, 220, 222, 224, 238
free-living stages, 51
Benedenia melleni
specificity, 237

Bile
  oxygen in, 136
Bile pigments
  in gut contents, 72
Bile salts
  action on cestode eggs, 80
  action on exsheathment, 83
  action on larval cestodes, 87, 230
  in gut contents, 72, 80
Body fluid of nematodes
  circulation, 152, 153
  haemoglobin, 154, 157
  hydrostatic pressure, 153
  osmotic pressure, 116, 118
  pH, 116
Bohr effect, 153–5
Bromelin
  action in cuticle, 246
Bromolysergic acid
  effect on *Fasciola,* 124, 125

C

Caenorhabditis briggsae
  culture, 176
Calliobothrium verticillatum
  urea in, 232
Camallanus sweeti
  infective stage, 38
Camallanus trispinosus
  haemoglobin, 154, 155, 157
Capillaria spp.
  egg-shells, 203–6, 208
Carbohydrates
  in eggs, 49, 50, 54, 56
  in larvae, 51
  in parasites, 159, 160–2, 177, 187
Carbohydrate metabolism (see also glycolysis, etc.)
  in Acanthocephala, 119–24, 161, 162
  in eggs, 57, 209
  in larvae, 58
  in nematodes, 100–6, 141–5, 177–9 187
  in parasites, 253
  in platyhelminths, 119–24
Carbohydrase
  in *Ascaris,* 169
  in *Strongylus,* 169
Cardiac glycosides,
  and eclepic acid, 89, 226
Cardiotonic properties
  hatching factor, 89, 226
Carbon dioxide
  effect on *Hydra,* 15, 91
  exsheathment of larvae, 15, 16, 81, 83, 226
  fixation in *Ascaris,* 56, 57, 103
  fixation in *Heterakis,* 16, 105
  penetration of egg-shells, 91
  production, 56, 57, 121, 222
Carbon monoxide
  affinity for haemoglobin, 159
  effect on respiration, 57
Catalase, 145
Catenotaenia pusilla
  nerve-muscle physiology, 124
Cellulases
  in *Ditylenchus,* 171
  in larvae, 90, 227
Cercariae
  glycogen, 64
  lipids, 64
  oxygen requirements, 64, 65
  specificity, 244
  water relations, 128
Cestoda (see also Platyhelminthes and generic names)
  absorptive surface, 182
  cytochrome, 122
  cuticle, 181
  eggs, 64, 79
  intermediary metabolism, 119–22
  life cycles, 29, 45, 48, 79, 80, 254, 255
  nitrogen metabolism, 123, 124
  nutrition, 180, 183, 184, 186–8
  process of infection, 79, 80
  source of energy, 168
  specificity, 228–30, 232
  specialization, 9
Chitin
  in egg-shells, 60, 78, 202–7, 211, 213, 214
  synthesis, 177
Chitinase
  action on egg-shells, 77, 78
  in *Ditylenchus,* 171
  in gut contents, 79
  in hatching fluid, 77, 78
Chitosan reaction, 204
Cholesterol
  hatching of eggs, 79

Choline acetylase
in *Schistosoma,* 125
Choline esterase
in *Fasciola,* 126
in *Taenia,* 125
Chondrichthyes
parasites, 231, 232, 234
urea, 231
Chorion, 208, 212
Chromosomes in *Strongyloides,* 215
Cilia in nematodes, 168
Circulation of body fluid, 152, 153
Cirripeda, parasitic, 29
Citrulline cycle, 110
Cittotaenia sp.
nutrition, 187
Coenzyme A, 180
Coenzymes
in parasites, 180, 189
required by parasites, 6, 7, 15, 167
Clonorchis sinesis
process of infection, 228
Collagenase
secreted by larvae, 88
Commensalism, 12
relation to parasitism, 244, 257
Contracaecum spp.
specificity, 223
Cooperia oncophora
oxygen relations, 146, 147
Cornea
Benedenia in, 237
Cortisone
effect on immunity, 237
Cotton rat
Litomosoides in, 235
Creatine phosphate, 100
Crepidobothrium lönnbergii
culture, 183
'Crowding effect' of tapeworms, 163
Crustacea
nitrogen excretion, 108
parasitism, 45
Cruzia sp.
egg-shells, 203–5, 208
Cryptocotyle jejuna
infection of snails, 223
Cryptocotyle lingua
host nutrition, 186
Culture of free-living stages, 51, 174, 176
Culture of parasites, 7, 8, 19, 119, 147, 168, 174–6, 180–7, 216
Cuticle of insects, 213
Cuticle of parasites, 255, 256
Acanthocephala, 126
amino acids, 115
carbohydrates, 116
collagen, 115
effect of proteases, 246
elastic properties, 36, 37
lipids, 116, 119
oxygen penetration, 151
permeability, 113, 116, 118, 169
plant parasitic nematodes, 116
Platyhelminthes, 126
proteins, 115
structure, 115
Cyanocobalamine
in *Ascaris,* 180
in *Nippostrongylus,* 180
Cyanide
penetration of egg-shells, 91
Cyanide-sensitive respiration, 57, 102
Cyanine dyes
effect on *Litomosoides,* 160
effect on *Schistosoma,* 162
Cyclocoelidae
egg-shells, 212
Cyclocoelum microstomum
culture, 186
Cyclophyllidea
egg-shells, 212
Cyclops, 37
Cylicostomes
oxygen uptake, 54, 64
Cysteine
effect on exsheathment, 83
effect on hatching, 75
Cysticercoids
Hymenolepis, 254
process of infection, 86, 87
Cysticerus spp.
excystment, 229
Cystine in egg-shells, 202
Cytochrome system, 253
Acanthocephala, 122
Ascaris, 57, 58, 102
Litomosoides, 102
platyhelminths, 122
Trichinella, 102
Trichuris, 102

D

Daphnia
haemoglobin in, 253
Dauer larvae, 253
Definitive host, 255
Deoxyribonucleic acid, 201
Developmental physiology, 60–2
Diapause, 31
Dicrocoelium lanceatum
haemoglobin, 163
Didymozoonidae
reproduction, 212
Diet and specificity, 13, 15, 19, 167, 177, 232
Diffusion of oxygen, 149–52
Digenea (see also generic names)
cuticle, 246
evolution, 255
life cycle, 49
specificity, 220, 223, 244
Digestive enzymes of hosts, 72
action on sheaths, 85
effects on eggs, 44, 78, 79, 86
effects on larvae, 44, 87, 228
effects on parasites, 245
Digestive enzymes in parasites, 168, 169, 171, 181
Digitalis purpurea
hatching factor, 227
3:4-dihydroxyphenylalanine, 213
Dioctophyme renale
egg-shells, 203–5, 208
haemoglobin, 155
size, 252
Dioecocestus spp.
reproductive system, 212
Diphosphopyridine nucleotide, 100, 101, 120
Diphyllobothrium sp.
specificity, 234, 235
Diphyllobothrium dendriticum
culture, 184
process of infection, 87
Diphyllobothrium latum
oxygen uptake, 161
Diplodiscus sp.
diet, 181
Diplostomum flexicaudum
culture, 184
specificity, 235
Dipodomys spp.
behaviour, 224, 256
feeding habits, 256
Dipylidium caninum
acetylcholine, 125
Dirofilaria immitis
glycogen, 177
specificity, 230
Dirofilaria repens
acetylchololine, 114
Disaccharides
nutrients for *Cittotaenia,* 187
Dispersal
mechanisms, 41, 253
stages in life cycles, 38, 42
Rhabditis coarctata, 34
Ditylenchus sp.
egg-shells, 203, 205, 208
Ditylenchus dipsaci
enzymes, 171
hatching of eggs, 62
Dorsal lines in nematodes, 152
Dracunculus insignis
carbohydrate metabolism, 144
Pasteur effect, 143, 144
Dracunculus medinensis
infective stage, 37
Duodenal mucus
effect on parasites, 234
oxygen, 152

E

Echinococcus granulosus
carbon dioxide, 121
glycolysis, 120
Pasteur effect, 122, 162
specificity, 219, 220, 230
Echinostoma revolutum
vitamin requirements, 186
Eclepic acid
action of, 89
cardiotonic properties, 226
constitution, 89
specificity, 227
Ecological specificity, 220, 223, 224, 244
Ecology and parasitism, 13, 14, 244, 248
Ectoparasites
origin of parasitism, 245
Eggs
ascarosides, 50
carbohydrates, 50, 56

carbon dioxide fixation, 56
cytochromes, 57, 58
development, 200, 201, 212
excretory products, 58, 59, 64
food reserves, 50, 64
glycogen, 50, 56, 64
hatching, 7, 16, 34, 43, 61, 62, 73–8
infective, 43–4
lipids, 50, 56, 64
maturation, 211
metabolism, 49, 56
oxygen requirements, 52, 63, 64
polar bodies, 211
production of, 11, 23, 29, 187, 215, 216, 251
respiratory quotient, 56
trehalose, 50, 56
unfertilized, 211, 212

Egg-shells
Acanthocephala, 69, 70, 213, 214
amino acids, 202, 209
Arthropoda, 211
chitin, 60, 78, 204–6, 211, 214
chorion, 208, 212
function, 209–11, 255
hatching fluid, 77, 78
lipids, 60, 202–6, 208, 209, 211, 214
Mollusca, 211
Nematoda, 201–12
operculae, 204, 212
permeability, 60, 91, 207, 209
Platyhelminthes, 212–14
primary layers, 201–7
proteins, 202–4, 208, 209, 213
structure, 60, 201–10, 213
tertiary layer, 208, 212
Yanagisawa's layer, 206

Energy sources for parasites, 14, 15, 134, 135, 140, 148, 159, 160
Enolase in *Ascaris,* 101
Enterobius vermicularis
egg-shells, 204–8, 209
process of infection, 91
Environments of infective stages, 30, 37
Environments of parasites
antibodies, 16
major components, 10, 13, 14
nutrients, 10, 14–16, 167–89
other organisms, 16, 17
osmotic pressure, 10, 71, 116, 245
oxygen, 10, 16, 71, 136, 137, 141, 163, 164, 173, 245, 247
physical features, 17
physico-chemical features, 17, 71, 246
stimulating substances, 15, 16
unfavourable factors, 10, 16
Eserine
effect on *Ascaris,* 113
Esterase in hatching fluid, 78
Ethological specificity, 220
Ethyl alcohol
produced by parasites, 122
Evolution of parasitism, 3, 11, 242–57
Acanthocephala, 242
cestodes, 242
Nematoda, 242
Eustrongylides ignotus
culture, 147, 148, 174
feeding habits, 160
haemoglobin, 153, 155
monosaccharides, 179
osmotic relations, 118
oxygen debt, 141, 142
oxygen relationships, 147, 148
Pasteur effect, 142–4, 160
Excretion of nitrogenous compounds, 58, 64, 106–11, 123
Excretory system and water balance, 59, 119, 126, 128
Excystment of larval tapeworms, 228, 229
Exsheathing fluid
action of, 80, 85, 86
activation, 85
inhibition, 85
site of secretion, 86
specificity, 86
Exsheathment of larvae
effect of temperature, 83, 84
physiology of, 80–6, 249
specificity, 225, 251
stimulus, 81–4, 88

F

Fasciola gigantica
miracidia, 88
nitrogenous excretion, 123
Fasciola hepatica
absorption of nutrients, 181

alimentary tract, 181
arginase, 123
body surface, 181
choline esterase, 126
culture, 128, 186
egg-shells, 213
haemoglobin, 163
hatching enzyme, 79
hatching of eggs, 65, 79
lyseric acid, 124
miracidia, 88
nitrogenous excretion, 123
Pasteur effect, 162
serotonin, 124
specificity, 219, 223
transaminase, 123
Feeding habits of *Dipodomys,* 224, 256
Feeding mechanisms in parasites, 160, 171, 172, 181, 247, 249
Fertilization, 225
membrane, 202
nucleic acids, 111, 201
Filariform larvae, 33
Filaroidea
infective stage, 49
Food reserves
eggs, 50
free-living stages, 49–52
parasites, 177, 183, 187
Formic acid
produced by *Moniliformis,* 122
Free-living organisms
ancestors of parasites, 253
dispersal, 34, 253
environments, 18, 37, 222
hydrogen ion concentration, 245
nematodes, 39
osmotic pressure, 245
oxygen requirements, 247
size, 252
temperature, 245
Free-living stages of parasites, 222
culture, 174, 176
food reserves, 49–52
oxygen requirements, 52–4
physiology, 27, 44–65
Strongyloides, 33
Fundulus heteroclitus
host for *Eustrongylides,* 174
Fumarase in *Trichinella,* 102
Fungal parasites, 250

G

Gastropoda
life cycles, 48
Genetics
adaptation to parasitism, 252, 254
basis of parasitism, 250
development of *Strongyloides,* 214, 215
natural immunity, 250
specificity, 250, 255
Globulins in acquired immunity, 236
Glucosamine from egg-shells, 204
Glucose
absorption in *Fasciola,* 181
culture of parasites, 175
metabolism, 58, 105, 178, 187
nutrient, 179
oxidation, 105
source of energy, 14, 134, 135
uptake in *Hymenolepis,* 162
uptake in *Litomosoides,* 144
Glucose-1-phosphate, 58, 100
Glutamic acid
culture of *Ascaris,* 111
Glutathione
effect on *Hydra,* 15
Glycerophosphate metabolism, 58
Glycine
culture of *Ascaris,* 111
excretion by *Trichinella,* 109
uptake by *Trichinella,* 110, 179
Glycogen
consumption, 142, 143, 162
in eggs, 50, 56, 64
in larvae, 51
in parasites, 159, 177, 187
synthesis, 100, 148, 160
Glycolysis
in nematodes, 58, 100, 101
in platyhelminths, 119–21
in parasites, 253
Gordiacea
life cycle, 48
specificity, 222
Growth
Crepidobothrium, 183
Eustrongylides, 175
Hyostrongylus, 31, 32
moulting, 36, 37
nematodes, 31, 32, 36, 37
Spirometra, 183

Schistosomatium, 184, 185
Guanase
in *Ascaridia,* 110
in *Ascaris,* 110
Gynaecotyla adunca
culture, 184
excystment, 184, 228
oxygen uptake, 161

H

Haematin
in parasites, 169
nutrient, 167
Haemoglobin,
absorption spectra, 154, 156, 158
affinity for oxygen, 155
deoxygenation velocity, 156, 158
digestion of, 169
culture of *Schistosoma,* 231
in *Daphnia,* 253
in nematodes, 151–8
in parasites, 254
in platyhelminths, 163, 254
in plants, 155
loading tensions, 153, 155, 157
physiological function, 159
unloading tensions, 154, 156
Haemonchus contortus
culture, 7, 8, 51, 176
egg production, 23, 216
exsheathing fluid, 85
exsheathing of larvae, 80, 81, 83
haemoglobin, 154, 157, 158
histotropic phase, 42
hosts' diet, 174
larvae, 251
life cycle, 36, 41, 42
oxygen relationships, 150, 151
oxygen uptake, 52, 138, 139
respiration *in vivo,* 139
specificity, 225, 226
Haemophilus influenzae
nutrition, 167
Halipegus eccentricus
hatching of eggs, 79
Haplometra cylindracea, 184
Hamsters
hosts for *Nippostrongylus,* 234, 237
Hatching of eggs, 21, 34
Ancylostoma, 61
Ascaridia, 75, 76
Ascaris, 73–8
cestodes, 80
digestive enzymes, 44
Heterodera, 16, 44, 62, 89, 90
osmotic pressure, 43
oxygen pressure, 52, 53
physiology, 62, 73–8, 88–90
trematodes, 79
relation to specificity, 225
Hatching fluid, 73, 77, 78, 85
Hatching factor (see also eclepic acid)
Heterodera, 16, 44, 88–90, 226, 227
Hermaphrodites, 199, 212, 214
Heterakis gallinae
carbon dioxide fixation, 16, 105
catalase, 145
egg-shell, 203, 205
haemoglobin, 154
Pasteur effect, 143
volatile fatty acids, 105
Heterodera sp.,
egg-shell, 203, 205, 208
Heterodera glycines
cuticle, 116
Heterodera marioni
egg mass, 209
Heterodera rostochiensis
egg production, 251
feeding habits, 171
hatching factor, 16, 44, 88–90, 226, 227
larval attractants, 89–90
life cycle, 34
process of infection, 88–90
sex ratio, 214
specificity, 226, 227
Heterotrophic organisms, 12
Heterogonic life cycle
Strongyloides, 215
Hexacanth embryo
activation, 79, 80
Hexachlorophene
effect on *Litomosoides,* 106
Hexokinases in trematodes, 120
Hexylresorcinol
penetration into *Ascaris,* 118, 119
Histamine
effect on *Ascaris,* 113
Histidine in egg-shells, 202, 209
Homogonic life cycle
Strongyloides, 215

Hoplolaimus tylenchiformis
cuticle, 116
Hormones
effect on parasites, 189, 234
Hyaluronidase
secreted by larvae, 88
Hydra
feeding activity, 15
differentiation, 91
reproduction, 15, 251
Hydrogen ion concentration
body fluid of *Ascaris*, 116
effect on exsheathment, 81–4, 225
effect on hatching, 74, 75
effect on *Strongyloides,* 215
gut contents, 71, 245
Hydrogen peroxide
Ascaris, 145
Hydroxyhentriacontane, 50, 207
Hydroxyproline in cuticle, 115
Hymenolepis citelli
excystment, 229
Hymenolepis diminuta
absorption of nutrients, 123, 182
amino acids, 123
carbon dioxide, 121
cuticle, 126
excystment, 229
glycolysis, 120
hosts' diet, 186
nutrition, 182, 186
oxygen debt, 161
oxygen uptake, 161
Pasteur effect, 162
proteins, 124
transaminase, 123
Hymenolepis nana
excystment, 229
infectivity, 72
life cycle, 29, 48, 254
oxygen, 163
specificity, 224
Hyostrongylus rubidus
growth, 31, 32

I

Immunity
acquired, 9, 16, 233, 248
natural, 9, 16, 248
of plants, 248, 250
relation to moulting, 256
Infection
adaptations for, 41, 136
barriers to, 244, 248
moulting of parasites, 37–42
of plants, 88, 89, 249
process of, 19, 20, 68–93, 224–8
Infective stage
Acanthocephala, 48
Ascaroidea, 38
Ascaris, 72
behaviour, 30, 48, 51, 251, 256
Camallanus, 38
cestodes, 48
characteristics, 30
dispersal, 42
Dracunculus, 37
eggs, 43, 72–9
excretory products, 58, 59, 64
food reserves, 49–52, 63
Filaroidea, 49
Haemonchus, 41
Hymenolepis, 72
larvae, 41, 42, 80–7
Nippostrongylus, 42
oxygen requirements, 63
physiology, 62–4
'resting stage', 10, 37, 38, 244
sense organs, 62
Schistocephalus, 72
specificity, 76, 222, 223, 225, 226
Trichinella, 49
Infectiousness
bacteria, 167
nutrition, 8
physiology of, 27, 68–92
study of, 5, 6
Insecta
chitinase, 79
metamorphosis, 31
Intermediate host, 29, 30, 255
Iodoacetate-sensitive respiration, 254

K

Keratin
egg-shells, 213
Ketoglutarate
metabolism, 58, 110
Kinorhyncha
moults, 34

L

Lactic acid
- Acanthocephala, 122
- energy relations, 134
- nematodes, 100, 101, 105, 144
- platyhelminths, 120, 121, 162

Lateral lines, 152
'Lethargus'
- development of nematodes, 36
- oxygen uptake, 54

Leucine
- egg-shells, 202, 209
- excretion, 109

Life cycles (see also generic names)
- adaptations to parasitism, 68, 69
- *Ancylostoma,* 35, 36
- *Ascaris,* 34
- Ascaroidea, 38
- *Atractis,* 49
- *Camallanus,* 38
- cestodes, 29, 45, 48, 79, 80, 255
- Cirripeda, 29
- Digenea, 49
- *Diphyllobothrium,* 29
- *Dracunculus,* 37
- Filaroidea, 49
- free-living nematodes, 39
- Gastropoda, 48
- Gordiacea, 48
- *Haemonchus,* 36, 41, 42
- *Heterodera,* 34
- *Hymenolepis,* 29, 48, 254
- infection, 29–46
- Mermithoidea, 48
- metazoan parasites, 44–6
- nematodes, 10, 31–3, 38, 44, 49, 255
- *Panagrellus,* 29
- physiology, 38–44
- *Probstmyeria,* 49, 199
- *Rhabditis,* 41
- specificity, 222
- Strongyloidea, 38
- *Strongyloides,* 33, 215
- *Syngamus,* 34
- trematodes, 86, 215
- *Wuchereria,* 29

Linum usitatissimum, 250
Lipase
- action on eggs, 77

Lipids
- in cuticle, 119
- in eggs, 50, 61, 64, 206–8, 211
- in gut contents, 72
- in nematodes, 108
- infectivity, 51, 52
- metabolism, 50, 56, 103–6, 145, 149
- nutrients, 179

Litomosoides carinii
- acetylcholine, 114
- acetylcholine esterase, 114
- acetylmethylcarbinol, 105, 106, 144
- culture, 147, 176
- cyanine dyes, 160, 162
- end-products, 144
- glycogen, 143, 177
- oxidative metabolism, 102, 105, 144
- oxygen requirements, 144, 145, 147, 148, 160
- Pasteur effect, 141, 143
- specificity, 235

Loading tension of haemoglobin, 153, 155, 157
Loligo, 137
Lysergic acid
- effect on *Fasciola,* 124, 125

Lysine in egg-shells, 202, 209

M

Macracanthorhyncus hirudinaceus
- egg production, 215
- egg-shells, 214
- Pasteur effect, 161
- transaminase, 123

Malaria, 256
Malic dehydrogenase, 102, 103
Maturation of eggs, 211
Mehlis' gland
- function, 212

Melampsora lini
- genetical bases of parasitism, 250

Meloidogyne arenaria
- hatching of eggs, 62

Meloidogyne hapla
- host relations, 89

Meloidogyne incognita
- nutrients, 173

Meloidogyne spp.
- egg mass, 209
- moults, 37
- pathogenesis, 214

specificity, 227
Mermithoidea
food reserves, 169
intestine, 169
life cycle, 48
sex ratios, 214
Metacercariae
encystment, 86
excystment, 228
food reserves, 183
infection with, 45, 86
oxygen requirements, 64
Metamorphosis
Acanthocephala, 45
Amphibia, 31
Arthropoda, 31, 44
and antibody production, 256
cestodes, 45
Digenea, 45, 88, 92, 223
free-living animals, 10
Insecta, 31
parasites, 10, 22, 31
physiology of, 46
stimulus for, 38, 39
Metastrongylus spp.
moults, 34
Methionine
excreted by *Trichinella,* 109
in egg-shells, 202
uptake in *Hymenolepis,* 123
Methylacetoacetic acid
synthesis in *Ascaris,* 104
Methylbutyric acid
synthesis in *Ascaris,* 103, 104, 144
Methylcrotonic acid
synthesis in *Ascaris,* 103, 144
Microfilariae
infection with, 87, 223, 230
Migration of parasites, 39, 231
Mineral deficiency, 173
Miracidia
Fasciola hepatica, 65
food reserves, 64
infection with, 21, 45, 88
location of hosts, 223
metamorphosis, 45, 88
process of infection, 45, 88
Schistosoma, 88
Mitochondria
in *Ancylostoma,* 172
in *Ascaris,* 103, 140
in cestodes, 122, 123
in *Parascaris equorum,* 253, 254
in Protozoa, 122
Molluscan parasites, 29, 45
Moniezia benedini
nitrogen metabolism, 123
Moniezia expansa
carbon dioxide, 121
glycolysis, 120
osmotic pressure of tissue fluid, 126
succinic acid, 121
Pasteur effect, 121
proteins, 124
Moniliformis dubius
aerobic fermentation, 122
carbon dioxide, 121
use of monosaccharides, 187
Monogenea
specificity, 237
Monosaccharides in gut contents, 72
Monosaccharides, nutritional value
in *Ascaris,* 179
in *Cittotaenia,* 187
in *Eustrongylides,* 179
in *Fasciola,* 181
in *Litomosoides,* 179
in *Moniliformis,* 187
Monoxenous parasites, 219
Moulting
Ancylostoma, 35
and antibody formation, 256
Arthropoda, 39, 44
Eustrongylides, 174
growth, 37
Kinorhyncha, 34
Meloidogyne, 37
Metastrongylus, 34
nematodes, 10, 22, 27, 31, 34, 36–41, 80–6
Nematomorpha, 44
nitrogenous excretion, 37
Paratylenchus, 89
Pentastomida, 44
physiology, 80
process of infection, 80
significance in parasitism, 37–41
Mucopolysaccharide
in egg-shells, 209
Muscarine
effect on *Ascaris,* 113, 114

Muscular contraction
Ascaris, 111–4
platyhelminths, 124

N

Natural immunity, 9, 221, 230, 234–7
Nematodes (see also generic names)
buccal capsule, 247
food reserves, 49–52
free-living stages, 31, 34, 39–42, 60–4
haemoglobin, 151, 153–9, 254
in soil, 248, 249
life cycles, 10, 31–3, 38–44, 49, 255
moults, 10, 22, 27, 31, 34, 36–41, 80–6
oxygen requirements, 52–6, 137, 159
plant parasites, 248
physiology, 49–64, 72–8, 80–90, 100–19, 137–60
Nematomorpha
moults, 44
Nematodirella
egg-shells, 60, 203
Nematodirus spp.
amino acids, 109
egg-shells, 60, 203
haemoglobin, 154, 158
oxygen requirements, 139, 147, 150, 151
oxygen uptake, 138, 139
peptide excretion, 109
Nematospiroides dubius
specificity, 237
Neoaplectana chresima
culture, 175
Neoaplectana glaseri
culture, 175, 216
oxygen uptake, 138
specificity, 175
Neoechinorhynchus emydis
culture, 186
Nereis diversicolor
water relations, 116
Neuro-muscular physiology
nematodes, 111–14
platyhelminths, 124
Nicotine
effect on *Ascaris,* 113, 114
Nicotinic acid, 180
Nippostrongylus muris
culture, 8, 51, 175, 180, 216
cuticle, 116
excretory system, 59
feeding habits, 170
glycolysis, 58
growth, 42
haemoglobin, 153–8
host resistance, 236, 237
in hamsters, 234
nitrogen metabolism, 58–9
nutrition, 174
oxygen relationships, 139, 150, 151
oxygen uptake, 52, 138, 139
process of infection, 42
respiration, 56, 57, 63
respiratory quotient, 56
tricarboxylic acid cycles, 58
vitamins in, 180
water balance, 59
Nitrogen metabolism
Crustacea, 108
platyhelminths, 123, 124
nematodes, 106–11
Nucleic acids
in nematode eggs, 111
specificity, 15
Nutrients
parasites, 15, 167–89
platyhelminths, 23, 180–9
nematodes, 168–80
specificity, 8, 13, 15, 18, 167, 177, 231–4
reproduction of parasites, 215, 216, 237
Nycticorax
host for *Eustrongylides,* 175

O

Oesophagostomum columbianum
free-living stages, 222
Oligoxenous parasites, 219
Oochoristica deserti
in *Dipodomys,* 224, 256
Oochoristica symmetrica
effect of bile salts, 121
excystment, 229, 230
glycolysis, 120
Oögonia
development, 200

Ornithofilaria fallisensis
specificity, 223
Origin of parasitism, 243
Osmotic pressure
body fluids of nematodes, 116, 118, 119
culture media, 119, 126, 128
effect on eggs, 43
effect on hexacanth embryo, 80
environments of parasites, 17, 71, 116, 245
urea, 231, 232
Osmoregulation
Acanthocephala, 128
nematodes, 115, 116, 119
platyhelminths, 126, 231, 232
Ostertagia circumcincta
culture, 216
oxygen requirements, 147
process of infection, 80
Oxaloacetic acid
in nematodes, 102
Oxidation-reduction potential
exsheathing of larvae, 16, 83, 225, 226
gut contents, 71, 246
hatching of eggs, 16, 76, 225
Oxidative phosphorylation, 102, 103
Oxidative processes
products from, 134, 135
Oxygen
availability to cestodes, 163, 164
effect on *Strongyloides,* 215
debt, 65, 140–2, 161
free-living organisms, 247
from host blood, 172
mitochondria, 253
transport, 149–57, 161–4
toxicity, 145, 148, 163
survival of parasites, 16, 145–7
Oxygen in parasites' environments
bile, 136
cold-blooded vertebrates, 137
gut contents, 16, 71, 136, 137, 245, 247
invertebrates, 137
mud, 137
plants, 137
pleural cavity, 141
stagnant water, 137
tissues of vertebrates, 137
Oxygen required for
free-living stages, 52–5, 64, 65
maturation of eggs, 211
parasites, 65, 134–64, 172
Oxygen uptake
eggs, 52–4, 56, 57, 63–5
larvae, 54, 59, 63, 65
parasites, 138–41, 161–2
relation to pO_2, 54, 56, 138, 139, 148, 161
Oxyuris spp.
egg-shells, 203, 205, 207, 208
feeding habits, 172
Oxyuroidea
egg-shells, 206, 208
fertilization membrane, 202

P

Panagrellus redivivus
life cycle, 28
Pantothenic acid, 180
Papain
effect on cuticle, 246
Paragonimus westermani
oxygen debt, 161
Paramphistomum cervi
carbon dioxide production, 121
oxygen uptake, 161
Paramphistomum explanatum
nitrogen excretion, 123
Parascaris equorum
ascaridine, 201
ascorbic acid, 180
cuticle, 115
egg-shell, 204–8
food reserves, 49, 50
mitochondria, 253, 254
osmoregulation, 115, 116, 118
oxygen requirement, 147, 148
oxygen toxicity, 148
oxygen uptake, 52–4, 210
Pasteur effect, 143, 144
respiratory quotient, 56
zygote, 211
Parasitic degeneration, 45, 46
Paraspidodera spp.
egg-shells, 203, 205
Paratenic hosts, 29, 41
Paratylenchus projectus
moulting, 89

Parthenogenesis, 199, 210–12, 214, 255
Passalurus ambiguus
eggs, 204, 210
sperm, 200
Pasteur effect
infective stages, 63
parasites, 105, 106, 121, 122, 135, 142–4, 148, 161, 162, 180–2
Pectinase
secreted by nematodes, 90
Pentose phosphate pathway, 101, 121, 253
Pepsin
effect on cuticle, 246
effect on sheaths, 85
Peptides
excreted by nematodes, 109
excreted by platyhelminths, 123
Perciformes
hosts for *Benedenia,* 237
Permeability
cuticle, 113, 116–9
egg-shells, 60, 207
Phenolase in vitelline glands, 213
Phenotypes and immunity, 230, 255
Phosphagens
in larvae, 58
in parasites, 14, 100, 121
Phosphate esters
metabolism, 58, 100, 101
Phosphoglyceromutase, 101
Phototropism of miracidia, 223
Phylogenetic specificity, 219, 220, 224
Pilocarpine
effect on *Ascaris,* 113
Plants as hosts, 248
infection, 249
haemoglobin, 155
Platyhelminthes (see also generic names)
coenzymes, 189
culture, 183–5
cytochromes, 122
egg-shells, 212, 213
free-living stages, 64, 65
glycolysis, 119–21
haemoglobin, 163, 254
mitochondria, 122, 123
neuro-muscular system, 124
nitrogen metabolism, 123, 124
nutrition, 180–9
osmoregulation, 126, 231, 232
oxygen transport, 163
oxygen uptake, 161
Pasteur effect, 161, 162
pentose phosphate pathway, 121
physiology, 64, 65, 119–28, 161–3
process of infection, 69, 70, 86, 228
proteins, 187
tricarboxylic acid cycle, 119, 122
Plasmodium vivax
specificity, 15
Plasmodium gallinaceum
effect of carbon dioxide, 91
Plerocercoids, 72, 86, 161, 183
process of infection, 86
Pleural cavity
oxygen in, 141
Polar bodies in eggs, 211
Polyembryony in trematodes, 215
Polymorphus
egg-shells, 213, 214
Polyxenous parasites, 219
Porrocaecum spp.
specificity, 223
Primary egg envelope, 201–7
Probstmyaria vivipara
life cycle, 49, 199
Proline
egg-shells, 202, 209
excreted by nematodes, 109
Propionic acid
in *Ascaris,* 103, 104, 105, 144
in *Heterakis,* 105
Prostigmine
effect on *Ascaris,* 114
Proteases
in *Ascaris,* 169
in *Schistosoma,* 231
process of infection, 77, 87, 246
Proteins
cuticle, 115
cyst-walls, 86
egg-shells, 60, 202–6, 208, 209, 213
hosts' diets, 173
platyhelminths, 124, 187
specificity, 15
Protozoan parasites, 14, 15
mitochondria, 122
nutrition, 167
physiology, 99
specificity, 15, 168
Pteroylglutamic acid
hosts' diet, 174

Purines
metabolism in nematodes, 110
Pyridoxine, 180
Pyruvate metabolism, 58, 102–6, 119–22

Q

Quinone-tanned protein
in cuticle, 115
in egg-shells, 60, 202, 203, 205, 206, 213

R

Rachis
in *Ascaris,* 200
Raillietina cesticillus
transaminase, 123
proteins, 124
Rattus norvegicus
host for *Litomosoides,* 235
Rediae
nutrition, 23
multiplication, 215
Reducing agents
attraction of *Meloidogyne,* 227
effect on eggs, 75, 76
effect on larvae, 81–4
Reproduction of parasites, 199–201, 212, 214, 215, 255
and nutrition, 215, 216, 237
Resistance (see also natural and acquired immunity)
mechanisms, 236, 237
nutrition, 173, 186
Respiratory quotient
Ascaris, 56, 64
cestodes, 122
Haemonchus, 56
Nippostrongylus, 56
Parascaris, 56
trematodes, 122
Respiratory surface, 149, 152
Resting potentials
in *Ascaris,* 111
Rhabditis coarctata
larvae, 253
life cycle, 41
Rhabditis elegans
temporary parasite, 54
oxygen uptake, 54, 56
Rhabditis pellio
temporary parasite, 246
Rhabditis strongyloides
temporary parasite, 54
oxygen uptake, 54, 56
Rhabditiform larvae, 33, 51
Riboflavin, 186
Ribonucleic acid, 201

S

Saprophytes, 8, 246, 247
Schistocephalus solidus
culture, 126, 183, 187
food reserves, 183
egg production, 21
osmotic relations, 126
oxygen requirements, 161, 162
Pasteur effect, 161, 162
plerocercoids, 72, 86, 161, 183
Schistosoma mansoni
acetylcholine esterase, 125
amino acid requirements, 231, 232
cercariae, 65
choline acetylase, 125
culture, 185, 189
cyanine dyes, 162
egg production, 186, 239
enzymes, 120
hexokinases, 120
hosts' diets, 186
oxygen debt, 161
oxygen requirement, 162
oxygen uptake, 161
Pasteur effect, 121, 122, 161
process of infection, 88, 223
protease, 231
Schistosomatidae
reproductive system, 212
Schistosomatium douthitti
nutrition, 184, 185
Sciurus carolenensis
host for *Hymenolepis,* 224
Scolex
evagination, 87
Scleroproteins in egg-shells, 202
Secondary egg envelope
platyhelminths, 212
Self-cure reaction, 256
Sense organs
in larvae, 62
in parasites, 253

Serine
egg-shells, 209
excreted by *Trichinella,* 109
Sheaths of third-stage larvae, 35, 39, 44, 85
structure of, 85
Sickle cell anaemia, 256
Sigmodon hispidus
host for *Litomosoides,* 235
Simulium venustrum
infection with microfilariae, 223
Sodium dithionite
effect on eggs, 75, 76
effect on larvae, 83, 84
Solanum
hosts for *Heterodera,* 89, 227
Spaerularia sp.
morphology, 33
Speciation
effect of nutrition, 167
parasites, 224, 242, 243
Protozoa, 168
Specificity
behaviour, 220, 222–4, 238
Contracaecum, 223
Echinococcus, 219, 220
ecological, 220, 223, 224, 244
ethological, 220
exsheathing fluids, 86
Fasciola, 219, 223
genetical basis, 250, 251
host immunity, 231, 232, 234–8
life cycles, 222
Neoaplectana, 175
nutrition, 8, 13, 15, 167, 177, 231–4
parasites, 11, 19, 219–41
phylogenetic, 219, 220, 224
Plasmodium, 15
Porrocaecum, 223
process of infection, 77, 78, 83, 91, 222, 224–6, 230
proteins, 15
Protozoa, 168
Stephanurus, 222
Taenia, 19, 224
temperature of host, 17, 225, 226, 234, 235, 245, 254
Trichinella, 19, 221, 223
Unionidae, 222, 223
urea, 231, 232
Wuchereria, 219
Spirocera sp.
haemoglobin, 155
Sporocysts
formation, 45, 88
nutrients, 23, 181
Spreading factors, 88
'Stationary layer'
in respiration of parasites, 151, 152
Stephanurus dentatus
free-living stages, 222
specificity, 222
Sterols in egg-shells, 207
Strongyloidea (see also generic names)
eggs, 60
egg-shells, 203, 205, 208, 209
fertilization, 255
infective stage, 38, 43
Strongyloides spp.
free-living stages, 33
glycolysis, 58
oxygen requirements, 54, 63
tricarboxylic acid cycle, 58
Strongyloides papillosus
oxygen requirements, 54
tricarboxylic acid cycle, 58
Strongyloides ransomi
oesophagus, 32
Strongyloides ratti
egg-shells, 210
glycogen, 51
glycolysis, 58
Strongyloides stercoralis
morphology, 33
Strongylus spp.
haemoglobin, 153–5, 157
Strongylus edentatus
digestive enzymes, 169
feeding habits, 172
Strongylus vulgaris
digestive enzymes, 169
feeding habits, 172
glycogen, 177
Strychnine
effect on *Ascaris,* 113
Succinic acid
Ascaris, 103
excreted by *Moniezia,* 121
metabolism, 57, 58, 102, 105, 119, 122, 253
muscular contraction, 114

Succinic dehydrogenase
Ascaris, 103
cestodes, 122
Survival of parasites *in vitro,* 16, 145–8
Susceptibility to parasitism, 14, 221
Syngamus trachea
eggs, 60
egg-shells, 203
life cycle, 34
Syphacea obvelata
egg-shell, 202–4, 208
Symbiosis, 12, 13

T

Taenia crassiceps
aldolase, 120
Taenia crassicollis
acetylcholine, 125
Taenia pisiformis
choline esterase, 126
excystment, 229
hatching of eggs, 79
Taenia saginata
egg production, 29
hatching of eggs, 79
pathogenicity, 252
proteins, 124
specificity, 19, 224
toxicity of oxygen, 163
Taenia solium
excystment, 229
specificity, 224
Taenia taeniaeformis
excystment, 229, 230
nitrogen metabolism, 123
Taeniidae
eggs, 79
Tagetes sp.
root diffusate, 256
Telorchis robustus
haemoglobin, 163
Temperature
activation of cestode embryos, 80
effect on plerocercoids, 86
exsheathment of larvae, 83, 84, 225, 226
hatching of eggs, 225
optimum for exsheathing fluid, 84, 85
specificity, 17, 225, 226, 234, 235, 245, 254
Tertiary egg envelope, 208, 209, 212
Tetrabothrius erostris
effect of urea, 232
Tetrameres sp.
haemoglobin, 155
morphology, 33
Thiamine
in nematodes, 180
uptake in cestodes, 182
Toxascaris leonina
eggs, 210
Toxocara sp.
egg-shells, 203, 205, 206, 208
haemoglobin, 155
Toxocara canis
ascorbic acid, 180
nutrition, 170
Toxocara mystax
process of infection, 72, 75, 225
Transaminases, 110, 123
Transport hosts, 29, 41
Trehalose in *Ascaris* eggs, 50, 56
Trematoda (see also generic names)
culture, 184–6
cuticle, 126
digestion, 181
life cycles, 86, 215
neuro-muscular system, 124
nitrogen metabolism, 123
respiratory quotient, 122
specialization, 9
Triaenophorus nodulosus
oxygen uptake, 161
Trilobus longus
sperm, 200
Tricarboxylic acid cycle
in eggs, 57
in larvae, 57, 58
in nematodes, 102, 105
in parasites, 253
in platyhelminths, 119, 122
Trichinella spiralis
amine excretion, 109
amino acid excretion, 109
amino acid uptake, 111, 179
culture, 176
cytochrome, 102
eggs, 210
glycogen consumption, 143
haemoglobin, 154
oxidation of lipids, 106, 145, 179

oxygen requirements, 148
oxygen uptake, 138, 139
Pasteur effect, 143
process of infection, 91
specificity, 19, 221, 223
Trichostrongyles
exsheathing, 80–6
histotropic stage, 42
sheath, 35
specificity, 222, 225, 226
Trichostrongylus axei
exsheathment, 80–6, 225, 226
specificity, 225, 226
Trichostrongylus colubriformis
exsheathment 80, 83, 86, 225
specificity, 225
Trichostrongylus retortaeformis
hatching of eggs, 60, 61, 62, 92
Trichostrongylus vitrinus
survival *in vitro,* 147
Trichuris spp.
egg-shells, 203–8
toxicity of oxygen, 145
Trichuris leporis
egg, 210
Trichuris vulpis
cytochrome, 102
Triphosphopyridine nucleotide, 103
Trypanosomes
antigenic structure, 16, 251
Trypsin
effect on cuticle, 246
effect on sheaths, 85
Tryptophane
uptake by *Trichinella,* 111, 179
Tubocurarine
effect on *Ascaris,* 113
Tyramine
effect on *Ascaris,* 113
Tyrosine
in vitelline glands, 213
uptake by *Ascaris,* 111
uptake by *Trichinella,* 111, 179

U

Unionidae
specificity, 222, 223
Unloading tension of haemoglobin, 154, 156
Urea
effect on cestodes, 231, 232, 234
excreted by nematodes, 37, 108, 110
metabolism in nematodes, 110
specificity, 231, 232
Urease in nematodes, 110
Uric acid
excretion by nematodes, 110
metabolism in nematodes, 110

V

Valeric acid, 144, 145
Valine in egg-shells, 202
Virus, 14, 167
Volatile fatty acids
synthesis, 101, 103–5, 144, 145
Vitamins
in hosts, 174, 186
in parasites, 180
in parasite nutrition, 173, 174, 180
Vitelline
fluid, 109
membrane, 60, 207
Vitelline glands, 212, 213

W

Water balance
Ancylostoma, 59
Angusticaecum, 116, 117, 119
Ascaris, 108, 116–18
eggs, 64
Nereis, 116, 117
Parascaris, 116, 118
platyhelminths, 126–8
Wuchereria bancrofti
life cycle, 29
specificity, 219

X

Xanthine
metabolized by *Ascaris,* 110

Y

Yanagisawa's layer in egg-shells, 206

Z

Zoogonus rubellus
oxygen debt, 65
oxygen requirement, 65
Zygote
in *Parascaris* eggs, 211